the
fireside
book
of
FOOTBALL

Edited by Jack Newcombe

SIMON AND SCHUSTER

NEW YORK • 1964

First Printing

Library of Congress Catalog Card Number: 64–19933
Manufactured in the United States of America
Designed by Betty Crumley
Printed by The Murray Printing Company, Forge Village, Mass.
Bound by H. Wolff, New York

ACKNOWLEDGMENTS: *The Editor wishes to express his gratitude to the following individuals and publishers for permission to include the following materials:*

"Midshipmen's Miracle" by Jesse Abramson. Copyright 1950 by the New York Herald Tribune, Inc., and reprinted by their permission.

"Undefeated, Untied, Unfounded" by Caswell Adams. Copyright 1941 by the New York Herald Tribune, Inc., and reprinted by their permission.

"The Glorious Slaughter" by Gerald Astor. Reprinted by permission from *Sports Illustrated,* November 27, 1961. Copyright © 1961 by Time, Inc.

Poems from *Goal Lines* by A. C. M. Azoy, Jr., and Frank Halsey. Reprinted by permission of Princeton University Press. Copyright 1922.

"The Kick" by John Baker. Reprinted by permission of the author.

"Gipp" by Jim Beach. Courtesy *Saga* Magazine. Copyright © 1958 by Macfadden-Bartell Corp.

"The Last Big Thursday" by Furman Bisher. Reprinted from *With a Southern Exposure* by Furman Bisher. Copyright © 1962 by Thomas Nelson & Sons.

"Mayhem Among the Ivies" by William Brothers Brook. Reprinted from *The Jester* of Columbia University.

"Some of My Best Friends Are Yale Men" by Heywood Broun. Copyright 1921, 1941 by Heywood Hale Broun. Reprinted by permission of Constance M. Broun and Heywood Hale Broun.

"Tribute to a Teammate" by Jimmy Brown with Hal Lebovitz. Courtesy of *Sport* Magazine. Copyright © 1963 by Macfadden-Bartell Corp.

"Football Girl" by Katharine Brush. From *Other Women* by Katharine Brush. Copyright 1931, 1933 by Katharine Brush. Copyright © renewed 1959, 1961 by Thomas S. Brush. Reprinted by permission of Holt, Rinehart and Winston, Inc.

"Eckersall's Last Game" reprinted from the Chicago *Tribune,* November 24, 1906.

"Riegels' Wrong-Way Run," reprinted from the Chicago *Tribune,* January 2, 1929.

"Boos" by Perian Conerly. From *Backseat Quarterback* by Perian Conerly. Copyright © 1963 by Perian Conerly. Reprinted by permission of Doubleday & Company, Inc.

"Middle Linebacker," originally titled "It's Tough to Get By Joe," by Myron Cope. Reprinted by permission of the author. Copyright © 1958 by the Curtis Publishing Company.

"First Helmet" by George Cuomo. From *Jack Be Nimble* by George Cuomo. Copyright © 1963 by George Cuomo. Reprinted by permission of Doubleday & Company, Inc.

"Bears 73, Redskins 0" by Arthur Daley. Copyright 1940 by the New York Times Company. Reprinted by permission.

"Ohio State–Notre Dame, 1935" by Allison Danzig. Copyright 1935 by the New York Times Company. Reprinted by permission.

"The Co-eds Were Real—The Boys Were Shadows" by Bernard De Voto. Reprinted by permission of Mrs. Bernard De Voto, owner of copyright.

"Radiator Rent" by Gus Dorais. Reprinted from *Football Record and Rule Book, 1945.* Copyright by the *Sporting News,* St. Louis, Mo.

"Broadcast of the Game" by Frederick Elbright. Reprinted from *Atlantic Monthly,* November 1950.

"Freud on the 50-Yard Line" by Thomas Hornsby Ferril. Reprinted by permission of the author and the *Rocky Mountain Herald.*

"Letter to Coach Crisler" by F. Scott Fitzgerald. Reprinted from *The Letters of F. Scott Fitzgerald* edited by Andrew Turnbull. Copyright © 1963 by

Contents

List of Illustrations

Preface

Of all the American games that small boys play and adults take seriously, football has been the most heavily romanticized in print. There is always the suspicion that this is because no one—except coaches, scouts and intellectually gifted players—really understands the game; that those who write about it are forced to lean on fancy rather than fact. But granted the complexities of modern football and the average person's inability to understand them, there is much in the nature of the game that has a distinctly romantic appeal. Pageantry, orderly violence, athletic skill and grace—these are football's components. The spectator may be attracted to one or all of them. Ask him why football is *his* sport and he is apt to admit to such nebulous appeals as the smell of burning leaves, the muffled sound of drumbeats beneath the stadium, the sight of a quarterback taking the snap from center, pivoting neatly and sticking the ball into the fullback's belly. Or he may get his satisfaction from the recurring images of colliding figures on his television screen.

"That football is one of those sports to which the human race clings because it satisfies a human, elemental need," wrote Wainwright Evans, "seems to be evidenced by the fact that it was played forty centuries ago in China; that the Greeks and Romans were playing it at the dawn of history; that the Irish played it two thousand years ago; that the Esquimaux and many other primitive peoples played games resembling it."

The elemental need may be—as, apparently, for the Esquimaux —simply exercise in a cold season; or it may be a need to self-identify with the hero on the field below and "experience something of what is meant by vanished glory."

In *The Crack-up,* F. Scott Fitzgerald turned to a "dream of a defeated dream" about football, in his efforts to overcome insomnia: "Once upon a time (I tell myself) they needed a quarterback at Princeton, and they had nobody and were in despair. The head coach noticed me kicking and passing on the side of the field and he cried: 'Who is *that* man—why haven't we noticed *him* before?' The under coach answered, 'He hasn't been out,' and the response was: 'Bring him to me.' . . . We go to the day of the Yale game.

I weigh only one hundred and thirty-five, so they save me until the third quarter, with the score . . ."

I would hope that this book is for everyone who, in dreams or actuality, has gone into the game in the third quarter. Included are reflections of the romanticism that caught Fitzgerald's imagination; there are explanations of the complexities that make football one of the most fascinating (and difficult) of games to understand. The sights, sounds and smells are here, too. This is a book for the football enthusiast who cannot say precisely why he likes to play pass-and-catch on the front lawn, watch the local high school team practice, drive to a college game on a gray Saturday morning, or see the pros on Sunday.

I have made no attempt to satisfy the football historian. The pieces offer some idea of the spread of the game, from other countries to the U.S. college campus and, most recently, to the boom in professional football. But there is no chronological coverage, for history's sake, of significant developments, famous games and players. I have included the Cleveland Browns, Southern California and Middlebury and omitted the San Francisco 49ers, Purdue and Knox. There is a description of a trick play that won a game for Minnesota in 1941, but no explanation of how Y. A. Tittle became pro football's leading passer at the age of thirty-six. I have included at least two stories in which football serves merely as a backdrop —as it often does in campus life.

The contents do not prove that there is, buried in the archives, a great, unearthed literature on football. The game has produced some excellent journalists; famous authors have commented on the sport. Yet most of the serious writers, i.e., those with sure literary qualifications, have written humorously about football and have chosen to expose the adult hypocrisies and youthful follies surrounding the game. Their satire belongs in this anthology as much as do the pieces of romance and reportage.

The fictional subliterature of football is, like most sports fiction, limited. It flourished when Ralph Henry Barbour, William Heyliger, Owen Johnson and others were writing boys' stories early in the century, but it gradually declined, apparently a victim of overemphasis on the game. I have included one chapter from Dink Stover's days at Lawrenceville. I found one example of recent football fiction worth preservation, a short story by Thomas Gallagher.

I concede that a football anthology of the future might include far more examples of sound reporting on the skills and techniques seen in the pro leagues and fewer expressions of "youthful joys and follies." By then, Notre Dame, the subject of a handful of stories here, may be a forgotten name on the scoring lists and the split T may be as outmoded as Pop Warner's double wing. Whatever the current rage, I hope that overexposure on television will not have drained all the romance from the game.

My appreciation goes to Peter Schwed, overseer of this collection, and to my wife, Trip, who helped put it together. The book is dedicated to Dick, a football fan, whose last autumn of life was made more enjoyable by the games he saw at Yankee Stadium.

Rye, New York   *Jack Newcombe*

the
fireside
book
of
FOOTBALL

When Army and Navy prepared to meet for the fifty-first time in 1950, the game had all the appearances of being the worst mismatch in the long series. Undefeated and untied Army was ranked No. 1 in the nation; Navy had lost six games, two of them to Ivy Leaguers. The illogical events that followed the kickoff were described in the New York Herald Tribune, *with customary clarity and style, by one of the best football reporters in the business.*

MIDSHIPMEN'S MIRACLE

Jesse Abramson

Navy defeated Army, 14–2, in their fifty-first football game before President Truman and a capacity crowd of 100,000 who were shocked and dazed into disbelief or delirium by incredible events in Municipal Stadium today.

The unfathomable stalwarts from Annapolis marched 33 and 63 yards in the late second period to their touchdowns, scored by 209-pound Bobby Zastrow, quarterback from Algoma, Wisconsin, on a 7-yard sneak and his 30-yard pass to end Jim Baldinger.

They gave Army its only points in the middle of the third period on a safety when Zastrow, fading back to pass from his 13, was rushed all the way into the end zone and dumped there by end Bill Rowekamp and guard Bob Velonnino. Roger Drew, Navy's place-kicking specialist, contributed both conversions.

Miracles such as this one are a dime a dozen in football history. It is frustrating to have to call it another miracle of football. A Navy team which had lost six of its eight games in one of its most disastrous seasons, had been beaten as badly as 22–0 by Northwestern and 27–0 by Tulane only a month ago, somehow managed to come up with a fantastic performance that no one believed possible.

But this one, of course, was against Army, which meant that Navy was starting a brand-new season from scratch. Forget the past. Against an Army team believed to be the finest team in the land, an all-conquering Army team which had won eight straight this year without being extended to its utmost; an Army team which had traveled twenty-eight games without defeat (two of them ties) and had won their last seventeen in a row; an Army team, favored by three touchdowns, to conclude its second straight perfect season and its sixth unbeaten season in seven years. An Army team which had assailed its opposition for an average of 400 yards a game and whose wonderful defense had strangled the enemy all year and had permitted only twenty-six points.

How, then, could such an Army team, bursting with health, boasting advantages in every department of play, deeper in man power, lose to such a badly beaten Navy foe?

The answer, of course, is simple. Football is, as Red Blaik has said, for everyone, a game of transcendent spirit played by American youth who will not concede anything in competition, no matter what the odds may be. Two teams of equal size and muscle met in a game and the team with the greatest emotional urge and drive

19

came through with a victory it wanted more than anything on earth this day.

As President Truman, his guests, members of his cabinet, generals and admirals by the bushelful and the eye-witnesses of this thrilling game slowly started out of the Stadium in the semi-darkness of a gray misty day, as the hysterical brigade of blue-coated Midshipmen swarmed onto the field of battle, as the winning players hoisted their new coach, Eddie Erdelatz, to their shoulders, a wild-eyed fan, obviously a Navy rooter, faced the press box and shouted: "Don't you dare call this an upset; Navy finally played the game it was capable of playing."

That was it, in a nutshell. Thank you, Navy fan. Navy hit and ran and drove with controlled fury that was overwhelming, churning the turf for two, three, four yards even after Army's fine defense had, to all purposes, stopped a play. Navy defended with eleven tacklers who swarmed over, ganged and smothered Army's swift runners, including even—and especially—the fullback, Al Pollard, who was rated the most unstoppable fullback in the country.

Navy's secondary covered Army pass receivers like leeches, so that even captain Dan Foldberg, one of Army's greatest offensive ends in history, was restricted to two catches and was never for a moment unguarded.

The pattern of this game was established early, never varied, insofar as Navy's crushing superiority was concerned.

Zastrow, a quarterback who had been so often the goat in Navy defeat, played the sort of game a boy plays in his dreams. He directed Navy's T-formation attack, with its brand-new spread features, with boldness and with superb skill, deftly handling the ball to his backs, Dave Bannerman, Frankie Hauff and Bill Powers, who rammed for short and consistent gains inside and outside Army's tackles. Zastrow ran for important yardage. Zastrow passed deftly.

In a duel of bruising, violent line impact, Navy in that decisive first half gained eight first downs to Army's one, and outpassed Army as well. Navy made its margin of superiority pay off for two touchdowns, Army could not mount an attack, rarely was across midfield and could not break Navy down even when it recovered a fumble and had a first down on Navy's 22 in the early minutes. The Cadets had to give up the ball on the 15, and did not get inside the enemy 30 the rest of the half.

Between the halves everyone marveled at Navy's remarkable play that was almost foolproof and fumble-free, wondered whether Navy could maintain its burning flame against an aroused Army foe. Army did rouse itself in the second half, Navy made a few errors, including the third-down pass try that led to a safety. Those two points might have been decisive if Army could score two touchdowns. But Army, getting opportunities, attacking remorselessly, in the fourth period, could not shatter Navy's valorous defense. Navy never lost its poise, or its control.

Navy, which scored its first victory in the series since 1943, was backed up against its goal through all of the last period in defense of a 14–2 lead, with Army at the 20 or inside it three times, and passing with desperation. In these pinches, Navy was unbreakable, stopping the Cadets with an interception by John Gurski on the 17, another interception by Bill Powers on the 8, stopping Army again on the 15. The Cadets, under exquisite pressure against the clock, fumbled twice and lost the ball in the waning minutes, on the 28 and on the 5, then ran into a final interception on the final play after blocking a punt and reaching the 3.

So Army was balked to the bitter end, unable to score a touchdown for the first time since it went scoreless with Illinois early in 1947.

The final figures indicated, too, how richly Navy earned this triumph. It outgained Army, 13 to 5, in first downs, 200 to 77 yards in rushing, with Bannerman and double-duty Hauff leading the way with 67 and 61 yards each.

Zastrow completed five of ten passes for 68 yards, all in the first half, while Bobby Blaik was held to five completions in twenty-two for a mere 54 yards, and the other Army passers hit for only one in three. Pollard was held to 52 yards in twenty-one tries, was often smeared at the scrimmage line by Fritz Davis, a demon left tackle of 6 feet 4 and 210 pounds, or Bob McDonald, his end neighbor. No other Army runner could dent Navy's ferocious line; the Cadets could not, with all their vaunted speed, get around the ends. Army attacked virtually all the way on the first count, but Navy, with shifting lines in four to eight-man alignments, was always ready for the Cadets. Army rarely changed direction on its plays, pounded Navy's left endlessly and fruitlessly.

Navy, for its part, came out with new stuff. Erdelatz installed a split end and a halfback or fullback flanker. Often the split end and flanker were on the same side; sometimes spread on either side. They got good blocking angles. Navy had deception and change-of-direction plays, and pulled a fancy wide reverse, a naked reverse by Powers which went for 22 yards, the biggest run of the day that set up

Navy's second score in the last minute before the half.

Though Francis Brady fumbled and recovered the opening kickoff, Navy wasn't a fumbling team today as it had been all year. Navy immediately began to move through Army. But on a fourth down at the Navy 35, Bob Cameron couldn't get his punt away, ran instead and was knocked down. He fumbled. Army had the ball at the 22, but gave it up on the 15.

The decisive second quarter opened innocently enough with Navy halted at midfield and punting. The next time Navy moved up 26 yards with two first downs, before Hal Loehlein, of Army, intercepted on his 33 and came back to the 43. On the first down, Pollard, who came into the game for Gil Stephenson in the second period, fumbled a pitchout and McDonald recovered on the Army 27. An offside penalty set Navy back to the 33 (the referee was stepping off six yards for five at this time), and Navy went for the score in four plays.

Zastrow, after a double fake into the line, hit Art Sundry on an 18-yard pass on the right sideline. Sundry made two yards. With the split end and halfback flanker to the right, Zastrow reached Hauff on the left with a 6-yard pass, Hauff sitting down on the catch.

On the next line-up, Zastrow burst through guard on a quarterback sneak, was stopped twice, but tore loose into the end zone. Drew kicked the point, and the Navy side, where the President sat (Navy was host), went crazy with excitement.

Army reacted vigorously to this challenge. Blaik hit Foldberg with a 26-yard pass to the 36, but Army picked up only two more yards and, conservatively, punted. Blaik kicked out on the 4. This should have set up an Army chance. But Army, getting the return punt on Navy's 39, couldn't go anywhere. Army got reckless. It tried a fourth-down pass on the 37 and lost the ball.

Navy, on fire, took it and went 63 yards in five plays against the clock to its second touchdown. Zastrow started with an 11-yard burst on a sneak, threw an incomplete pass, then Powers, on the naked reverse, got loose around Army's left for 22 yards to the 30. Another incomplete Zastrow pass, then Zastrow faded to his left and threw to Baldinger in the end zone.

The hoax described here is probably as close as anyone will ever come to turning Rackety Rax (see page 269) into reality. It was the most imaginative play of the 1941 season.

UNDEFEATED, UNTIED, UNFOUNDED

Caswell Adams

Far above New Jersey's swamplands
Plainfield Teachers' spires
Mark a phantom, phony college
That got on the wires.
Perfect record made on paper,
Imaginary team!
Hail to thee, our ghostly college,
Product of a dream!

A group of Wall Street brokers, with time heavy on their hands, recently perpetrated a classic gag on the newspapers, a gag which was exposed only after considerable investigation into the whereabouts of Plainfield Teachers —unbeaten and untied in six games this season (although there's no such place or no such team). The brokers had been reporting the scores of this phantom institution of learning to newspapers all autumn, and the New York *Herald Tribune,* the *Times,* the *Post,* the Associated Press accepted the information, dutifully printed it, and eventually longed for more news about John Chung, "stellar Chinese halfback" for Plainfield Teachers.

This modern version of Joel Sayre's *Rackety Rax* was the brainchild of a few stockbrokers

at Newburger, Loeb & Co., who were wondering one day how such places as Slippery Rock got their scores into the newspapers. This led to the founding of Plainfield Teachers in the hope that dear old P.T. could get some space, too. The brokers took turns calling the papers on Saturday afternoon to report new victories for the team—and then gleefully awaited the Sunday editions. They even had a Philadelphia outlet, which hoodwinked the *Record*—and the leak finally came from there. At least that's what they believe after they had been tracked down and made to come clean. The leak reached *Time* magazine, which carries an item on the gag in the current issue. The brokers tried unsuccessfully to talk *Time*'s editors out of printing it. When they knew the jig—or gag—was up they sent out one last publicity release and then had the one telephone at Plainfield Teachers disconnected.

The last publicity blurb, sent out by a press agent here, was to the effect that because of a phalanx of flunkings in the midterm examinations Plainfield Teachers was forced to call off its last two scheduled games, with Appalachian

Tech, November 15, and with Harmony Teachers, Thanksgiving Day.

"Among those thrown for a loss at examination time was John Chung, stellar Chinese halfback of the team, who has accounted for 69 of Plainfield's 117 points," the blurb read. Plainfield, according to the record, had trampled successively on Scott, Chesterton, Winona, Randolph Tech, Ingersoll and St. Joseph. And Appalachian was to be stifled, 20–2, and Harmony was to put up a great game but succumb to Chung's wizardry, 40–27.

When the hoax was thriving Herb Allan in the *Post* printed a glowing piece about Chung's exploits and the brokers decided that they needed a publicity man and a telephone. They invented the name Jerry Croyden for the tub thumper, and had a phone installed in Morris Newburger's office. But the phone was discontinued Wednesday. The telephone service cost $5.

After the exposé there were suspicions that a betting coup was involved in the scheme, but there was no such thought. Plainfield Teachers wasn't a money-maker; it was just plain fun. When the cultured voice of "Jerry Croyden" called a newspaper the other night and gave the score of the Randolph Tech game (35–0), the rewrite man asked where Randolph Tech was. "Delaware," was the prompt reply. "Wilmington?" queried the rewrite man. "No, just outside," said Jerry Croyden.

*For some reason, the season of 1916 was particularly merciless on the downtrodden
in football. Oberlin was humiliated by its big neighbor, Ohio State, 128–0; Missouri
Mines crumbled before Tulsa, 117–0; the Shawnee Catholic Indians fell before Oklahoma,
140–0. But the most inflexible punishment of all was received by little Cumberland College
(in Tennessee) at the hands of Georgia Tech. The score, 222–0, is a record that will
surely withstand the passage of time and the changes in the rules. The game seemed to
prove a favorite theme of Georgia Tech's famous coach John Heisman: comparative
scores are meaningless in football. It also proved that when your team is trailing 126–0
at halftime—as Cumberland was—things are bound to get better.*

THE GLORIOUS SLAUGHTER

Gerald Astor

A football game between Georgia Tech and
Cumberland College was played on October 7,
1916, and the one thing never in dispute about
it was the score. The most devoted Cumberland
alumnus was not prepared to holler robbery, for
Georgia Tech won 222–0. But everything else
about the game is argued morbidly, and Cumberland rooters hate any suggestion that theirs
was not the rout of the ages. The game lasted
only forty-five minutes. Who—Cumberlanders
ask haughtily—has ever been beaten more decisively in so short a time?

The myths and facts are not easy to sort out,
but something like the following seems to have
taken place. Around the turn of the century
Cumberland in Lebanon, Tennessee played
formidable football but by 1916 enthusiasm for
the sport had waned until it was little more
than a casual pastime for undergraduates and
students at the one-year law school. They
organized teams and scheduled games hap-
hazardly, meeting prep schools one week
and colleges the next. Football schedules
in 1916 were more informal than they are
today.

Georgia Tech was looking around that fall
for an opponent to fatten its prestige, of which
it already had a lot. Since Cumberland had
humiliated Tech in baseball the preceding

spring, football offered a chance to work off
the grudge. Tech offered a $500 guarantee, and
Cumberland agreed to the game.

Cumberland's coach was a law student named
Butch McQueen. He scoured the campus to
pick up sixteen of the healthiest and most experienced specimens around. One of them was
Gentry Dugat, who said recently, "I played once
in high school and once in prep school. But
they promised me the first Pullman ride of my
life and a chance to visit the home of my idol,
Henry Grady (the editor of the *Atlanta Constitution*)."

The Cumberland squad practiced hard and
worked up a simple series of set plays to use
against Tech. To strengthen the team Cumberland hoped to pick up some "Hessians" from
Vanderbilt College when the team's train
stopped at Nashville on the trip from Cumberland to Atlanta.

Instead, the first casualties were suffered in
Nashville. Three members of the team missed
the train after the layover. Worse, additional
troops could not be hired, for Vanderbilt had a
tough game coming up and did not care to risk
its prize specimens against a reportedly strong
Georgia Tech team. Shaken but determined, the
small Cumberland squad advanced on Atlanta,
determined at least to collect the guarantee.

24

They didn't figure to win, but they thought they would put up a good fight.

They reckoned without the character of the Georgia Tech coach, the able and devious John Heisman, one of football's hallowed names. Heisman was a great coach. It was he who got the forward pass legalized, he who originated the hidden-ball trick, he who introduced the center snap and he who invented the scoreboard, which listed downs, yards to go and other data.

Heisman was also a great eccentric. He outlawed soup and hot water for his players on the grounds that it weakened them. He banned from the training table any foods he himself did not like, such as nuts, coffee and apples. He liked raw meat, and the team got lots of that. His creed would have pleased Machiavelli and alarmed Lord Acton. "The coach should be masterful and commanding, even dictatorial," Heisman once said. "He has not the time to say please or mister . . . he must be severe, arbitrary and little short of a czar."

Shortly before the Cumberland game, Heisman became infuriated with newspaper stories that assigned great value to the margin of victory. Heisman recalled his indignation in murky rhetoric a year after the game. "I have often contended that this habit on the part of sportswriters of totaling up the number of points each team has amassed in its various games and comparing them with one another was a useless thing. . . . Finding folks are determined to take the crazy thing into consideration, we at Tech determined last year, at the start of the season, to show folks it was no difficult thing to run up a score in one easy game, from which it might perhaps be seen that it could also be done in other easy games as well."

Unaware that Heisman planned to try out his grisly theory on them, the Cumberland football players marched onto Grant Field in Atlanta. On hand to observe the skirmish were 1,000 spectators.

Tech won the toss and performed its only act of charity for the afternoon by electing to kick off. Cumberland's Carney received on his 25-yard line and was dropped immediately. Attempting to block for Carney on this play, Quarterback Edwards was knocked senseless and Morris Gouger (later a banker in Robstown, Texas) took over the direction of the team. Gouger went over tackle and gained three yards. It was Cumberland's biggest rushing gain of the day.

When McDonald made no yardage on his try at the line, Cumberland punted. Everett Strupper, a future All-Conference back for Georgia Tech, returned the ball all the way to the Cumberland 20. On Tech's first play Strupper swept left end for a touchdown. Jim Preas kicked the extra point, and Tech led 7–0.

Cumberland returned the ensuing kickoff to its own 10, but on the first play from scrimmage there was a fumble. Tech Halfback Guill scooped up the ball and ran into the end zone for a second touchdown. Preas kicked the extra point.

The pattern continued for two more touchdowns. Georgia Tech would kick off, Cumberland would try futilely to gain, Tech would take over and score with insulting ease. Behind 28–0, Cumberland shifted strategy. Instead of receiving, they would kick off, forcing Georgia Tech deep into its own territory. On the first such attempt the kickoff was returned 70 yards to the Cumberland 10. It took two plays to put the ball across the goal line. The next Cumberland kickoff was returned to Tech's 40. On the first play from scrimmage Everett Strupper went 60 yards for another touchdown, Jim Preas kicked his sixth extra point and Georgia Tech led 42–0. Cumberland kicked off again. Its defenses stiffened, and Georgia Tech needed three plays to move 65 yards to another touchdown.

Cumberland went back to receiving. They failed to gain, punted and watched Strupper return the ball 45 yards for six more points. Cumberland went back to kicking off. Spence returned the kickoff 90 yards for a touchdown, and the quarter ended with Georgia Tech leading 63–0.

In the second quarter Cumberland numbly gave up kicking off and took comfort in holding the ball as long as possible between touchdowns. In no case did that interval last very long for Cumberland never made a first down, and Tech never needed more than two plays to reach the Cumberland end zone. Sometimes it took fewer. With Georgia Tech leading 105–0, Preas kicked off to Gouger, who fumbled. Preas picked up the ball, ran for the touchdown and then made the extra point. The half ended with the score 126–0.

Early in the second half Georgia Tech, for the first time during the game, exhibited signs of something other than cold efficiency. J. C. Alexander, a massive Yellow Jacket tackle, had never experienced the thrill of scoring a touchdown. He was handed the ball on the Cumberland 10-yard line and aimed toward the goal but, as a big joke, nobody on Tech blocked. Alexander could get the ball only to the three-yard line. As if shocked by their lack of professionalism, Tech stopped its nonsense and Strupper took the ball over on the next play.

Midway through the third quarter, Strupper rounded right end for yet another touchdown, and the extra point pushed the score to 154–0, which set a world's record. John Heisman still had a point or two, however, to make in his argument with the newspapermen. Georgia Tech continued to bowl along, scoring every time it got the ball.

In the final quarter McDonald of Cumberland completed a pass to Murphy for ten yards —the biggest Cumberland gain for the afternoon. Since two previous running plays had lost 18 yards, it was not enough for a first down.

By this time the tiny Cumberland squad was nearing exhaustion (Tech was pretty tired, too, but only from running). George Griffin, quarterback for the Engineers, recalls a moment when Heisman discovered a couple of Cumberland players seated on the bench. "He yelled at them to get back to their side of the field. They said, 'Give us a break. Don't make us go back. We'll have to go into the game.'"

Battered as they were the Cumberland players stuck it out, trying to hold the score down by clinging to the ball. From the bench George E. Allen, the student manager of the team (and later close friend of four U.S. presidents), encouraged the team not to quit, for they would then have to forfeit the game. Over the years Allen has embellished his part in the debacle. He claimed that he was the fullback when another player fumbled and yelled at Allen to fall on the ball. Allen is supposed to have replied, "Not me. I didn't drop it."

Any suggestion of cowardice on the part of the Cumberland players still angers survivors of the game. "We may have been unskilled and badly beaten," says Gentry Dugat, "but we were not yellow."

The pattern of the game left a permanent mark on one member of the team, punter R. E. Gray. After every unsuccessful attempt to make a first down the team called for a kick with the signal, "Gray back." It was called so often that the punter has carried the nickname, Grayback, ever since.

Georgia Tech amassed 528 yards rushing, returned punts 220 yards and kickoffs 220 yards. It threw no passes. Cumberland lost 45 yards rushing, completed two of 11 passes for 14 yards and fumbled nine times.

Forty years after the game Gentry Dugat, at a reunion of both teams, spoke the Cumberland football epitaph. "Little did we realize we were playing ourselves into immortality that day. We made you of Georgia Tech a great team."

If you're of the opinion that Princeton men have always had a stodgy, single-wing attitude toward the game, read these lyrics by two Princeton men.

From *GOAL LINES*

A. C. M. Azoy, Jr., and Frank Halsey

The 1921 Backfield

Lourie and Garrity, Gilroy and Cleaves,
Footballers flightsome as autumn-blown leaves,
Filling the Princetons with riotous joy,
Lourie and Garrity, Cleaves and Gilroy.

Gilroy and Cleaves, and Lourie and Garrity,
No hope for Harvard or Yale to get charity;
Worthy a wager of all your wife's dowry—
Garrity, Cleaves, Gilroy and Lourie.

SCHEERER'S SPRINT
OR
The Battle Hymn of the Bowl
Princeton 13, Yale 6
Yale Bowl, November 10, 1919

Now glory to the Lord of Hosts, from whom all glories are!
And glory to that agile youth, whose fame has gone afar!
Now let there be the merry sound of music and of cheers,
Albeit Prohibition's come and we're done out of beers.
And thou, New Haven-on-the-Sound, proud city of the Yales
Again let gloom enshroud thy walls and loudly rise thy wails.
As thou wert joyous in our ills, be saddened in our joy;

For Justice now has seen the light, and wrought thy team annoy.[1]
Huzza! Huzza! A single run did turn the chance of war!
O sound the brass for little Joe, and twang the light guitar! [2]

Gosh! how our hearts were beating, when near the end of day,
We saw the Bulldogs [3] in the Bowl, drawn out in long array;
Eleven doughty warriors, bedecked with azure wool,
And Kempton playing quarterback, and Bullet Jim at full,
And Yale with three points to the good—ah, shame that this should be—
To see the scoreboard give Yale 6, and Princeton only 3!
But lo! Frank Murrey kicks a goal, and now the score is tied;
At least Yale does not *win* the day, whatever else betide.
Yet loud we cry unto the god who rules the fate of war
To grant us one, or two, points more—we're not particular!

McGraw is come to marshal us, in all his armour dress'd,
But he has bound no snow-white plume upon his gallant crest.
(He has no snow-white plume to bind, but O his shining eye!)
He look'd upon the Elis, and his glance was stern and high;
Right graciously he smiled on us as skyward rose our hail,
And from the stands we loosed the plea that fits be given Yale.
And yet we knew not, nor did he, what was to turn the tide,
But none the less he smote his breast and manfully he cried:
"Look well to see some round dome shine amidst the ranks of war,
To be your oriflamme today—a helmet of Navarre!"

Zowie! The foe are moving. They catch the kicked-off ball,
But in their haste to run it back they do not gain at all.
Now Fido Kempton runs *à gauche;* [4] he makes a sideways pass—
But there is none to catch it, and the ball is on the grass!
The ball is on the grass alone—O men of Old Nassau,
Charge for the Tiger Lilies! [5] Unsheath the Tiger's claw!
A hundred cleats dig in the turf, two score of arms reach out—
Look you, someone hath seized the ball! Hark to the Princeton shout!
Confusion worse confounded! But, like a guiding star,
Joe Scheerer's helmet leads the way, like that one of Navarre!

With blanching cheeks and fevered brows, the Yales rush up pell-mell,
But Raymond gets right in their way, and Garrity as well;
Likewise McGraw and Trimble find a way to block the path
Of all the frenzied Bulldog host who—tell it not in Gath,—
Are perjuring their little souls with heartfelt statements mighty,
The while they struggle just to get one hand on Joe the flighty;
But Joe has influential friends who help him on his hike,
As through the serried ranks of blue he flashes serpent-like.
He dodges here, he dodges there, he's almost down—*he's up!*
O never was a game like this since Hector was a pup.

Allah be praised! the day is ours, for Joe hath crossed the line,
And Yale hath cried for water, full half her team supine.
Their ranks have broken like thin clouds before a Biscáy gale;

[1] An unusual form, used as Macaulay used it in a rather decent poem of his quite similar to this one. Means, in this sense, "annoy."
[2] Or twang the heavy one, for that matter; it's nothing to us.
[3] Goldfish come in bowls all through the year, but bulldogs only seasonally.
[4] Or, as the French say, *to the left.*
[5] In other words, say it with flowers.

The field is heaped with broken hearts and wet with tears of Yale.
And all Yale's stands are hushed, are hushed—but loud across the field
The gladsome shouts of Princeton men are pealed and pealed and pealed.
Behold! the goal is kicked forthwith and addeth one point more,
And Princeton 13 to Yale 6 is now the tidy score.
Oh was there ever such a run, in football or in war,
As that of Joe's—although Yale thinks he went a bit too far!

Ho! men of Skull and Bones, and ho! [6] ye men of Scroll and Keys!
Get out your votive offerings, and bend your pious knees;
Enshroud the Old Yale Fence in black, the Taft go hang with crepe,
Have stilled all campus laughter, each merry quip and jape;
In sackcloth and in ashes, go jump off Savin Rock,[7]
And call down everlasting hate upon J. Scheerer's block!
For this day ye have lost the fight, the fight [8] you've lost this day,
And all your prayers and curses that fact cannot gainsay.
So glory to the Lord of Hosts, from whom all glories are!
And glory to Joe's headguard, that new helmet of Navarre!

[6] At the second *ho!,* Yale men customarily leave the room for, as in the Ku Klux Klan, the secrecy of these Yale societies is preserved by certain klegalities. It has something to do, we believe, with the Tap Room in the Taft, mentioned two lines further down in the same stanza.

[7] The name, not of a geological formation, but of a beach resort, so-called for the same reason that summer hotels two miles inland are always named "Ocean View," and those on the sand-dunes, "The Bluffs." Or possibly its name is derived from that once popular lullaby, *O come to Savin, Rock and Rye.* We do not remember how the rest of the song goes, but why go further?

[8] To *fight* add: *football game, bets,* and *temper.*

Cornell vs. Rochester, 1889

LINE UP FOR YESTERDAY

The T-formation crouch, 1900

The flying wedge, 1890

When Southern California defeated Notre Dame, 16–14, in 1931, by scoring all its points in the last period, the Hollywood finish evoked one of the biggest outbursts of patriotism ever seen in Los Angeles. Long-time residents of the area still refer to Johnny Baker's winning field goal, which temporarily ended Notre Dame's long domination of college football, as The Kick. This is Baker's description of The Kick and the moments that surrounded it. Unrecorded here is the reaction of Coach Howard Jones, SC's revered "Head Man." After the placement Jones raced onto the field and kissed Captain Stanley Williamson who had just bussed Johnny Baker. Later he steadfastly defended the right of Williamson and Quarterback Orv Mohler to reject the substitute that he had sent in for the last play.

THE KICK

Johnny Baker

There were only four minutes left and the ball was on our own 17-yard line. We were trailing Notre Dame, 14–13, and the chances of our moving 83 yards for the score that would break Notre Dame's victory streak of twenty-six games seemed remote. But a tremendous team effort on a pair of passes—and a little luck—suddenly put us within striking distance.

The passes—one from Gus Shaver to Sparling and the other from Shaver to Hall—gained 63 yards. An offside against Notre Dame and a running play put the ball on the 13-yard line. A pass by Orv Mohler intended for Clark was knocked down. Now with third down and the clock running out we went back into the huddle as fired up as any Trojan team I've ever played on.

There wasn't a dissenting voice when Quarterback Mohler called for a place-kick. But the goose pimples almost sprouted through my jersey because it meant that I would do the kicking and Mohler would hold. Although I had never kicked a field goal in a regular game, Mohler and I had practiced together for two years.

As we ran to our positions the whistle blew and my first thought was that the game had ended—although I was sure we had nearly two minutes left. My heart sank right into my shoes but then I noticed a substitute dashing in from our bench. He was Homer Griffith, sophomore quarterback, coming in to replace Mohler. Griffith had no more than reached the field when he was waved back to the bench by Mohler and our captain Stanley Williamson. It was apparent what Coach Jones wanted. In countermanding the order Williamson was indicating that the right play had been called and the team had preferred the ball be held by Mohler rather than Griffith.

The whistle blew again and we moved into our positions—and a thousand thoughts went through my mind in the next few seconds. I knew I could not go back to Los Angeles if I missed. Howard Jones had been coaching at Southern California since 1925 and in those seven years his teams had lost ten games. But —and this was what was racing through my mind—five of the defeats had been by the margin of one point. Three of them had been at the hands of Notre Dame! I had heard those one-point defeats rehashed at fraternity houses and on campus until I felt I had actually played in every one of them. Anyway, the one-point jinx was staring us in the face again as Mohler called the signals for the kick. Gus Shaver, our fullback, had taken my place at guard and we were as ready as we ever would be.

I took a long look at the crossbar and then lowered my head. Williamson snapped the ball to Mohler—a fine pass and Orv set it up perfectly. My foot went forward, my head stayed down, and I had no idea whether the kick was successful until Mohler shouted, "It's good!" I looked up and saw the ball in the air, sailing into the solid mass of spectators at the end of Notre Dame Stadium. Then my teammates were pounding me on the back and Williamson raced up and kissed me—which shows you what a football player will do when he gets excited.

CARTOON BY GEORGE PRICE

© 1951 The New Yorker Magazine, Inc.

Football was banned in England by King Henry II (1154–1189) because the villagers were foregoing archery practice to kick the bladder around. The antifootball laws lasted for nearly four hundred years but, as Poet Barclay's lines indicate, the prohibition was not completely successful.

ECHE TIME AND SEASON

Alexander Barclay

Eche time and season hath his delite & joyes,
Loke in the stretes, behold the little boyes,
Howe in fruit season for joy they sing and hop,
In Lent is eche one full busy with his top
And nowe in winter for all the greevous cold,
All rent and ragged a man may them beholde,
They have great pleasor supposing well to dine,
When men be busied in killing of fat swine,
They get the bladder and blow it great and thin,
With many beanes or peason put within;
It ratleth, soundeth, and shineth clere & feyre,
While it is throwen and caste up in the ayre.
Eche one contendeth and hath a great delite
With foote & hande the bladder for to smite:
If it fall to grounde they lifte it up agayne,
This wise to labour they count it for no paine,
Renning and leaping they drive away the colde.
The sturdie plowman, lustie, strong & bolde
Overcommeth the winter with driving the footeball,
Forgetting labour and many a grevous fall.

35

Did George Gipp, as he lay dying in a hospital, tell Rockne that he hoped some day Notre Dame would win one for him? And did Rockne ask his players before the 1928 Army game to win it for the Gipper? The answer to the first question is that such a romantic notion would have been completely out of character for a pool player and gambler like Gipp. But it would have been natural for Rockne to use Gipp as an emotional prop in one of his pre-game pep talks. Chet Grant, a teammate of Gipp's, says that Rockne actually pulled the "win one for the Gipper" stunt for the first time at the 1921 Indiana game, the year after George Gipp died. Chet was quarterback then and the Irish beat Indiana easily, 28–7. "Winning one for the Gipper" belongs to the folklore of the game; the real Gipp was a remarkable young man whose interest in adult games gave him precious little time to devote to football. This is an unadorned story of a vagabond athlete whose name became legend.

GIPP

Jim Beach

At seven o'clock on the bone-chilling winter evening of December 14, 1920, a young man lay close to death in St. Joseph's Hospital, South Bend, Indiana, suffering from a streptococcus infection that had now reached its critical phase.

At that hour the entire student body of the University of Notre Dame was joined in prayer. Some of the boys were kneeling in chapels on campus; others knelt in the snow, reciting the Rosary on the hospital grounds.

At the Oliver Hotel on North Main Street, there was a spirit of gloom in the rooms where the smart money guys, card sharks, and traveling salesmen had gathered for the nightly dice, poker, and rummy sessions which the sick man had regularly attended.

A few minutes past seven, the hotel lights dimmed and flickered, and although there had been no prearranged signal, this message from the desk clerk was correctly interpreted to mean that George Gipp was dead.

George Gipp—the first Notre Dame man to be chosen All-America by Walter Camp—was a football star who in his brief twenty-five years on earth had been raised to the stature of a demigod. His astounding feats inspired Ring Lardner to write that the Notre Dame team seemed to have only one formation and one

signal: ". . . line up, pass the ball to Gipp and let him use his own judgment."

The innocent years immediately preceding, during and following World War I are commonly thought of as the "Old Siwash" era. It was an era typified by a mole-skin-clad lad named Gipp, who could run with the speed and power of a stallion, pass a football through a needle's eye at 40 yards, punt soaring spirals and drop-kick field goals with the precision and poise of an automaton. George Gipp was a national celebrity, regarded with the same awe as Woodrow Wilson, "Black Jack" Pershing and Douglas Fairbanks.

As a youngster living at Laurium, Michigan —a small mining and industrial community located near the shores of Lake Superior—Gipp first revealed his athletic ability. In those days, baseball and basketball were his sports. He did play some football at Calumet High School, but he was slight of build and got banged up too often. On the basketball court George made up for his fragile frame with speed and accuracy, and he starred on a team that won twenty-four out of twenty-five games and brought Calumet its first regional championship. It was baseball, however, that brought him hometown fame. Old codgers around Laurium still recall him as a dark-haired, gangling school-boy who could belt the ball for extra bases against grown-men pitchers.

While he excelled in sports, his scholarship was a different story. He managed to get passing grades, but after he and some of his buddies were accused of vandalism, George was suspended from school. The result was that he didn't get a diploma and took a job driving a taxi.

Hacking soon put Gipp wise to the shadier aspects of life in the tough copper country. He matured far beyond his years in many respects, but he had no plans for the future.

"George," his older brother Alex finally told him, "the best thing for you is to get out of town."

George spoke in short, clipped sentences. "I like it here," he replied. "Besides, who are you to give me advice? You came back home after college, didn't you?"

"But you've got the brains in this family, kid," Alex argued.

But the most Alex could accomplish was getting George to go to work on a line gang for the Michigan Bell telephone company—rough and dangerous work. The lanky twenty-year-old had the strength and stamina required, and he was agile and quick climbing telephone poles to string and repair wire. Away from the job, though, George was restless and unable to settle down.

His stern, bearded father, a hard-working carpenter and laborer who had sired a family of eight children, and his gentle, Scotch-Irish mother didn't approve of their youngest son's shiftlessness. They were alarmed, too, at the time he spent hanging out in saloons and pool parlors.

"Matthew," his mother would chide her husband when he criticized George's shiftlessness, "he'll find out what he wants to do soon enough."

George resented the strict Baptist discipline maintained in the Gipp home. He escaped from the constant prodding and carping by following a well-worn path away from the frame house on Hecla Street toward the bright lights of Calumet. He would prowl the honky-tonks, shooting pool and playing cards with pals from his Calumet High days, and he indulged in the conventional vices.

A girl named Hazel—the town beauty—was one of the reasons George remained in Laurium. But because he considered her to be on a higher social level, George admired her from afar.

The mounting friction in the Gipp household reached a climax in the summer of 1916, when Bill Gray, a baseball catcher who had been signed by the Chicago White Sox after playing college ball at Notre Dame, returned home to Calumet for a few days. Bill told George he would be a cinch for a scholarship at Notre Dame—then a minor university—and that he thought he could arrange it for him. Although George expressed little interest, Gray got him an offer of free tuition if he would play baseball. He could earn his bed and board working as a waiter in a student dining hall.

At the age of twenty-one, George Gipp packed his pool cue and some clothes and set out for Notre Dame.

When Gipp came down the pike it wasn't difficult to pass muster at the registrar's office. He indicated a willingness to study and was assigned a bed in the Brownson Hall dormitory. To his dismay, he had to pay for books, classroom supplies, registration fees and other routine expenses, and was charged for his laundry and other incidental items. It wasn't long before he had only fifteen cents left.

Notre Dame was primarily a poor man's school, where virtually all students dressed in the same manner and ate the same meals regardless of blood lines, bank accounts or religious background. The average fellow thought he was flush if he had a dime and a nickel to rub together. It was a Spartan existence, characterized by a strong spiritual undercurrent from which George felt apart. Men like the Fathers and Brothers of the Congregation of the Holy Cross who taught and administered at the Catholic university were strange to him. Although it took him a while to become accustomed to the strict ways of life in a Catholic college, George grew to respect and admire the priests for their devotion, sacrifice and faith. But, as in the case of Hazel, he admired from afar and followed the path that led him to the bright lights of South Bend.

One afternoon, Knute Rockne, then a Notre Dame chemistry instructor who doubled as assistant to football coach Jesse Harper and as team trainer to supplement his meager income, was strolling across the recreation field alongside Brownson Hall. Suddenly, he stopped in his tracks and watched a 60-yard punt sail over his head. He looked around to see who had kicked it and there stood George Gipp—wearing street shoes. By now, George was a 175-pound six-footer with lean muscles, long legs and broad shoulders.

"Why aren't you out for the freshman

squad?" the burly man with the knuckle-dented nose asked.

"Football isn't my game," Gipp replied.

"Afraid?" Rockne said, laughing.

"Like hell I am!"

"Oh, you're tough?"

"As tough as I need to be."

"Think it over. I'll be handing out equipment over at the Field House in an hour or so. I've got just the pair of cleats for you."

"A special pair?" George asked.

"Yeah," Rock said, "they belonged to Ray Eichenlaub."

"Who is he?"

"Around these parts he was known as a *real* Notre Dame man."

Rockne had gauged the kid correctly. The barb stung Gipp's pride, and he reported for practice.

The name George Gipp first appeared in sports page headlines a few weeks later. He made the freshman team and was a starter at left halfback against Western State Normal School at Kalamazoo, Michigan, where his brother Matt was living. In the fourth quarter the score was tied, 7–7. Notre Dame had yardage to go for a first down. On fourth down, quarterback Frank Thomas barked the signals for a shift from the "T" to punt formation, with Gipp back in kicking position. As the ball was snapped from center, Notre Dame end Dave Hayes took off at full speed to get down under the punt. He sprinted straight for the Western State safety man, but slowed down when he saw the player turn around to face his own goal. Then Dave became conscious of the cheering crowd.

"What happened?" Hayes asked.

"That sonofabitch kicked a field goal," the State safety man told him.

Gipp, not wanting to settle for a tie, had drop-kicked—62 yards between the uprights and over the crossbar. The record still stands in the books.

Gipp wasn't at all ruffled by the applause he received for his remarkable feat at Kalamazoo, and he accepted prestige as a matter of course. Once his status as an athlete was established, he moved from Brownson Hall to Sarin Hall, where he bunked with athletic scholarship men. Yet he still had to don a waiter's white jacket and sling hash.

George played freshman basketball that winter and ran anchor in the intramural track relays. The evening hours usually were spent in the recreation room with his roommate and friend Elwyn "Dope" Moore.

"Make you a proposition, Dope," Gipp said one night. "You teach me three-cushion billiards and I'll stop taking your money at pool."

"Since I lose to you all the time, old buddy," Moore said, "I guess that's a pretty good deal for me. You've got yourself a teacher, and I'm the best."

"The best for now, but not for long," George said.

For a number of weeks afterward George concentrated on perfecting his smooth cue stroke at billiards, a game he found both challenging and stimulating. Meanwhile, he shot Kelly pool and snooker for small change. Since the financial returns were limited around the campus, George soon set out in search of bigger action. This meant taking the Hill Street trolley to the billiard halls of South Bend.

Playing pool, George was, as always, the picture of nonchalance. He would saunter into the room, remove his jacket and hang it on a wall peg. Then he would take his stick down from the rack and chalk up, all the while sizing up the skills of the men at the tables. Having selected his victim, he would begin the customary pregame con.

"How many will you spot me?" he would ask an unwary stranger.

The poolroom loafers who had seen George play, or who knew him by reputation, would cluster around the table as Gipp flubbed a few practice shots.

"It would be foolish, you playin' me," the mark would say.

"Put some money where your mouth is."

"Okay, laddie buck. I'll spot you ten balls. For ten bucks."

At this point, Gipp would dangle a cigarette from the corner of his mouth and say, "Why not make it more interesting?"

"Are you good for twenty-five?"

"If he ain't, I am," the proprietor would say.

"It's like a license to steal," the patsy would remark. "Anytime you're ready, Buster."

Gipp would always lose the first game. Then he'd ask, "How about a chance to get even?"

"Be my guest," the stranger would say.

"For a hundred bucks?"

"You got yourself a bet."

George's opponent would then scatter the balls and Gipp would settle down to work. It wasn't at all unusual for him to make fifty consecutive shots when it was worthwhile. It was worthwhile. It was how he made his living.

Gipp's behavior was not unusual in a period when the tramp athlete was a fixture at most colleges. Notre Dame had adopted strict standards of eligibility for athletes—insisting on a 76 per cent grade instead of the 70 per cent commonly accepted by most of the big colleges. But George took advantage of his growing fame, and his individuality was regarded with leniency by certain members of the faculty.

Knute Rockne, himself a non-conformist, made it his business to be Gipp's protector and apologist. He had a deep-rooted fondness for George, based on respect for his native intelligence and athletic ability.

In football, George applied himself solely to theory. It bewildered his coaches that he improved as a player without going through the intermediate steps of instruction and practice.

"He doesn't have to be told anything twice," Rock said to Harper. "And more often than not, he does the correct thing the first time without being taught. For him, football is strictly a game of brains. . . ."

George absorbed most of his knowledge of football at the noon chalk-talks conducted in in the off-season by Harper and Rockne. He was counted on for regular varsity duty in his sophomore year, 1917, when America entered the war and ten Notre Dame lettermen enlisted.

Gipp spent the summer vacation playing professional baseball. When the squad assembled for fall practice, George was among the missing. Rockne finally learned that he was playing for the Simmons Baseball Club in Kenosha, Wisconsin. Rock chased up north to investigate and found George sitting on the bench.

"Hiya," the coach said. "Been playing much?"

"Some."

"The manager tells me not at all. Guess he was afraid it would cost you your amateur standing."

"Maybe."

Rockne told Gipp he had no future knocking around the country, picking up a few dollars here and there. And when George argued that there was no percentage in it for him to go back to college, Rock had the answers to prove George was wrong. They talked well into the night, but Rockne knew he needed Gipp, and when he took the train back to South Bend, his star backfield man went with him.

The subject of Gipp's border-line professionalism was kept secret. It never came up again, even though George would often pick up a few dollars playing "town ball" under assumed names on Sundays. But Rockne couldn't kick—he had done the same thing in his undergraduate days at Notre Dame.

In 1917, Gipp showed signs of fulfilling his promise of gridiron greatness. He was hampered by a muddy field in the Nebraska game. But under the same weather conditions at West Point, he stole the show from Cadet Elmer Q. Oliphant by playing the full sixty minutes and sparking Notre Dame to a 7–2 victory.

When the team arrived at the South Bend railroad station after the Army game, George flashed a wry smile as the students mobbed him. Then he left the party to join some of his downtown cronies. He had bet some money for them and was bringing home the winnings, part of which was his commission for handling the transactions.

Gipp's first varsity season was cut short the following Saturday. In a game with Morningside at Sioux City, Iowa, he was tackled and thrown against an iron post near the sideline. His leg was broken. After spending a short time in the infirmary, he went home to Laurium on crutches.

The following spring George still walked with a limp, and the draft board deferred action on his case. But when word reached the board the next fall that Gipp was playing football, an induction notice was drawn up and mailed special delivery, ordering him to report for military duty at South Bend on October 19, 1918. But the Armistice was signed on November 11, and Gipp's only uniforms were baseball flannels and a blue football jersey with a big 66 on the back.

In the 1918 season—Rockne's first as head coach—Gipp became a full-fledged star. Yet, he never had the spirit and attitude expected of a football hero.

Football ordinarily requires a basic urge for tooth-rattling, rock-'em sock-'em body contact. The average player gets fun out of the sport by putting his strength, skill and courage to the bloody test without hesitation. Gipp was an exception. It wasn't that he disliked the game; he just took no particular delight in it. Moreover, his physical condition was seldom up to taking the punishment. A priest at Notre Dame once asked him why he didn't do more blocking and make more tackles. "I let the strong boys do that," George answered.

In Sarin Hall bull sessions, Gipp was often the Number One topic. Right halfback Grover Malone, whom George preferred to have blocking for him, spoke with authority on the subject. "The thing that makes him a slick customer is that he avoids trouble. When he is hit with a solid tackle, he relaxes and goes down. He's always saving himself for next time."

George made his own hours on the practice

field, and he wouldn't work out more than three times a week. The other players were usually taped, suited up and gone before Gipp wandered into the locker room. They had been catching punts and running wind sprints for half an hour when he finally joined the practice. George would kick a few and say, "Let's go. I'm ready."

During the play, Gipp disguised whatever excitement he may have felt with a quiet calm. He used razzle-dazzle to good advantage, and speed was his strongest point. He had the habit of talking to his blockers as he advanced downfield: *"Take him to the outside . . . Let this one go . . . Go after the safety man."* Then he would slither off tackle, change pace to outrace the secondary and, using the crossover dodge, fake other defenders with a hip, an eye and a burst of power that left them grabbing at a shadow.

One of the compensations for the grind, the bruises and the post-game exhaustion was the hero-worship of thousands of cheering sports fans. But more important, football gave him a chance to make money—by betting on himself.

Notre Dame went through its schedule undefeated in 1919 and much of the credit was given to Gipp. And all the while George was paying less and less attention to his classroom studies, barely skimming through as a pre-law major.

"The faculty is getting on my neck," Rockne told him one day.

"What are they kicking about?"

"They say you never crack a book."

"That's for the grinds," George sneered.

Eventually there came a showdown with one of his law professors. "Tell me, Mister Gipp, how were you able to answer the examination questions when your notebook contains nothing but blank pages?"

"A friend loaned me his notes," George said. "College isn't hard when you know the short cuts."

"That's an arrogant remark, Mister Gipp. You have a flair for evasive tactics—"

"Have I been evasive with you?"

"No, you've been forthright. And in being forthright you have revealed your weakness. God blessed you with a remarkable intellect, but you are letting it lie fallow."

George always weathered his scrapes with the faculty with an air of toughness and self-assurance. He was popular and he was witty, but he was distant and aloof, except with his few old-time buddies.

Gipp began spending more and more time in downtown South Bend and made Hullie & Mike's poolroom on Michigan Avenue his headquarters. After beating the best pool sharks in northern Indiana and surrounding territories, he branched out. He supported himself for a while at three-cushion billiards, then he turned to the poker tables. Eventually he and a man named Peaches Donnelly rented a suite of rooms and conducted their own card games.

From the time Gipp first arrived in South Bend, he was a big man with the ladies. Hazel had married soon after he left Laurium, but his soft-spoken charm registered strongly with the Indiana girls.

"George was always a gentleman," said one lovely blonde, whom he numbered among his intimate friends, "and he always treated me like a lady." This particular gal was always good for a touch when Gipp suffered a streak of bad luck gambling, but he never failed to pay her back. Another girl he favored was the manicurist in a downtown hotel. Also there was a pretty little French girl, who was sometimes seen with him in side street cafés. And then there was Irene.

Irene was the girl George loved. Other girls were good for laughs, but she was the girl he wanted to marry. Irene adored George—despite her family's disapproval of him—and reached him in a way no one else ever had. She was sensitive, cultured, tender, comforting and encouraging. George loved her, but he couldn't marry her. She was already married, though separated from her husband. They finally broke off their romance, and George resumed his carousing.

Finally his hell-raising came to the attention of the priests at Notre Dame, when he was caught in an off-limits South Bend hangout. He was immediately expelled from the university. George packed up and went to Indianapolis to get a job with that city's American Association professional baseball club. By now, however, he was famous as a football star, and Indianapolis knew nothing of his baseball ability. They advised him to peddle himself to the independent team at Lafayette, Indiana. When George failed to sell his baseball services in Lafayette, he reasoned that he had but one alternative open to him.

For months Gipp and several other Notre Dame players had been receiving offers to play football for the University of Michigan. There was a big drive on by the Michigan alumni to recruit all state residents playing for other colleges. Two men who were prime targets in the campaign were Bernie Kirk, the Notre

Dame left end, and George Gipp. Kirk accepted the profitable deal, and George went with him. Gipp actually went to the Michigan campus and remained for two weeks before deciding just as suddenly that he couldn't play for Fielding H. Yost, a long-time antagonist of Rockne and Notre Dame.

Another offer that had come to him was from the University of Detroit. Leonard "Pete" Bahan, a Notre Dame halfback, had already accepted the bid to switch to that college, and George decided he would join him. Part of the arrangement with Detroit called for a summer job in Flint, Michigan, playing baseball with the Buick-Chevrolet team.

West Point was also after Gipp. General Douglas MacArthur, superintendent of the Military Academy, had instituted a new system for recruiting sports stars into the ranks of the Corps of Cadets. On July 27, 1920, a telegram arrived in Laurium from West Point:

YOU HAVE BEEN RECOMMENDED FOR APPOINT-MENT TO UNITED STATES MILITARY ACADEMY . . . PLEASE WIRE ME COLLECT WHETHER OR NOT YOU WILL CONSIDER ACCEPTANCE.

CAPT. PHILIP HAYES
CHARGE OF A.A.A.

George never received that telegram. His family had no idea where to forward it.

Gipp was floundering badly at this stage of his young but full life. He was running away from the only security he had known since growing into manhood—his football fame at Notre Dame.

That summer in Flint, George became interested in the Catholic religion for the first time. He borrowed prayer books and pamphlets from Pete Bahan. Notre Dame, and what it stood for, became more important to him. And when Rockne traced him and offered him an assistant coaching job for the following year so he could complete his law courses, Gipp reversed his plans and took a train for South Bend.

In the meantime, Rockne, confident that he could get George to return, had sold the priests on giving Gipp an examination to make up the previous year's class work. But the panel of professors was instructed to throw the book at George, who they felt was a bad influence on the other students and a detriment to the reputation of Notre Dame.

Rockne chewed a cigar butt to shreds waiting in his office while George was undergoing the ordeal calculated to flunk him out of college.

"How'd it go, George?" Rock asked when it was over.

"I passed," Gipp said.

And he had—with flying colors. Gipp's brilliant mind had saved him. It was the general impression that he was finally ready to knuckle down. However, it wasn't long before Gipp began to crack under the restrictions of school life. Because he preferred to be alone, he registered at South Bend's Oliver Hotel. And within a few days he fell back into his old pattern of behavior.

Prohibition had been in effect in Indiana long before the Volstead Act was passed, but it didn't bother the South Bend citizens. Speakeasies were open for business all over town, and Gipp was a good customer. The long hours spent in dissipation began to show on him. His complexion, always pale, faded to a pasty white. He was losing weight, and in the shower his teammates noticed his ribs sticking out. But on the field, he continued to be the big attraction that drew the crowds.

In the opening game that year—only four days after George had been readmitted to school —he was stricken with a sudden attack of nausea. The attacks recurred every game.

In one game Joe Brandy called for Johnny Mohardt to run. "Check!" Gipp shouted. Brandy repeated the signal, but Gipp checked again. When this happened a third time, Rockne knew that something was wrong. He waved Brandy over to the sidelines and, upon learning the trouble, yanked Gipp. Star or not, George was told in no uncertain terms that he was to obey the quarterback. George took the reprimand and used different tactics to gain his point from then on. When signal-caller Chet Grant, a crafty war veteran who was even older than Gipp, entered the Nebraska game with instructions to play it safe, George told him that some of his South Bend friends had bet that Notre Dame would win by a greater margin than 16–7—the score at that moment, late in the fourth quarter.

Gipp said, "Let me throw one. We need another touchdown."

Grant made Gipp promise that he would pass long to avoid an interception, and he let George toss twice to end Eddie Anderson. Both were incomplete.

Grant said, "That's all, George."

Gipp shrugged his shoulders. "All right," he said.

The players who didn't know that Gipp was gambling heavily on the games mistakenly thought he had developed a star complex. But the few guys who knew the truth worked all the harder for him, trying to get him even. They knew he was betting $500 and $600 each week, big money in those days.

The week before the Army game, George placed a bet that he alone would score more points than the entire cadet team.

On October 20, 1920, when the teams were going through warm-ups and signal drills at West Point, Gipp gave the 15,000 fans a fabulous demonstration of drop-kicking skill. Russell "Red" Reeder, the Army point-after-touchdown specialist, was matched against him in an impromptu competition, but he dropped out when Gipp backed up to the 40-yard line. Then George walked to the mid-field stripe and called for four footballs. From there he kicked two balls aimed at one goal, then, turning around, sent two more toward the opposite goal. All four balls sailed between the goal posts.

The game that day was the dramatic crest of Gipp's football career. He gained 124 yards from scrimmage, threw passes for 96 yards and ran back kickoffs and punts for 112 yards—a grand total of 332 yards accounted for by one out-of-condition young man.

But he blew his big bet. For in that game, if in none other, he was a team player. On defense he was far from great, as he sat on his rump and watched Cadet Walter French scamper for two long runs, one of them for a touchdown. But on offense, he recovered a fumble, punted beautifully to keep Army in its own territory much of the time, and time after time acted as a decoy while other players cashed in on the opportunities he had set up. Mohardt scored twice, as plays were run to the left to outsmart an Army team that was prepared to stop Gipp on the other flank. Wynne plunged over for a third touchdown while the cadets chased George as he ran wide. Gipp threw a pass to end Rog Kiley for one more touchdown in the Notre Dame 27–17 victory. George himself marked up three points on conversions. He did win some money, however. The entire team did, with the exception of Chet Wynne, who hadn't had any money to bet. When George heard about this, he hit his teammates for a percentage of their winnings, put ten dollars in the pot himself and handed it over to Chet with the comment: "Here, you earned it."

After that wonderful Army game, George suffered a decline. He injured his left arm in the first half against Indiana, when Notre Dame was trailing 10–0. Rockne taped him from shoulder to wrist, however, and he went back

on the field. Although he had a relatively poor day as a ground gainer, he contributed to a close Notre Dame victory by setting up one touchdown and pulling off an amazing fake while Joe Brandy sneaked across for the score that won the game.

George didn't get off the return train at South Bend that night. Instead he continued on to Chicago to help out Grover Malone, a Notre Dame graduate, who was coaching a high school team. But George and Grover never got around to teaching the finer points of football to schoolboys. They went on a rip-roaring three-day drunk, stopping at every joint they could smell out. When Malone poured Gipp aboard a South Shore railway car headed for South Bend, he noticed that George was coughing.

"Better take care of that, kid," Malone said.

"I've already swallowed the best medicine for what ails me," Gipp told him.

On Saturday Rockne didn't put Gipp in the starting lineup. It wasn't until the second quarter that George trotted to the center of the stage in front of the first Homecoming crowd at Notre Dame. Two plays later he sprinted 70 yards and over the goal line. But the play was called back and Notre Dame was penalized 15 yards. Again Gipp carried—and this time went 85 yards to plant the ball in the Purdue end zone. George was untouched but completely bushed.

Rockne with his keen sense of showmanship, coupled with worry about George's health, substituted for his first-string left halfback. "Always leave 'em wanting more," he told Gipp.

By the middle of the week George had developed a sore throat that complicated his sick condition. He didn't mention this to Rockne, but it was evident to the coach that the infection had sapped Gipp's strength and energy.

"You're sitting out the Northwestern game," Rock told George.

"That's jake with me," George said.

"Feel well enough to come with us?" Rock asked.

"Oh, sure."

"Good. At least we'll give the people who pay the money a look at you, huh?"

But the fans in Evanston, Illinois, wanted more than a look. *We Want Gipp!* they yelled without letup.

"What do you say, George?" Rock asked between halves.

"Why not?" Gipp answered.

In that game he threw two incomplete passes and was smeared catching a punt. That was all

Rockne could bear to watch. Rock couldn't know then that Gipp's playing days had ended forever.

The night of the annual South Bend community banquet for the Notre Dame team, Gipp excused himself early, whispering to Rockne on his way out that he was sorry to disappoint the loyal rooters. The day of the game against the Michigan Aggies in East Lansing, his name was on the critical list at St. Joseph's Hospital.

Father Cornelius Haggerty was assigned by Notre Dame to look after George's spiritual needs. "Anything I can do to help?" the priest asked.

"No thanks. I'll pull through this," George said. "Everything's jake."

Telegrams arrived by the batch to wish him a speedy recovery. Among them was a wire from Bill Veeck, Sr., of the Chicago Cubs, confirming details of a contract agreement already worked out that was to pay George the high salary of $3,500 for his rookie year in major league baseball, plus a bonus of $1,500 if he should make the regular batting order.

But George's mind was occupied with other affairs, and he had long conversations about himself with a nun who nursed him. It was that good sister who called in Father Pat Haggerty the day Doctor McMeel gave up all hope of saving Gipp's life.

In the privacy of the hospital room, George examined his life and his cynical outlook, and by the time the priest arrived he had come to a conclusion. "I want to be a Catholic," he said.

"Have you been baptized?" Father Haggerty asked.

"As a Methodist, in my mother's church," George said.

"Then I'll have to give you conditional baptism in the Catholic faith," the priest said.

"No, better not. Not now, anyway. My mother would be furious."

For a number of days George stalled the priest. Intermittently he had lapsed into delirium, but once his mind was clear he said, "Father, be sure and don't let me go out without being fixed up."

Rockne telegraphed Laurium when George began to sink fast. George's father couldn't get time off from his job, but his mother made the fearful trip. Matt, Jr. met her at the train, and George's sister Dolly came, too.

At four o'clock on the afternoon of December 14, George was given conditional baptism, conditional absolution and the sacrament of extreme unction, the last rites of the Catholic Church. Then he went into a coma and died three hours later.

It is uncertain whether or not Gipp really made the famous deathbed speech so often attributed to him: "Sometime, Rock, when the team is up against it, when things are wrong and the breaks are beating the boys, ask them to win one for the Gipper. I don't know where I'll be then, Rock, but I'll know about it and I'll be happy."

But that is the version Rockne is supposed to have related to his players before the 1928 Army-Notre Dame game to inspire his underdog team to victory.

Shortly after Gipp died, Rockne told a few intimate friends a different story.

"It must be tough to go, George," Rockne said.

"What's tough about it?" Gipp rasped through a lopsided grin.

Possibly Notre Dame had had some influence on George Gipp after all.

"Et tu, Marjorie?"

CARTOON BY MIRACHI

© 1961 The New Yorker Magazine, Inc.

For many years arch rivals Clemson College and the University of South Carolina had a day all to themselves to settle their bitter differences on the football field. Their game was always played on Thursday, in late October, at the state fair grounds in Columbia, South Carolina. Because of the special staging, the attention of football fans across the U.S. was drawn to this traditional event where spirits soared as high as they do around any football field on any Saturday afternoon. Furman Bisher, a frequent observer of the game for the Atlanta Constitution, *laments the passing of this day.*

THE LAST BIG THURSDAY

Furman Bisher

As streaks of eastern light cracked the skies of South Carolina this Thursday morning, many a Sandlapper arose from his bed and dressed in his garish best while in the kitchen his bride packed the picnic basket. Flasks were filled with tonic water, in case venomous snakes were encountered on this hazardous journey, and shortly they set out, hardy pioneers advancing on the state capital.

From Wampee to Walhalla, from Yemassee to Tamassee this little drama of the dawn was enacted. Fathers, mothers, daughters and sons, alumni, alumnae and spiritual affiliates, politicians, storekeepers and bankers, doctors, lawyers, bakers and thieves, alcoholics, teetotalers, preachers and bartenders all were going the same way.

There was a funeral of an old friend to attend.

This is a strange way to prepare for a funeral, but this is a strange old friend. Precisely at 2 P.M. in Carolina Stadium, a steel saucer located on the state fair grounds in Columbia, last rites would begin for Big Thursday.

This 1959 game is the last of the series between South Carolina and Clemson that began in 1896 and reached such a degree of bigness as to become a national classic in itself. This is

because it is the only college football game played in America on this day, and because it therefore enjoys the undivided attention of the nation.

This had become too much for Clemson College. Each year the Tigers had to play their most important game on the soil of their most vicious rival. Win or lose, whatever came afterward was a letdown for one or the other. It might be said, however, that Clemson did make the most remarkable resurgence of any Big Thursday victim last year.

Slaughtered 26–6 at the State Fair, the Tigers moved on to the championship of the Atlanta Coast Conference and played to millions in the Sugar Bowl.

Nevertheless the game had become so big that Clemson, its highest authorities, its coach and athletic director, Frank Howard, its alumni and its students had reached a common agreement. South Carolina should be met on Clemson soil at least once every other year. Negotiations began. Old-liners didn't like the idea. Gamecocks didn't like the idea. Downstate Clemson alumni didn't like the idea. But Clemson liked the idea, and since Clemson owned one of the football teams appearing, and since Clemson was able to muster enough support in the state

45

legislature, Clemson swung things Clemson's way.

Big Thursday was declared dead. The Clemson-South Carolina game was moved to the last Saturday of November, to be played alternately in Carolina Stadium, seating 42,000, and Clemson Stadium, seating 40,000 and equipped with an elevator to the press box.

This day will be no different from any of the rest, except that it will be the last of the Big Thursdays. These Sandlappers will come out and they will whoop and they will holler. There will not be enough tickets for all who'd like to see it. Some will get too drunk and have to be toted home. Some will sing and celebrate until their heads split.

Because this is the kind of day it is, and because it enjoys national exclusiveness, whatever has happened here has been magnified. Two events, however, would have forced attention on most any occasion, for they shall never be forgotten.

There was the year the former baseball umpire and associates forged about 10,000 tickets and distributed them about the state. A few minutes before the kickoff a wild commotion arose at the stadium gates. People with legitimate tickets were being turned away and people with bogus tickets were demanding admittance.

The thwarted ones vowed to get in somehow and somehow they did. There were two huge wooden gates at one end of the stadium and the angry ticketholders amassed at this entrance. Together they pushed and they shoved until about midway of the first quarter the gates came crashing down and 5,000 to 10,000 humans surged into Carolina Stadium.

There weren't enough police in South Carolina to restore order and so the human cattle milled about the place until the surface of the football field was the only patch of earth left exposed. Gregarious fans intermingled with players and coaches. Generously some of them offered players drinks from their flasks.

One man sidled up to Rex Enright, then the Carolina coach, and said, "Why don't you put ol' 67 in, Coach? He's from my hometown and they's a crowd of us up here'd like to see him play."

That was in '46. It was a year later, I think, that some Clemson gallant rushed out onto the field, captured Carolina's gamecock mascot and ran up and down the field wringing the poor fowl's neck. This almost started a war. Not only were Carolinians irate but the Society for Prevention of Cruelty to Animals rose up in protest. Clemson is said to have punished the game student but I've always suspected that as soon as he returned to the old campus he was extolled as the autumn hero.

In '48 the only perfect team in the history of the two schools used this game as a springboard but it wasn't at all easy. Clemson won in the last few minutes on a blocked punt by Phil Prince and a touchdown recovery by Oscar Thompson, a runty little end from Columbia.

Carolina had led almost from the start when Bo Hagan, now backfield coach at Rice, threw a scoring pass to Red Wilson of Macon and Bayard Pickett kicked the extra point. Clemson scored, but missed the extra point; then the game was in the dying stages, Carolina punting to protect its lead when the punt was blocked and suddenly it was Clemson's day.

Big Thursday isn't exactly dead in South Carolina. It merely moves to November and becomes Big Saturday. But for the rest of the nation which has shared the high moments of this Roman holiday in October, it dies at sundown, or when the last drop is downed, and when the last weary body has been returned to its bed back in Wampee, Walhalla, Yemassee or Tamassee.

The versatile Indian, Jim Thorpe,
ran wild for Carlisle in 1911
and 1912 (see page 234) before turning
to professional exhibitions and
games. Thorpe could run and kick—
and could do anything else in
football that caught his fancy.

KICKS FROM CARLISLE AND HARVARD

Charley Brickley, Harvard's
All-America of 1912, 1913, was an
early-century version of
today's pro kicking specialist. In
the 1913 Harvard-Yale game he
kicked five field goals. Here
he makes a postgraduate boot
at the Polo Grounds.

From Columbia University's undergraduate humor magazine, the Jester, *comes this satire on the evolution of dirty play in the Ivy League.*

MAYHEM AMONG THE IVIES

William Brothers Brook

With the last Ivy League football season safely tucked away, an analysis of a new and startling trend can be made with a reasonable degree of accuracy.

First, a bit of history is in order. In 1913, seven football players in schools that were later to become members of the Ivy League were killed in intercollegiate competition; twenty-two were maimed for life; and nearly forty-seven received temporary injuries which required immediate medical treatment. That was the year in which the immortal Bronk Slivovitz of Princeton was brutally beaten into insensibility by members of the Yale team, before the eyes of thousands of terrified spectators. That was the year in which one coach commented that "nothing I seen in the Spanish-American War comes up to today's game." That was the year in which the playing fields literally ran with blood (see R. Whitmayer's *The Brutal Decade: Collegiate Football 1903–1913*).

The result of all this was the now-legendary Coaches Conference, held at Harvard from March 3 through March 7, 1914, at which there was adopted, unanimously, a code of rules and restraints which specifically forbade gouging, stabbing, trampling, punching, throttling, kick-

ing, and the use of knives, clubs, rocks, billies, blackjacks, chest armor, sharpened shoespikes, brass knuckles, nooses, and missiles of all kinds, including helmets, pebbles, signal-markers, and boomerangs. Every effort was made to keep the game as humane as possible, and the custom of spitting on a fallen opponent, which resulted in three fatal fist fights in 1906 alone, was made punishable by suspension for the duration of the season, and, if repeated, by permanent disqualification. Football, at least on the eastern seaboard, became a gentleman's game, a fine and chivalric sport.

It remained fine and chivalric for more than forty years. In all that time, there were only three fatalities in the colleges that later became members of the Ivy League. With the formation of the Ivy League, however, a subtle change in attitude entered the atmosphere.

Widely heralded as a progressive and forward-looking achievement, the Ivy League actually crystallized existing rivalries and, for the first time since 1913, introduced an element of *hate* into the game. Winning, and not the game itself, became the important thing. Gradually, the atmosphere of Ivy League football became ugly and tense.

The new attitude first became apparent in

the behavior of the spectators. Fist fights broke out in the stands, stabbings occurred in the Yale Bowl men's rooms, and it was not uncommon to see some partisan spectator or other being hurled headfirst from the upper reaches of the stadium to the field. Periodically, horrible shouts and screams would echo from the stands, and students earning their spending money by vending candy or hot dogs stood the risk of brutal attack by the "visitors," together with the total destruction of their wares.

Sooner or later, the atmosphere was bound to affect the players. And it did. In 1955, a single Ivy League school, Cornell, suffered the following injuries: 17 black eyes, 15 bloodied noses, 4 simple fractures, and 1 concussion. In 1956, this skyrocketed to 28 black eyes, 22 bloodied noses, 10 simple fractures, 7 compound fractures, 4 concussions, 2 fractured skulls, 1 broken nose, and 1 fractured spine. In 1957, the fantastic total of injuries shot up still further: 35 black eyes, 29 bloodied noses, 12 simple fractures, 10 compound fractures, 7 concussions, 2 fractured skulls, 2 broken noses, 1 partial blinding, 1 broken neck, 1 injured spine, and 1 broken jaw. Similar statistics were reflected in the medical reports of other Ivy League teams.

It soon became clear that a new order of ethics had quietly been introduced into the game. The first concrete proof of this came in an article written for the Yale *Daily News* by Somerset B. Winston, a Yale quarterback. "The Coach," Winston wrote, "he told us to get in there and win and even if we had to kick their ***** in to do it. I kicked one guy in the face when nobody was looking, and the Coach he said that was fine so I kicked another guy in the face too. The Coach he told us even if we fouled the h*** out of them it didn't matter, and we should do anything just so we should win, so we fouled the h*** out of them." Winston's article opened the floodgates, and the confessions began to flow. A weeping, memory-haunted Dartmouth junior admitted having used a well-directed kick to halt an opponent—a kick that resulted in an eight-month hospitalization for the unfortunate player. At Brown, players confessed that a complete "armory" was maintained for the team, consisting of small, easily concealed hand weapons, including a devilishly clever slingshot which could hurl an iron bolt over a distance of thirty yards.

The admissions have continued to pile up. It is crystal clear that dirty football has returned to the Ivy League. What are we going to do about it?

The late Heywood Broun is remembered as the champion of the underprivileged, for whom he spoke out so eloquently in his famous newspaper column, It Seems to Me. *But when Broun, a reformed sportswriter, was not commenting on the politics or society of his time he often turned to lighter matters, such as the inequalities between the Harvards and Yales.*

SOME OF MY BEST FRIENDS ARE YALE MEN

Heywood Broun

Oh, Harvard was old Harvard
  when Yale was but a pup,
And Harvard will be Harvard
  still when Yale has all gone up,
And if any Eli——

This is about as far as the old song should be carried. Perhaps it is too far. Our plea today is for something of abatement in the intensity of the rivalry between Harvard and Yale. To be sure, we realize that the plea has been made before unsuccessfully by mightier men. Indeed, it was Charles W. Eliot himself, president of Harvard, who rebuked the students when first they began to sing, "Three cheers for Harvard and down with Yale." This, he said, seemed to him hardly a proper spirit. He suggested an amendment so that the song might go, "Three cheers for Harvard and one for Yale." Such seventy-five per cent loyalty was rejected. Yale must continue to do its own cheering.

Naturally, it is not to be expected that Yale and Harvard men should meet on terms of perfect amity immediately and that the old bitterness should disappear within the time of our own generation. Such a miracle is beyond the scope of our intention. Too much has happened.

Just what it was that Yale originally did to Harvard we don't profess to know. It was enough we suppose to justify the trial of the issues by combat four times a year in the major sports. Curiously enough, for a good many years Yale seemed to grow more and more right if judged in the light of these tests. But the truth is mighty and shall prevail and the righteousness of Harvard's cause began to be apparent with the coming of Percy Haughton. God, as some cynic has said, is always on the side which has the best football coach.

Our suggestion is that whatever deep wrong Yale once committed against Harvard, a process of diminution of feeling should be allowed to set in. After all, can't the men of Cambridge be broadminded about these things and remember that nothing within the power of Yale could possibly hurt Harvard very much? Even in the days when the blue elevens were winning with great regularity there should have been consolation enough in the thought that Harvard's Greek Department still held the edge. Seemingly nobody ever thought of that. In the 1906 game a Harvard halfback named Nichols was sent in late in the game while the score was still a tie. On practically the first play he dropped a punt which led directly to a Yale touchdown and victory.

Throughout the rest of his university career he was known in college as "the man who dropped the punt." When his brother entered Harvard two years later he was promptly christened, and known for his next four years, as "the brother of the man who dropped the punt."

Isn't this a little excessive? It seems so to us, but the emphasis has not yet shifted. Only a month or so ago we were talking in New Haven before an organization of Yale graduates upon a subject so unpartisan as the American drama —though to be sure Harvard has turned out ten playwrights of note to every one from Yale —and somehow or other the talk drifted around to football. In pleading for less intensity of football feeling, we mentioned the man who dropped the punt and his brother and told how Yale had recovered the fatal fumble on Harvard's 19-yard line. Then, with the intention of being jocose, we remarked, "The Yale eleven with characteristic bulldog grit and courage carried the ball over the line." To our horror and amazement the audience immediately broke into applause and long cheers.

Some of my best friends are Yale men and there is no basis for the common Harvard assumption that graduates of New Haven's leading university are of necessity inferior to the breed at Cambridge. Still, there is, perhaps, just a shade of difference in the keenness of perception of wit. Practically all the Harvard anecdotes about Yale which we know are pointed and sprightly, while Yale is content with inferior and tasteless jibes, as the falsetto imitation which begins, "Fiercely fellows, sift through." Even the audience of graduates to which we referred was singularly cold to the anecdote about the difference in traditions which prevails at New Haven and at Cambridge. "When a Yale man is sick, the authorities immediately assume that he is drunk. When a Harvard man is drunk, the authorities assume that he is sick."

Nor were we successful in retelling the stirring appeal of a well-known organizer who was seeking to consolidate various alumni bodies into a vast unified employment agency for college men. "There should be," he cried, "one great clearinghouse. Then when somebody came for a man to tutor his children, we could send him a Harvard man and if he needed somebody to help with the furnace, we'd have a Yale graduate for him."

Joking with undergraduates we found still more disastrous. After the last Harvard-Yale football game—score Harvard 9, Yale 0, which doesn't begin to indicate the margin of superiority of the winning team—we wrote an article of humorous intent for a New York newspaper. Naturally our job as a reporter prevented us from being partisan in our account of the game. Accordingly, in a temperate and fair-minded spirit, we set down the fact that, through the connivance of the New York press, Yale has become a professional underdog and that any Harvard victory in which the score is less than 42–0 is promptly hailed as a moral victory for Yale.

Developing this news angle for a few paragraphs, we eventually came to the unfortunate fist fight between Kempton of Yale and Gaston of Harvard which led to both men being put out of the game. It was our bad luck to see nothing but the last half-second of the encounter. As a truthful reporter we made this admission but naturally went on to add, "Of course, we assume that Kempton started it." For weeks we continued to receive letters from Yale undergraduates beginning, "My attention has been called to your article" and continuing to ask with great violence how a reporter could possibly tell who started a fight without seeing the beginning of it. Some letters of like import were from Princeton men.

Princeton is always quick to rally to the defense of Yale against Harvard. This suggests a possible common meeting ground for Harvard and Yale. Of course they can hardly meet on the basis of a common language, for the speech of Yale is quite alien. For instance, they call their "yard" a "campus." Also, there are obvious reasons why they cannot meet as equal members in the fellowship of educated men. Since this is a nonpartisan article designed to promote good feeling it will probably be just as well not to go into this. Though football is the chief interest at New Haven, Yale men often display a surprising sensitiveness to attacks on the scholarship of their local archeologists. Nor will religion do as a unifier. Yale is evangelical and prays between the halves, while Harvard is mostly agnostic, if it isn't Unitarian. No, just one great cause can be discovered in which Harvard men and Yale men can stand shoulder to shoulder and lift their voices in a common cause. Each year some public-spirited citizen ought to hire Madison Square Garden and turn it over to all graduates and undergraduates of Harvard and Yale for a great get-together meeting in which past differences should be forgotten in one deep and full-throated shout of "To Hell with Princeton!"

Ernie Davis, the first Negro ever to win the Heisman Trophy, did not live to show how well he could play with the pros. Yet he was around the Cleveland Browns long enough in the last courageous year of his life to have a tremendous impact on those who got to know him. One who knew him best was Jimmy Brown, who had expected to stand beside Ernie in the Cleveland backfield. Jimmy's tribute to Ernie, written with the collaboration of Cleveland sportswriter Hal Lebovitz, also had its impact on many people. Sport Magazine, where it first appeared, received more mail on this article than any it has published in the last ten years.

TRIBUTE TO A TEAMMATE

Jimmy Brown with Hal Lebovitz

We were on our way back from Elmira, New York, in a four-engine plane chartered by the Cleveland Browns football team. We had flown there—our coaches, and the players who lived around Cleveland—to attend the funeral of a teammate who had never played a game with us.

Leukemia had taken Ernie Davis at the age of twenty-three.

At Elmira we had seen a city stop to pay him tribute. People had filled and surrounded the First Baptist Church, where funeral services were held; they had lined the road to Woodlawn Cemetery, where Ernie was buried. A complete silence had fallen over Elmira.

Except for the hum of the motors, our plane was equally quiet. It was a place and a time for contemplation. Ernie Davis in his 23 years captured the heart of his home town. In the few months he spent with us in Cleveland he made more friends than a man does in a lifetime.

His impact—an impact he didn't try to make—was so strong that Arthur Modell, owner of the Browns, broke down and cried at the news that Ernie was gone. Ernie's roommate, John Brown, a giant of a football player, wept quietly. I was stunned beyond belief.

I've always felt the words "great" and "courage" have been overused and abused. I have never been one to take them idly. I say with the utmost sincerity: Ernie Davis, to me, was the greatest, most courageous person I've ever met.

Though death is sad and often tragic—and these elements were present in Ernie's death—his is not a sad story. He made our lives better, brighter and fuller because we were privileged to know him.

Ernie would rebel at my effort to tell about him. He never wanted to be singled out. He never wanted to be different. He never sought praise or acclaim. He shunned interviews and adulation. Even during his illness, when he wrote a story in an effort to reject sympathy (it was titled *I'm Not Unlucky*), he worried afterward that readers might have misinterpreted it as bragging, or as an attempt to say he was something special.

But he *was* special. Samuel Clemens, better known as Mark Twain, is also buried in Woodlawn Cemetery, and he once said, "Among the three or four million cradles now rocking in the land are some which this nation would preserve for ages as sacred things, if we could know which ones they are."

Ernie's memory is being preserved. In Elmira the junior high school Ernie attended has been named after him. The All-America Football Game, held each summer in Buffalo (Ernie played in the first one in 1962), has established a memorial trophy given in his name annually to "the player who most impressed his coaches with a general attitude of cooperation, leadership, cheerfulness and all-around conduct on and off the field." The idea for the award came from Buffalo citizens who had known Ernie personally and had found these qualities in him.

An Ernie Davis Leukemia Fund, affiliated with the American Cancer Society, has been created by the Cleveland Browns. The Browns started it with a large contribution, and it is the hope of Arthur Modell, who conceived it, and the American Cancer Society that "Ernie Davis Chairs" will be set up in several medical schools for research devoted to the cause and cure of leukemia.

Why is Ernie's memory being "preserved for the ages?" Because he died at the prime of his life of leukemia? Because he was a fine football player?

Not really. Countless others suffered equally from this blood disease. And in football he never did get to prove himself professionally, the goal Ernie had set for himself.

Obviously, his illness and his athletic achievements are emotionally involved in his memory. But it's so much more than that. It's the way in which he carried himself through his life. Always humble, but with dignity, pride and strength. And always with an unforgettable selflessness, a compassion for others.

I met him for the first time when I was a senior at Syracuse University. He was a high-school star at Elmira, a scholastic All-America as a junior. It was suggested I visit Ernie and tell him about Syracuse.

I met him at the home of Anthony De Filippo, an Elmira attorney and a Syracuse alumnus. Tony De Filippo was like a father to Ernie (Ernie's father had died shortly after Ernie was born). Somehow I had expected Ernie to be a smart, flashily dressed teen-ager. Instead I met a clean-cut young man, dressed in the manner of an Eastern college student. This might be a funny thing, but his neatness made an indelible impression on me.

He also seemed to be a shy individual. I found this to be not completely true. His shy manner was really a reticence toward acclaim. To friends he always opened up.

I talked to Ernie differently from the way coaches would. I told him exactly what he could expect at Syracuse, the good and the bad. We talked about the social life and how a Negro was treated. Ultimately he decided to attend Syracuse, mostly because of Tony De Filippo's influence. The big thing that worried him about going there was me. I had broken football records there, become an All-America. My shadow fell on Ernie. Would he be as good as Jim Brown? Would he be better than Jim Brown? Did he want to be another Jim Brown? These were the questions immediately asked by the sportswriters.

By saying the wrong things, he could have put both of us in a funny spot. He handled the delicate situation perfectly. He simply said he respected my ability, but that he wanted to make it on his own, in his own way. To me, this is the mark of a great athlete and I developed the deepest respect for him.

I rarely saw him play at Syracuse, but I followed his accomplishments. He broke all my records, he was an All-America, he was the first Negro ever to win the Heisman Trophy, awarded annually to the outstanding college football player in the nation. He led the graduation parade at Syracuse, an honor given to the senior who contributes the most scholastically and athletically; he received and, of course, accepted an invitation to meet President Kennedy.

Though I rarely saw Ernie play football, I did meet him from time to time. He always talked to me about pro football and told me that more than anything else he wanted to play pro football.

After his senior season, he was the No. 1 draft choice in the National Football League and the American Football League, and he also became the top target of the Canadian Football League. The Browns, in a trade with Washington, received the NFL rights to sign Ernie, and Modell signed him for a $15,000 bonus (he sent the check to his mother so she could pay off her obligations) plus a three-year contract calling for an additional $65,000. It was an excellent contract, but he turned down a better one from Buffalo. He could have forced Modell to go higher, but, truthfully, Ernie would have signed for less if necessary. He simply wanted to play for the Browns.

Probably no one was closer to Ernie than his roommate, John Brown. They were buddies at Syracuse before coming to Cleveland. (Ernie always ran the two names together and called him "Johnbrown.") John told me: "Some people play for money or for other reasons.

Ernie wanted to play pro football just because he wanted to play. He loved it."

Ernie came to our early summer camp for advance schooling, then headed for Chicago where he was to play with the College All-Stars against the Green Bay Packers, the NFL champions. A few days before the game he developed symptoms that required an examination. The doctors at Evanston General Hospital diagnosed his illness immediately as leukemia, and called Modell, who went there with Tony De Filippo.

Ernie wasn't told what he had. He thought it might be mumps or mononucleosis. But he knew he was out of the game and when Modell and De Filippo came into his room they found him sitting at the edge of the bed, crying.

This was the only time he showed loss of composure. "They really were tears of disappointment," Modell told me later. "He was bewildered, confused. He felt fine and wanted to play but was told he couldn't. He was unable to understand why."

I knew almost immediately that Ernie had leukemia. Modell and the doctors leveled with his close friends and sportswriters, asking them for Ernie's sake to keep it off the record. Otherwise, he was certain, the news would leak out.

I can't say enough about the manner in which Modell treated Ernie. He had become fond of him during their period of negotiations and now, regardless of the blow Ernie's loss was to the Browns, the team president wanted to do everything possible, at whatever the cost, to make Ernie's few remaining months (the prognosis given at Evanston) as pleasant as possible.

He had Ernie flown back to Cleveland for further examination and to put him in an environment among friends. We visited him in Marymount Hospital that night. John Brown and John Wooten and I drove in from training camp to sit in Ernie's room. We turned on the television set and watched the All-Stars play the Packers in the game Ernie had so wanted to participate in.

Not once did he talk about himself, or his disappointment. Instead he told us about players on the All-Star team, how big they were and their abilities. He was obviously touched when it was announced that the Packers had voted to award him the game ball.

Ernie was allowed to come to camp to visit us, but had to return to the hospital each evening. We often asked ourselves: "Does he know how sick he really is?"

The question was answered for us silently a few weeks later. He was sent to Bethesda,

Maryland, for a checkup and when he returned, Modell and De Filippo found on the back seat of the car, where Ernie had been sitting, a booklet of burial masses. It had slipped out of his pocket.

In Cleveland, Dr. Victor Ippolito, the Browns' team physician, called in Dr. Austin Weisberger, a professor of medicine at Western Reserve University and one of the nation's foremost hematologists, to take over Ernie's case. As it was with everyone who got to know Ernie, a close friendship grew between the two.

We continued to see Ernie as often as possible. He no longer was confined to the hospital, going there only for medication and examinations. He moved into an apartment with John Brown and attended our exhibition games.

Suddenly, something happened that Dr. Weisberger still describes as "semimiraculous." Ernie entered a state of complete remission, meaning tests showed his blood count normal in all respects. He explained it's not uncommon for adults to become remissive but the completeness of Ernie's, he said, was remarkable. How long the temporary state would last was a matter of speculation.

It was agreed by the doctors and Modell that it was time to tell Ernie exactly what he had. There was too much whispering. John Brown told us Ernie went to a movie and a stranger came up and asked him: "Are you Ernie Davis?"

According to John: "Ernie never wanted anybody to make a fuss over him so he said, 'No.'

"The man said, 'You're lucky, because Ernie Davis has leukemia and he's going to die in six months.'

"Ernie replied quietly: 'I'm Ernie Davis and I'm not going to die.' "

He explained to John afterward: "I didn't want to hurt that man but it might keep him from being cruel to somebody else."

Dr. Weisberger broke the news to Ernie gently. The doctor and Arthur Modell described the meeting to me. The doctor cushioned the blow by telling Ernie the remission was so complete he could now play football. This news brightened him considerably but it didn't eliminate the fact that he finally knew he had leukemia.

Ernie's first comment was: "Can I lick it?"

Dr. Weisberger replied that people have been known to live normal lives for a long time with it.

Ernie perspired a little and remained quiet.

The doctor said, "You're an intelligent person. You must have had some inkling."

"Yes, I thought about the possibility," Ernie said. "But I made myself stop thinking about it. I had made up my mind that whatever I had I was going to have to live with it and make the most of it."

Dr. Weisberger told me: "I don't believe for a minute that he wasn't upset, but he never showed it. Not once."

Ernie asked that his illness be kept a secret but he was told his ability to play football would be a lift to other leukemia patients and he finally agreed to a carefully worded statement to be issued to reporters.

Ernie began to work out every day. He'd run and do calisthenics. He seemed in better shape than many of us. He ran longer and harder. We played golf together, went bowling. It was amazing to me that in a relatively short time he knew as much about the defenses of the other teams as I knew. He studied the game thoroughly. I'd say, "What do you think of so-and-so as a linebacker" and he'd give me a complete analysis which often helped me. He was absorbed in football.

But it soon became evident to all of us that, despite the doctor's full permission, Paul Brown wasn't going to give Ernie a chance to play. On the practice field Ernie would be forced to condition by himself. Paul didn't bring him into the huddles even as a listener. Undoubtedly he had his reasons.

At the end of the season Paul Brown was fired. A great majority of our players, myself included, said publicly we were glad of the change. We felt we couldn't play our best under him. But Ernie Davis, the man who suffered the most, the man who wanted to play pro football more deeply than any of us—if only for a token quarter to see his dream come true—said only: "From the little I know of Paul Brown, I think he is a fine gentleman."

These words from the man who always hopefully signed his autograph, "Ernie Davis, Cleveland Browns, 1962," were not said in cover-up. Ernie always said what he meant. Many times in private conversations I would try to probe him about Paul Brown. He always spoke respectfully about the coach.

When Paul Brown had made the trade for the draft rights for Ernie, he planned to use a "two-fullback" offense. The Packers had that offense with Jim Taylor and Paul Hornung. Ours was to be built around Jim Brown and Ernie Davis. I didn't agree with it completely. I wasn't for it or against it. I wanted to study Ernie on the football field—to analyze him, to see what he had—before I decided whether it would work. In football I never got the chance.

But on the basketball floor I found out this man would have been all he was cracked up to be. We have a Cleveland Browns basketball team which plays during the winter. Ernie had the doctor's okay to join us. In our first game we met a strong team, one that had beaten us the year before. The gym was packed. Ernie was like a tiger on the floor. He never let up. Near the end of the game I got a rebound and the instant he saw me grab it he was streaking for the other basket. He continued to play that way and we won the game by a couple of points.

The way he fought I knew I didn't have to look at him in a football uniform to realize what might have been. I've thought about it often. He could have contributed so much.

I didn't get to play much basketball with him after that game. In February he began to slip out of his remissive state and was advised by the doctor to stop playing basketball "for a while." All Ernie said to Dr. Weisberger when he was told that further blood therapy would be required again—medication and transfusions—was "Darn."

"That was the only complaint, literally and truly, that Ernie ever made in all the times I saw him," the doctor told me. Not once was a tranquilizer needed. The doctor said Ernie's refusal to complain made it necessary to evaluate his condition by examination of the blood rather than symptoms which Ernie might relate. He always told the doctor, "I feel fine. I feel strong." He didn't want to be a bother to us.

That's how he was with us. We knew the remission had disappeared but he wouldn't let on. He continued to play golf with us, to go to movies and parties with us. He always was part of the crowd. Once he had a piece of cotton in his nose to stop some bleeding. He hid it with his hand so we wouldn't see it.

When he needed transfusions, he wouldn't stay in the hospital overnight. He didn't want anyone to know about them. John Brown told me: "If I didn't know from the doctor that Ernie was sick I'd swear he was perfectly normal. He never gave any indication that anything was wrong." He wanted to preserve an image of strength. He didn't want anybody to see him lying down.

Ernie was religious and went to church regularly, and John says each night he would shut the door to his room for a few moments of privacy, probably for prayer.

Just once after the remission disappeared,

Ernie hinted at his illness. He and "John-brown" were conversing in the quiet of their apartment. John told me: "I was talking about marriage, life, the hard road you have to travel, you're sometimes afraid to take a step."

Ernie said softly: "I may not make it, John. But that doesn't mean I have to quit trying."

This was his philosophy, the reaction of a fierce competitor. And he didn't quit. He refused to remain idle. He talked about next year when he would be playing for the Browns. He went to the Browns' office and offered to help in any manner he could. Modell assigned him to study movies of opposing teams, similar to the analysis done by the coaching staff. He was given the films of our games with the Giants and Redskins and he worked on them for two weeks at home and in the office.

The job he did caused Dick Evans, one of our coaches, to doubt the work had been done by someone without any coaching experience. "It was a helluva study," Dick told me. "He put down every move. It's really fantastic."

The staff considers it a major contribution for the 1963 season. If we are more successful against these two tough teams, Ernie will have played a vital part.

Two weeks before he died Ernie bought a set of golf clubs and displayed the set as a "bargain." He was becoming a good golfer. He took me to a clothing store in New York where we purchased car coats for the "coming winter." He talked about the new car he would buy "next year."

He also told Dr. Weisberger he planned to get married. He and a lovely Syracuse coed, Helen, were deeply in love. The doctor said it might be a good idea and mentioned he would like to talk to the girl. Ernie came back from the visit and reported he had decided to wait until next year. The doctor feels Ernie changed his mind because he didn't want to take the chance of being a burden on her. I believe this, too, for I know she would gladly have married Ernie had he asked.

Toward the end Ernie's neck swelled up and he was in great pain. But all he said was he might be having some tooth trouble.

Two days before he died he had an appointment with Dr. Weisberger. John Brown woke him up to remind him of the appointment, and then left for work. Before going to the doctor, Ernie went to the Stadium to visit Modell. "This was strange," Modell told me later. "He usually phoned first. Now I realize he was coming in to say 'goodbye.'"

When John Brown came home that night he found a note from Ernie: "Have to go to the hospital for a few days. Don't tell anybody. I'll see you around."

That was all. None of us ever saw Ernie alive again, and yet I find it difficult to realize he's gone. Maybe it's because I never saw him sick or never heard him complain. The way he acted he had me believing he'd make it. Even now I find myself talking about him in the present: "Ernie is," not "Ernie was."

He was the finest guy I've ever met. Not because he was always smiling, soft-spoken, gentle, seemingly shy. But because he was so honest, so realistic, so considerate of others. Simply by being himself he won over people who were hard, suspicious and critical. And he did it without trying. He wasn't a middle-of-the-roader, still he was like a connecting link between groups of guys.

With Ernie around there were no cliques.

I knew Ernie when he was perfectly healthy. I knew him when he was sick. I watched him when I knew he had leukemia but he didn't. I watched him after he found out. I tried to see a difference. There wasn't any. He asked for nothing, wanted no special consideration but always was grateful for whatever he received. And his greatness was that no one ever tried to take advantage of his good heart.

The dictionary defines courage as "a mental or moral strength enabling one to venture, persevere and withstand danger, fear or difficulty firmly or resolutely." Ernie's actions fit this definition. He took his illness on his own shoulders, carried it, lived normally, simply. It was a tremendous thing to watch.

People say, "Hate me or love me but don't be indifferent to me." Ernie asked for none of this. To go without complaining, without a fuss—this is the greatest courage.

When a person as fine as Ernie, who had so much to live for, is taken away at such an early age, the natural reaction of his friends is: "Why did it have to be him?" John Brown confessed he gave this question much thought and finally concluded:

"Everybody was born with a purpose. Perhaps his was to make an impact on the sports world, on all of us. We let little things bother us. Here Ernie had a real big thing—he was fighting for his life. Still he never whined, never felt sorry for himself. When I feel low I think of how Ernie stood up under his burden and it gives me strength. He's an inspiration to me. I'm a better man because I knew him."

Arthur Modell keeps a large photo of Ernie above his desk at the Browns' office. "When I need a little extra lift I think of him," he told me.

Ernie's life has been an inspiration to me, too, but not in the same way as it has inspired John. I'm at a stage of life where I think I know myself pretty well. I know I'm not as high class as Ernie. I'm basically a skeptical person. I've seen so much hyprocrisy, so many phonies, so many pseudo guys. Then I see this Ernie Davis, so straight, so honest, so genuinely considerate. I've looked deep into this guy and what's there is real. And this is where he's been an inspiration to me.

I say to myself, "If there's one guy like that, there must be others. Maybe there are millions like him. Which is good. If so, this isn't such a bad world after all. There's hope for it."

Maybe I'm not a better man, as such, for having known Ernie but at least now I have more faith in people. I've never been quite as honest as this guy. By his example he taught me a greater tolerance and understanding of others.

Dr. Weisberger told me he recently received a letter from a little boy which touched him deeply. It read, "I met Ernie Davis. He was so nice. I loved him. Here is twenty-five cents in his name to fight leukemia. I'll never forget him."

Neither will I.

"Oh, for goodness' sake!
Are you going to watch him run the whole 80 yards?"

CARTOON BY CHON DAY

Ted Coy, Yale, 1909

CULVER PICTURES

BROWN BROTHER

Red Grange, Illinois, 1924–1925

Hail the college football hero—for a season or two. Edward H.
(Ted) Coy, captain of the 1909 Yale team, was one of the first of a
long line of young Americans who went to college as schoolboy
football players and graduated as national idols. For most of them fame
was intoxicating and brief; for a few, like Red Grange, the publicity
became an enormous burden, to be endured because of the riches
it promised. Ernie Nevers, probably the best all-around back ever produced
on the West Coast, arrived, as did Grange, in the middle of the
hero-worshiping 1920s. Jay Berwanger, the one-man gang
at Chicago, was more admired than idolized during the Depression.
The most glamorous of the postwar heroes, Doak Walker, accomplished
what is expected of a genuine college football star these days:
he hit it big in professional football, too.

Ernie Nevers, Stanford, 1925

Jay Berwanger, University of Chicago, 1934–1935

59

Doak Walker, Southern Methodist, 1948–1949

Anyone who has taken a girl—young, special and a little delicate—to a cold stadium on a Saturday afternoon has experienced something of this. The author was writing of the Jazz Age. But the girl and the scene remain unchanged.

FOOTBALL GIRL

Katharine Brush

"It's cold in this stadium," said the girl behind me.

She had a slow little voice, clear and sweet, with a trace of Southern accent. Just a trace. You thought perhaps she visited in Macon or in Memphis—it was that much of an accent and no more. She had just arrived at her seat, escorted by a long-legged undergraduate in a ponderous black bearskin coat. They were late. The game had begun some moments before.

I knew what she looked like though I did not turn around. I had watched her coming up the steps. Everybody in thirty rows had watched her. She was that sort of girl. Little she was, and slim in a coat of soft tan fur, belted tight at the waist with broad brown leather. The collar of the coat was high and puffy and immense: it held her face as velvet holds a jewel. She was very young. She could not have been more than sixteen or seventeen. An exquisite child, with black hair curling below a tilted patch of hat, with a spoiled red mouth, with extravagant dark-blue eyes. The eyes were older than the girl. They were adult with self-assurance. They had a lazy stare for the staring world.

The boy was mad about her. He had looked it, coming up the steps—though he had tried hard not to, he had looked almost fatuously proud. Now, when she remarked that it was cold in this stadium, he repeated, "Cold?" in instantaneous alarm.

"Wait!" he said. "Wait'll I get this ole robe unfolded. You won't be cold with this ole robe around you."

"My face will be," she said.

On the field a halfback made a gain of 13 yards.

"Lift your feet a minute," said the boy, "while I tuck it under. There! How's that? Okay?"

"I guess so."

"Warm enough now?"

"Maybe I will be in a minute," she said doubtfully.

In a minute she said, "It's cold underneath, that's the trouble. It's sitting on this icy cold stone."

"Well, here," said the boy. "Sit on one of these programs. Get up a minute—Now, try that."

"That's slick," said the girl. "And let's put the other one under where my feet are, hummm'm, Tom? Because my feet always practically freeze."

"They're so little," the boy said, in the voice

of one bent double. "There now!" he added more clearly. "Now you're all set."

"Um-hmm. Now I am. What's the score?"

"Nothing to nothing."

"Oh," said the girl, "then we're not really late. You kept saying we were going to be late."

"Well, we were, a little."

"I'm never late," the girl said dreamily.

The boy did not answer. *"Watch that pass!"* he shouted hoarsely instead. *"Watch it!"*

"Look," said the girl. "Before you get all excited, may I please have one of your cigarettes?"

"Ye-e-eah!" the boy was yelling. "Get 'im! Nail 'im! *Ye-e-eah!* What's the trouble, baby?" he added softly.

"I want a cigarette."

"Oh, gosh," said the boy, "now where did I —Wait a minute."

"Ye-e-eah" he cried again, but faintly now. He began a subdued muttering. "Wallet," he said. "Keys. Lighter. Handkerchief. 'Nother handkerchief. Powder—here's your powder gadget, Jill. And here's your purse, and here's your comb. And your rouge or whatnot. But where in hell're the cigarettes?"

"Isn't my lipstick there?" the girl asked anxiously.

"I'll look."

"I never saw so many pockets."

The cigarettes were finally found, but the rejoicing was halfhearted. The lipstick, it appeared, was missing still.

"It was the one I bought in Paris," the girl said sadly. "And now it's gone goodness knows where through a hole in your pocket."

"But I tell you it couldn't've, honey! This is a new suit!"

"It was a new lipstick. It was a bra——"

"Here it is!" he crowed triumphantly. "I've got it!"

"Oh, good. I'm so glad."

"Here, take it," said the boy. "Don't you want it?"

"Uh-uh," said the girl. "Not now. I just wanted to be sure it wasn't lost . . . Look, Tom. This lighter won't light in this wind."

"Sure it will. Give it here."

"I told you," the girl said presently. "Haven't you got some matches?"

Matches were borrowed, and many were scratched in succession. This took some time, and a touchdown was meanwhile made by the visiting team. In the accompanying tumult the girl's small voice was lost to me. I thought she was saying, "Try putting your head inside your coat and lighting it, why don't you?" But I could not be sure.

The first quarter ended shortly. The boy, withdrawing his gaze from the sky, where he had been urged to direct it with a view to determining whether it wasn't really terribly, terribly dangerous for that plane to be swooping down so low over all these people—the boy remarked the end of the first quarter with surprise.

"Say," he said, "it's the quarter already."

"Oh, is it?" said the girl. "Well, now's our chance to fix this robe. I didn't tell you, but I've been getting chillier by the minute."

"Say! You haven't!"

"Oh, it'll be all right when we fix it," she assured him soothingly. "The trouble is that it's *over* me and then tucked under, instead of *under* me and then wrapped *over*. Do you see what I mean?"

He did. He was able to fix it in a little less than four minutes.

"There!" said the girl. "That's marvelous! I won't be cold now. . . . Oh, look, they're all playing down our end of the field."

"You bet they are!" said the boy. "And we're going to score—we're gonna *sco-o-re—There you* GO!" he howled. "THERE YOU—oh, tough. Tough. *Hard luck, Red, old boy! Next time!"* He beat his hollowed gloved palms together once, making a loud report. *"Come on, TEAM!"*

"Tom," said the girl. "I smell something burning,"

"What?"

"I smell something burning. I think the robe must be on fire. I think," said the girl, "we must have wrapped my cigarette up in it."

It turned out after a wild interval that she was partly right, though only partly. It was her cigarette, but it was the robe of the gentleman next her.

"What a time!" she sighed exhaustedly, when it was all over and the boy was carefully wrapping her up again. "After that, I'll have to have my make-up, please, Tom. Not the rouge. Just the powder and the lipstick."

"You look all right," he demurred. "You look great."

"Oh, no I don't. I'm all hot and bothered. Such a horrid mean old man I never did see in all my days," she added clearly.

"Hush!" said the boy. "Here! Here're your things."

"And may I have your hanky? Because mine must have blown away." Her next remark was about a cheerleader. It was her most enthusiastic remark so far, though it was brief. It was, "Oh, looky! *Who's he?*"

"Who?"

"That cheerleader!"

"Oh, him," said the boy. "I believe his name's Adams or something. Or maybe it's Andrews. Something like that."

"But I want to *know*, Tom!"

"What for?" Tom asked suspiciously.

"I just do. Listen, wouldn't he be in the program somewhere?"

The boy didn't think so.

"Well, look and *see*, silly!" the girl suggested sweetly, adding, "You can take the one that's under my feet. It isn't keeping them a bit warm anyway."

The search for the cheerleader occupied the boy for quite a while. He said nothing, but he was to be heard turning pages rapidly. "Don't go so fast," the girl said once, and once she accused him of skipping. She had previously explained that she herself would look through the program "—only my hands would freeze if I didn't keep them in my sleeves."

There were several interruptions. Once the girl sneezed, a tiny sneeze like a little cat's, and the boy was obliged to produce his handkerchief again in a hurry. "And the powder again too," said the girl. "Oh, and the lipstick! Because look, it all rubbed off on your handkerchief."

Somewhat later she said suddenly and pitifully, "I'm hungry."

The boy stopped turning pages. "Hungry?" he said. "But you just had lunch!"

"I didn't have anything but that old salad."

"Well," said the boy, "can you wait till between the halves? I can get you a hot dog or something then."

"I suppose I can if I have to," the girl said. "But I'm awfully hungry."

"Well, shall I go out now and try to find something? I will if you say so, only you'll be all alone—"

"No," sighed the girl. "I'll wait."

"But I'm awfully hungry," she added low, a moment later.

"Smoke another cigarette," said the boy. "Maybe that'll help."

"All right," said the girl. "You light me one."

The intermittent hissing of matches began again.

"Look at that child," the girl observed, in the midst of it.

"Where?"

"Two rows down. Climbing all over his father's lap. Can't you see him?"

It was a little bundled red-faced boy about five years old, with the feather of his father's alma mater in his cap.

"Imagine bringing a child that age to a football game!" the girl said. "Imagine *bothering!*"

The youth agreed with her. It was plain from his tone that he wagged his head.

"Can you beat it?" he demanded solemnly.

Walter Camp of Yale is generally recognized as the father of football's All-America teams. But Camp may not have originated the scheme at all and he must at least share authorship of the very earliest All-Americas with one Casper Whitney, who began picking them for The Week's Sport *in 1889. Casper kept the selections simple by restricting them to Harvard, Yale, Princeton and occasionally Pennsylvania. Camp has clear title to the* Collier's *All-America, which he started in 1898. He made his annual selections for* Collier's *until his death in 1925; then Grantland Rice took over as the master selector. The All-America did not die with* Collier's; *but it has now acquired so many sponsors as to be virtually meaningless. Below are Camp's choices for '98, including his critical evaluation of the players. They appeared in* Collier's Weekly *under the department "Sports of the Amateur on Field and Water." With them went this reminder:*

> Who misses or who wins the prize,
> Go lose or conquer as you can;
> But if you fail or if you rise,
> Be each, pray God, a gentleman!

COLLIER'S FIRST ALL-AMERICA

Walter Camp

FIRST ELEVEN	SECOND ELEVEN	THIRD ELEVEN
Palmer, Princeton	Poe, Princeton	Folwell, Penn
Hillebrand, Princeton	Steckle, Michigan	Sweetland, Cornell
Brown, Yale	McCracken, Penn	Randolph, Penn State
Overfield, Penn	Cunningham, Michigan	Jaffray, Harvard
Hare, Penn	Boal, Harvard	Reed, Cornell
Chamberlin, Yale	Haughton, Harvard	Foy, West Point
Hallowell, Harvard	Cochrane, Harvard	Smith, West Point
Daly, Harvard	Kennedy, Chicago	Kromer, West Point
Outland, Penn	Richardson, Brown	Raymond, Wesleyan
Dibblee, Harvard	Warren, Harvard	Benedict, Nebraska
Herschberger, Chicago	O'Dea, Wisconsin	Romeyn, West Point

The lesson of the season of 1898 to players and coaches was the demonstration of the value of the kicking department. This, in a way, is opposed to what had become such a predominant factor; namely, team play, as evidenced in the running game and special formations. The kicking branch, given an ordinarily good line, is a question of individual ability in the kicker and ends. Get a man who can punt accurately and far, and two ten-second men who can tackle when the ball drops, and the combination shows for itself what a feature individual ability may become. And since so much has been made of mass plays and long-studied interference, since the accomplishment of getting eight men into the push at the same moment has been regarded as such a feature of the play, it is good for the game and good for the sport to have it shown that individual skill and individual speed are still tremendous factors in winning games. Again, it is individual work pure and simple to catch punts. And two at least of the big games of this season were lost through a woeful lack of this individual ability. Football takes on at once fifty per cent more interest, especially to the spectator, now that he knows the possibilities and probabilities of his seeing the ball are thus increased. To watch the struggling mass of players move painfully two or three yards at a time, while it becomes exciting to the partisan when the play reaches the five-yard line, can to the general onlooker never compare in point of interest with the interchange of kicks, the swoop down the field of two ends, the dodge and run back of the good catcher, or the fatal muff and scurry to secure the ball, and perhaps a touchdown and victory, involved in the punting game.

In selecting an All-America Team last year and this year, I have endeavored to follow out consistently what would be the course of the management if such a team were to be a real one, destined to meet an outside rival, and equipped as well as are our big teams in point of material. Every big university has for its team not eleven men, but a first eleven and a second eleven, and as many more available men as would go to make up a third eleven. Harvard played something like sixteen men in only one of her big games, and, as noted in an earlier portion of this review, could have fully equipped three elevens. We should hardly do less in our selection for a national team.

ENDS Hallowell has all the family football characteristics. He possesses a keen eye for the ball, good speed, and that ability to break interference without which the modern end can hardly be said to be equipped for his position. In both the Pennsylvania and Yale games it was his work in getting down the field, together with that of his comrade end, that made Haughton's kicking so wonderfully effective. Nor was Hallowell caught by trick plays, delayed passes or end runs; and this is the true test of the football caliber of an end today. To be fast, to break interference, and to be wise about the time of going in, make up the requisites of an end rusher, and all these Hallowell possessed in a marked degree. Hallowell showed his speed in the Pennsylvania game and his judgment as to going in in both that match and the later one at New Haven. In both games, and during the entire season, his tackling was hard and clean. Smith of West Point and Snow of Michigan were the only ones who could pick out the man with the ball as well. Poe took greater advantage of fumbles, but was not as able in meeting interference, especially where it was close, and his light weight handicapped him.

Palmer was one of the most effective of the ends of the season, owing in a large measure to his speed. He is probably the fastest end on the field today, and with that speed he combines good judgment and strong, clean tackling. The man who gets by him has to take big chances and make the most of them. While not a showy player, he was a careful one. When interference or a long or double pass tended to get the runner out beyond him, he usually managed to keep getting out with the play, so that, although a slight gain might be made, he prevented that fatal circling of the end which a runner must accomplish in order to net a large gain. It was due to his speed that De Saulles never had that one chance for a run back for which he would have sacrificed that ankle.

Poe of Princeton made the most remarkable single run, and by far the most telling runs of the year, but he might have made that run from any other position than that of end, and his general performance throughout the season, while of the highest grade, could not quite place him ahead of Palmer and Hallowell. Yet none compared with him in these wonderful dashes. In the Annapolis game 80 yards, in the Brown game 40 yards, and in the Yale game 95 yards, and touchdowns in every case, ought to fill this young man's cup to the brim. Folwell of the University of Pennsylvania and Cochrane of Harvard were both very strong men, and Cochrane had an additional ability to kick; but the fact that Cochrane was unable to play out either of his two big matches, and that Folwell was unable in the Harvard game to prevent the running back of Hare's kicks, prevents them from being set up with Palmer and Hallowell. Cochrane of Harvard was first-class, had an ability to kick and was a dashing player, but he failed to last out either of his big games. Smith of West Point and Hedges of Pennsylvania both played some remarkable games, and the former had exceptional ability in reaching the man with the ball. Snow of Michigan was one of the best ends the West has developed and close to some of the best in point of speed. Anderson of Wisconsin is also an end deserving of mention, and so is Stringer of Nebraska. Chadwell of Williams kept up his good work and exhibited the results of experience. Hubbell of Yale was at times a most striking example of good end play, but he was not in condition. Hamill of Chicago was another man of ability, but at Philadelphia was unable to cover Herschberger's punts, owing to slow starting. Womble, a University of California freshman, did capital work, and if he keeps in the game will be heard from. Parker of Stanford displayed in this his second year good speed.

TACKLES Hillebrand, while he did not allow his captaincy to interfere with the play of his position, undertook at times more of the work than ought to fall to the share of the tackle on a well-balanced team. This was due not a little to the makeup of the Princeton line, where the chief resisting force lay in the three men in the middle, but the weight of these three men made quick shifting of their positions impossible. Hence Hillebrand had plenty to do, and was literally all over the field. He is one of the exceptions to the general rule of men who undertake such a practice, for he was safe and steady, as well as at times brilliant. While the work he had to do gave him an opportunity of showing his great ability for close following of the ball, Hillebrand has never since '96 had a chance to show to the full his ability, and what it would be on a well-balanced team. In that year he was young and green, but good, and with the added experience with the same backing, he would have shone out this season in a way to make a name for himself among the star tackles of the past. As it was, he has made sure of a place, but not the lasting fame of a Cowan or a Church.

Chamberlin, the other captain of the season of 1898 to stand in the tackle's position, while perhaps not as aggressive as in '97, was well up above the rank of the ordinary tackle both in offense and defense. Added to that, he performed some kicking, as did Haughton of Harvard. Between the two, as far as kicking went, there was no comparison. Haughton outclassed him, as he did practically all the Eastern kickers, especially in the point of accuracy. But in the ordinary work of the tackler's position, taking the season through, Chamberlin performed the duties of the place with more uniform certainty than any other tackle save Hillebrand, particularly when it is considered that the Yale man had to bolster up a line that had several seriously weak points. Time and again in the Princeton game it was the Yale captain, who, performing the work that should have been accomplished by the ends, would bring down the man who was attempting the run to kick back. His tackling was certain as the grip of a steel trap, and he never missed his man. It is his unerring selection of the moment and the man that has always made Chamberlin such a valuable tackle, and this year he repeated his own individual good work, though less strongly in the Harvard than in the Princeton game.

Haughton was far and away the best kicker on the Eastern gridiron this fall. He had dis-

tance, height and accuracy, and, added to all these, he kicked a ball which, while it looked to the spectators to be an easy one to handle, proved the bane of every man who during the season was called upon to catch it. I have it on the authority of Mr. Forbes that not even Daly and Dibblee, after a season's work upon it, could make sure of catching the punts that Haughton drove. This may be some measure of consolation to the men on the Pennsylvania and Yale teams who had this work to do in the big games. Moreover, the Haughton of 1898 was a very different Haughton from the man who played in the last Yale game at Cambridge. He was active, confident and aggressive. He improved steadily as the play went on, and his exhibition in both his big games has not been equaled by any kicker for many years. In fact, the net result of his work is probably greater by actual measurement of gains than that of any kicker in any of our big matches. If this could properly be regarded as work belonging to the tackle position no competitor could equal him. But it is not a prerequisite of a tackle that he should be a punter. In fact, other things being equal, a punting half or fullback is better than a punting tackle, because it should enable an eleven to get off a kick against opponents when less prepared for that particular play. As a tackle pure and simple, Haughton was undeniably good, but not as shifty or experienced as either Chamberlin or Hillebrand. As heavy a man as Hare could not have got to the outside of either of these men.

Steckle of Michigan is a star tackle, and while he has not perhaps shown the fullness of general development exhibited by Hillebrand and Chamberlin, it has been because the general opportunity of acquiring a wide experience has not been offered to him. Foy of West Point is well up. Sweetland of Cornell followed the ball most closely, and with Donald gained a touchdown thereby in a big game.

GUARDS Hare, in spite of all the work that was thrown on his shoulders in the way of punting, running and defense, was undoubtedly the guard of the season. He was pretty well hammered to pieces before the end, but for all that his injuries were hardly apparent in his play, save when he had to perform his kicking. He is a natural player, has unlimited spirit and dash, and is for a guard exceptionally fast. He can make ground with the ball, he can aid in the interference, he can tackle, and he can block. In addition to all these, he is a fair punter when in condition, but liable to kick too low for his ends. But kicking has not been regarded, and may not fairly be regarded, in a guard's province. For two years this man has demonstrated that he can perform all the duties of the guard's position as well, and in several respects better than any man he has faced, and, in fact, better than any man occupying the place on any team. That he has been able, in addition to this, to help out a lamentable weakness in the kicking department of his team does not detract from his record.

Brown made his mark last season, and this year was equally steady and reliable. So far as the proper duties of the position are concerned, there was no man who could perform them better. He was not tried at running with the ball, nor at kicking, but in defensive work, and in opening holes in the opposing line, under legal restrictions, he was at the top of his class. Like Chamberlin, his captain, he had to help out men on either side of him, and the task was a large one, but his play in the Princeton game alone would have insured him the place even without the other good work that he performed throughout the season. He is a student of the game, and before he came to college developed a strong school team. He knows why his position requires certain qualities and what to do under the most trying circumstances. He is fully competent to cope with the unexpected, and is what may be termed a thoroughly experienced and extraordinarily well-equipped guard. In the Harvard game he was put in the position of having to do a share of the work of men on each side of him. I doubt very much if any guard of this season, save possibly Hare, would have been able to stand it out with anything like the success that Brown exhibited upon that occasion. He might have been content with showing off simply as a guard, but Brown is not that kind of a player, and, seeing the need, he supplied it to the best of his ability.

McCracken, had he been in first-rate condition through the season, would have crowded Brown very closely, although he could not equal his teammate, Hare. Boal of Harvard and Reed of Cornell are likewise close to the leaders, and played consistent football throughout the season. Wheeler of Brown, Burnett of Chicago, and Townsend of Wesleyan also deserve special mention for reliability in the straight work of the position. Burden of Harvard was good in defensive play and strong on his feet. Randolph of Pennsylvania State was the strongest of his team, and that team was a good one.

CENTERS Overfield seemed to be, barring Hare, almost the only man on the Pennsylvania team who throughout the season kept up a consistent, steady advance. It is even more creditable to Overfield that he was able to perform such excellent center work from the fact that physically he is not heavy enough to be on an equality with the men he is likely to face. It was necessary, therefore, for him to make up with skill what he lacked in pounds. This he did, playing a hard, vigorous and thoroughly scientific center work throughout the season. And, with the exception of the last few minutes of the Cornell game, lasting through his games in spite of the handicap. He is one of the speediest centers we have ever had, and, under usual conditions, accurate and always careful. Flanked by two big guards, who can with their weight help him out, he plays an ideal game. His tackling is first-class and his getting down the field under kicks remarkable, when one considers his position and the way in which most centers stand still after snapping the ball and let the rest of the line men do the running. My own feeling has always been that men of the type of Overfield and Lewis, the old Harvard center, might be fully as effective if played at tackle. However, although Harvard hammered Boal and Reid straight into Overfield when he was being practically held down in close quarters by big Jaffray, the gains were so modest that, after battering out some 20 yards or so, they changed. That showed Overfield's caliber, and he has always demonstrated his exceptional activity.

Cunningham of Michigan deserves mention in this connection, and the game he put up against Cavanaugh showed that he is to be classed among the good ones of this year. He is strong and active, never lets up, and keeps his man on the go from the very start. Cavanaugh of Chicago gave Overfield plenty of work, and while perhaps not as quick on his feet, certainly exhibited a remarkable ability in checking plays in his vicinity, and, added to this, got the ball back with the greatest accuracy of any center of the year, save possibly Jaffray. The latter, during the two half times that he played in big matches—namely, the Pennsylvania and Yale games—exhibited form of the highest class, and had he played out both games, displaying the same ability, would have displaced Overfield. There is no line man today who could so exasperatingly occupy space and prevent the opposing center and one guard oftentimes from getting into the play as could this tall and strong product of Cambridge. Burnett, Jaffray's understudy, was quick and strong, but we shall have a chance to see him develop further, and Daly did not seem to handle his snapping as easily as he did Jaffray's. Booth of Princeton was a safe player, and Yale could find no way through the middle of Princeton's line, for with Edwards and Crowdis the trio was absolutely impregnable.

QUARTERS   Daly has earned the right to be classed as one of the best quarters who has ever passed a ball. He has all the requisites that go to make up the man for such a position. He is steady, he drives his men well, he tosses an easy ball to handle, and he thinks of every play. Besides this, his tackling—note two particular instances, that of McCracken in the Pennsylvania game and that of Ely in the Yale game—is certain and deadly. Finally, he can handle the ball when it is kicked by the opponents, can run it in or can punt it a long, hard drive down the field when it is necessary to return it. All in all, the man who would try to improve upon Daly as a quarterback would either not know Daly or else be ignorant of the requirements of the place.

In quarterbacks, after Daly of Harvard, Kennedy of Chicago and Kromer of West Point deserve the place. Both were steady men, Kennedy the stronger on plays in offense and defense where weight was required, but Kromer offsetting this by his added ability to kick. Hudson of the Carlisle team continued his exceptional work as an accurate dropkicker, and one that could be relied upon in actual contests.

Young of Cornell and Ely of Yale both exhibited under trying circumstances the qualities and the skill that might have earned them the place under different conditions, but both these men had too much to do in the way of work outside their positions on account of the weaknesses of their own team, and thus marred their showing in a measure. Smith of Union was a man who on a larger team would have made his mark. Owens of Kansas and Griffith of Iowa both did clever work, the former being especially strong in advancing the ball. Further West, Murphy of Stanford, though with a game leg, did some hard playing upon a defeated team. His run, when he caught his own high punt and redeemed his poor kick by carrying the ball some 80 yards, was enough to entitle him to mention.

HALFBACKS   Dibblee is one of those men who are naturally football players. Of medium build,

compact and strong, he has within him that spirit which seems to be more than matter, and which acts as a steel spring within him when he starts on a run. He is fast, a good dodger, and seldom fumbles. He is a good catcher and a fair interferer, that part of his play being especially good in assisting a single runner in a broken-up field. Mated with Daly, the two men make the safest as well as the most certain combination of players behind the line that any team has had in a long time. He has improved in following interference, and is able to make use of it in scrimmage plays, while his natural dodging and shifting for himself when once well started or in a broken field make him doubly dangerous to his opponents.

Outland showed himself one of the best general runners that ever stood behind a line. By this I particularly mean that he could either buck the line or go out around the end. Besides that, he was cool when once under headway, and had the weight and strength to throw off a man when necessary. In two important games by exceptional runs he turned the tables in Pennsylvania's favor when they were behind. And, after all, that is what we must judge by—not what a player might do, but what he did do, and in this Outland stands forth without challenge as next to and very close to Dibblee.

Herschberger was played by Chicago as a halfback, but it has come to be the fact that the three men behind the line are practically interchangeable, and a halfback must be regarded in the same light as a fullback. Warren of Harvard, after Dibblee and Outland, supposing that Herschberger on account of his kicking is classed as a fullback, would be called a close second, although Richardson of Brown, Raymond of Wesleyan, Benedict of Nebraska, McLean and Widman of Michigan, and, when in shape, Reiter of Princeton all push him closely. Whiting of Cornell, had it not been for his injury, which for a time incapacitated him, and which certainly detracted very materially from his ability in the latter half of the season, would have pushed Outland hard, and would have been ranked very close to Dibblee. Croelius of Dartmouth put up a strong game. Durston of Yale as a line-bucker pure and simple was the strongest of the entire lot, but his more natural position was that of tackle, and he has not the speed for circling runs, which must be regarded as part of the equipment of a halfback today. Waldron of West Point is likewise a strong line-plunger, and Dudley of Yale, upon the one or two occasions when he was in condition, showed some of his old-time form. Townshend of Yale was light, but very promising until he hurt his knee. Gordon of Buffalo, Wilcox of Syracuse, and Folger of Hobart are all men who would be noticed if they had powerful line men in front of them. Both the captains of the Pacific Coast teams were good halfbacks, Fisher at Stanford a sturdy line-bucker, but Hall at Berkeley the better ground-gainer.

FULLBACKS Herschberger of Chicago, in his performance against Pennsylvania, exhibited the best all-around kicking of the season, punting, place-kicking and drop-kicking with equal accuracy and facility. Barring O'Dea of Wisconsin, he is the longest kicker, so far as public form is concerned, of the year. To say that O'Dea can outdistance him is a statement that will make those in the East open their eyes, but it is nevertheless a fact. But in running and other points of a position behind the line, Herschberger is conceded to be the better man; in fact, it ought to be enough praise for one man to be able to outpunt such a kicker as Herschberger. The tackling of the latter in the Pennsylvania match was not quite up to the standard, but the work he had to do, coming as it did principally in the second half, and when his line was letting men come through more than they should, was sufficiently trying to stand as a fair measure of excuse. With Palmer and Hallowell to cover his kicks and prevent running back, he could let out another link, and the team that had to meet his kicking game would needs make the most of themselves to equal the gains. With the demonstration given the kicking game this season all players will realize what it means to a team to have a kicker who can be relied upon to send the ball high enough for his ends, and yet cover over 55 yards with accuracy and consistency. This, with the ends named, would mean the certain encroachment of 10 to 15 yards on every interchange with the 40- or 45-yard punter, and, other things being equal, the final victory. Or, to turn it another way, Herschberger has demonstrated in actual contest with first-class teams, notably in the match with Pennsylvania, and under trying conditions, that it is not safe to give him a kick from a fair catch anywhere from 45 to 55 yards of the opponent's goal. Owing to his superiority in punting, it must devolve upon the opponents to kick out, and there are very few backs who can send the ball beyond the middle of the field, and certainly not if kicking against the wind.

Of the men who occupied the position of fullback, O'Dea, with his tremendous punting power, would be a factor on any team. Reid of Harvard, Romeyn of West Point, and Wheeler of Princeton showed the most general and even consistency of work. But Haughton did most of Reid's kicking and Wheeler was not in shape to play until nearly the end of Princeton's season. McBride, erratic in his punts, was an exceptional man on interference and defensive play. Slaker of Chicago, Bray of Lafayette, Irvin of Nebraska, Cure of Pennsylvania State, and Perry of Northwestern, all showed good qualities.

Walter Eckersall of the University of Chicago was named on Walter Camp's All-America teams for three successive years (1904–6)—once as an end and twice as a quarterback. Before the forward pass was an accepted weapon, Eckie won the hearts of Chicago fans with his twisting touchdown runs and his unerring dropkicks. He and Willie Heston of Michigan were the first big football heroes in the Midwest who were properly recognized as such on the Eastern seaboard. When Eckersall played his last game the University arranged a fitting farewell ceremony.

ECKERSALL'S LAST GAME

Chicago Tribune

Dazzling as the bright, clear sunlight which added splendor to the occasion, was the finale of the football season of 1906 in Chicago yesterday—the closing chapter in the history of one of the greatest gridiron stars America ever has known.

Chicago closed its football year with a brilliant, clean-cut victory over Nebraska by a score of 38–5, putting far in the shade Minnesota's 13–0 against the same Cornhuskers. Walter Eckersall finished his phenomenal athletic career with a performance which for scintillating, spectacular effects surpassed anything even he had shown in the four years he has been tearing across the chalk lines. Five times he dropped goals from the field, equaling his 1905 record against Illinois, and he exhibited a generalship which brought out the full strength of his team.

When the last whistle blew, the doughty little Maroon hero, whose stature gives no indication of the veritable giant he is, was carried in triumph from the field to the gymnasium by the proud admirers and worshipers who were fortunate enough to reach him first, while thousands fought to get near him, cheering madly all the way. Then the famous captain became an ordinary American citizen, but none the less a hero, whose fame will last for as long as exists the game or the institution he has represented so well.

It was a fast, dashing exemplification of the best there is in "new football," between two elevens possessed of speed, alertness, and brains, although they were nowhere equally matched, as the result indicates. That Eckersall did not shine even more brightly in his last game was due partly to the fact that it had been advertised so widely that he was to be the centerpiece of the day, the pivot of many plays, some of them especially devised to give him an opportunity to add to his reputation.

In consequence, the Cornhuskers, having been warned and coached in advance, watched the Maroon captain like hawks, taking particular care that he never had a chance to get entirely free and holding his running feats down to normal proportions.

This confined Eckersall's scoring to his field goals, which netted Chicago an even 20 points. The five successful efforts were made at distances ranging from 18 to 35 yards and at all angles. Ten times altogether, Eckie tried field goals, but most of the five unsuccessful attempts were made from distances of 45 yards or more. A single exception was an attempt from the

20-yard line at an extremely acute angle. One of Eckersall's failures was from the 50-yard line.

Between the halves Capt. Eckersall was the center of all eyes as he was lifted to a bench beside Dr. Goodspeed, the university's registrar, in front of the Maroons' cheering section, and after a special speech bristling with encomiums by the registrar, was presented with a diamond studded watch, the gift of the students and faculty of the university. Contributions to the fund were limited to twenty-five cents.

The watch is a unique testimonial and souvenir, as its face bears in place of the letters or figures usually designating the hours, pictures of the 1906 varsity team. At the top, in place of noon, smiles Director Stagg's face, while at the opposite side, in place of the "VI," is Eckersall's picture. The faces of the other ten regulars are arranged to represent the other hours.

"Offsides! Offsides!"

CARTOON BY GALLAGHER

Reproduced by permission, *Sport* Magazine, © Macfadden-Bartell Corp.

Unlike most classic blunders in sports there was never much controversy about this one, which happened in the 1929 Rose Bowl game. 70,000 witnesses saw Roy Riegels grab the fumble and head in the wrong direction. As he raced toward his own goal Riegels could not hear the warnings for the roar: "No, Roy, no! Not that way!" The following account of the unfortunate reverse was sent special from Pasadena to the Chicago Tribune.

RIEGELS' WRONG-WAY RUN

Chicago Tribune

Georgia Tech's Golden Tornado this afternoon defeated University of California's Golden Bears, 8–7, before a crowd of 70,000, and in the contest another tragic figure was added to the Hall of Goats.

Until today professional baseball boasted the prime goats of sports. Fred Merkle, who failed to touch second and cost the New York Giants a pennant; Fred Snodgrass, who lost a World Series with a muff; Heinie Zimmerman, who chased a winning run across the plate to decide a World Series. Fine goats, these, but none so tragic as Roy Riegels, captain-elect of California's 1929 team. Roy decided today's game by running 69½ yards to his own 6-inch line where he was tackled by one of his teammates. A safety followed a few seconds later and that safety decided the outcome.

The score was 0–0 when Riegels suffered his terrific lapse. California was operating deep in Georgia Tech territory. Three plays had failed to gain the prescribed 10 yards for the Golden Bears. Benny Lom shot a bullet pass to Barr on fourth down, but it was too hot to handle. Tech's ball.

Not much noise from the California section for an instant. Then a roar of ecstasy. On the first play, Mizell of Tech fumbled on the 25-yard line. Joy was great when the Californians saw Riegels seize the loose ball and start for the enemy goal, little more than 30 yards away.

Then there was a hush. Riegels had whipped about-face and was starting on his historic dash —SIXTY-NINE AND A HALF YARDS IN THE WRONG DIRECTION!

Riegels is a lineman—a center. And centers aren't supposed to be the fastest of runners. But Riegels was grasping at the stuff of which heroes are made. He sprinted like one possessed. Benny Lom was among the first to see the bottom had fallen out of the world—and Benny is the fastest of California's speedsters. He tried to overtake Riegels, shouting frantically the while. But the center outran him until he was just about to cross his own goal. Then Lom pulled Riegels down with a herculean tug at the latter's arm. The ball was down 6 inches from California's goal.

The score was still 0–0. A good punt would, perhaps, save Riegels' name from going into the book as one of sports' greatest goats—the "bonehead" of his era.

The two principals in the drama took their places in the play they hoped would stave off years of humiliation—Riegels as the ball passer, Lom as the punter. But the panic was on. Maree

71

WIDE WORLD

The sequence of confusion that sent Roy Riegels off on his
60-yard wrong-way run in the 1929 Georgia Tech-California Rose Bowl game
(see preceding page) is shown in this film strip. A Georgia Tech fumble
is grabbed by Riegels, who cuts away from Tech players and
breaks for the goal line—his own. On his lonesome run Riegels
is pursued by teammate Benny Lom, who finally overtakes him just short
of the goal. Later a stricken Riegels was consoled by other
California teammates.

73

UPI

of Tech broke through and blocked the kick. California recovered, but the score was Tech, 2, California, 0.

Riegels, a dejected, pitiful figure, moved to the sidelines after the scoring play. Onlookers thought he had been withdrawn but it was revealed later that he had wanted to leave the Rose Bowl forthwith.

But teammates wouldn't have it. Eventually the captain-elect yielded to their entreaties, and when the whistle blew for the start of the second half, California's greatest goat was in there battling for all his life was worth.

In the next quarter—the third—the Golden Tornado, still merry from the stimulating effects of the unbelievable break, hammered its way to a touchdown, then failed to add the point.

The score at the end of the third quarter was Tech, 8, California, 0. Though it couldn't have happened under the ethics of the battling game of football, it perhaps would have been humane for California to have eased up its offensive. The boys then could have consoled themselves they would have been beaten, regardless of the tragedy play.

In the fourth quarter, however, California put on a desperate drive and scored a touchdown and extra point. That made the fatal safety the key to victory. Throw out poor Roy's 69½-yard run and the score would have been California, 7, Tech, 6. Right there is at least ten years' food for the California chapter of the Brotherhood of Second Guessers.

•

When Charlie Conerly retired from pro football and returned to his native Mississippi, New York lost not only a famous quarterback but also a popular sports columnist. Charlie's wife, Perian, had been contributing witty, informative articles on the game to the newspapers. Fortunately, many of her views and experiences were bound up in a book called Backseat Quarterback. *She and her husband are authorities on this subject.*

BOOS

Perian Conerly

Stormy weather? . . . No reminiscence would be complete without some mention of The Lean Years—when the Polo Grounds was festooned with *Back to the farm, Conerly* signs; when catcalls rang out because Charlie often found it necessary to "eat the ball"; and when newspaper accounts of Giant games were frequently unfriendly.

I am told that human nature kindly endows us with the tendency to suppress unpleasant memories and recall more vividly the happier experiences. Nevertheless, in answer to a question about how the foregoing unpleasantries affected our lives, I could not, in good conscience, admit to anything so dramatic as a poignant family scene, fraught with emotion, in which either Charlie or I was visibly desolated by the press notices or the signs or the boos. Not even for the sake of a good story.

I am sure the expressions of disapproval left their scars, but Charlie is a master at hiding his feelings . . . even from me. Describing him as a stoic would not be far from the truth. He never complains. He never offers an alibi. He rarely allows disappointment to affect him. (Exceptions: an unsatisfactory game of cards or golf.) He accepts undeserved criticism and

valid censure with equal calm—and without expressing malice toward his detractors in either case. The ravings of his severest critics after a poor performance could never compare with the reproach he gave himself.

As for me, I am a most un-stoical creature. I *do* complain. I alibi. I can always manage to find someone or something to share the blame for anything. Therefore, I too am able to exhibit a calm exterior in the face of adversity. I live in a little world where I am Queen, and the unseemly subjects who berate My King are several kinds of idiot. I must admit that I was taken aback when exposed for the first time to a thunderous chorus of boos directed at Charlie. I had been reared in accordance with my parents' practice that "If you can't say something nice about somebody, don't say anything at all." And of course in college, fans blame the *coach* for everything. I really believe the worst part of it all is feeling the eyes of the other wives as they look sympathetically down the row to see my reaction to the uncomplimentary vocalizing. But I just used to sit there, staring straight ahead, playing Queen.

I think it actually became fashionable to boo Charlie in the early fifties. In one game he

75

completed the first nine passes he threw. When the tenth fell incomplete, the stands booed lustily!

Miles of copy have been written about the fact that the protection given Charlie by his line some years left something to be desired—and that his receivers in those days were not always terribly sure-fingered. I have had players apologize to *me* after a game in which Charlie absorbed a particularly stout drubbing.

"I'm just not big enough," an offensive guard told me once. "I weigh 220 and some of those guys across from me weigh 260. I just can't keep them off of Charlie. What makes it worse, he never complains. Just once I wish he'd give me a little hell in the huddle. It wouldn't make me try any harder, cause I'm trying as hard as I can right now, but I think I'd feel better."

Occasionally shouts of abuse are directed at the wives, but I never reply in kind because that would gratify the insulters. Boo birds are practiced in their art. They have a repertoire of standard replies with which I could never compete and are anxious for the opportunity to play comedian for their fellows. Generally when people sitting near us realize we are players' wives, they tactfully tone down any uncomplimentary remarks that come to mind.

However, after one game during which the Stadium air had been rent with cries of "Get Conerly outa there. We want Heinrich!" a very excited woman was waiting for us at the end of the wives' row. As we approached, she began to shake her fist and shout, "Your husbands stank today, the bums! Especially that bum Conerly!" And on and on.

I ignored her tirade, pretending I was somewhere else (waltzing in the palace ballroom, perhaps). But the fair complexion of the wife walking with me always belies her fiery temper. Whenever she becomes unduly excited a spot of brilliant red appears on each cheek. (We often tease her with, "What's the matter now, Barbara? You've got your clown rouge on.")

Barbara sprang into action. "Let me tell you one thing . . ." she began, her nose almost touching that of the vehement dissident.

The woman was startled, but not silenced. "Eat the ball! Eat the ball! That's all that dumb coward Conerly knows how to do . . ."

Barbara's cheeks turned the color of strawberry soda. "It's obvious that you don't know anything about football or you'd know it takes guts to eat the ball and be plowed under two or three big linemen. Dumb, you say? I'll have you know it takes quick thinking and skill to

deliberately throw the ball away when your receivers are covered—just close enough to your own man so the official can't call it intentional grounding, but far enough from the defender covering him to prevent an interception. And if Charlie had had a line in front of him today, he wouldn't have had to do either . . ."

"You must be Mrs. Conerly," the woman jeered.

"No. I am Mrs. *Heinrich!*" Barb replied grandly. Whirling, she took me by the arm and flounced up the steps as only Barbara Heinrich can flounce.

Meanwhile, down on the field . . . "I guess all pro players have 'rabbit ears,'" Charlie observes, "but I imagine quarterbacks have the most sensitive hearing of all. At the Polo Grounds, in order to reach the playing field, we had to pass within a few feet of a section of bleacherites who evidently spent most of their spare time between Sundays thinking up new insults. I think it was a kind of game with them to see who could come up with the cleverest abuse. The fastest running I did on any Sunday was sprinting past that section. I'd always put on my helmet too—to help drown out the static. I don't think the remarks affected my performance one way or the other. But it gets to some fellows. Maybe we should have put up some of those signs they have in zoos: 'Please don't annoy the animals'! Sometimes they would actually lean down and take a swipe at us as we ran by. I'm glad no one ever succeeded in hitting me. I couldn't have ignored that."

As a matter of fact, Charlie did slap a "fan" once. I got the word first from one of the players who preceded him to the apartment after the game. "Well, Charlie hit a kid today," he said, smiling. "I was standing right there and I don't blame him a bit."

I was frantic. A series of imaginary headlines flashed through my mind. POOR SPORT CONERLY ATTACKS CHILD. FATHER INSTITUTES MILLION DOLLAR SUIT. My fears were calmed somewhat as the story unfolded. On the way to the dressing room after a Giant loss, Charlie had been accosted by an unruly teenager, who was as tall as he and much stockier. The big youth cursed Charlie, who ignored him and tried to pass. He blocked his path and began to shove Charlie, calling him every vile name he could think of.

"Take your hands off me . . ." Charlie began. His warning was interrupted as the teenager drew back and threw a punch which glanced off Charlie's shoulder. Charlie slapped him in the face, hard, and ambled off the field.

"I guess I should have turned the other shoulder," he told me later. "I can take the talk, but when somebody starts shoving me around . . ."

Ironically, though the incident followed a Giant defeat, newspaper accounts described the game as "one of Charlie's finest performances." Perhaps the frustrated youngster had bet his week's allowance—from the Parole Board—on the Giants. Or his hard-earned wages—after selling hubcaps.

With the exception of an occasional "Ya bum ya!" directed at Charlie by a dissatisfied customer who recognized him on the street, such expressions of discontent were generally confined to game day. However, one extra-curricular demonstration stands out in my memory. Back in 1952 or 1953 the Giants and their wives were invited by the management of Madison Square Garden to attend a Ranger game. Since many of us had never seen ice hockey played, over half the team accepted. We were enjoying the thrilling sport immensely, but our pleasure was short-lived. During an intermission (or third-time) the announcer boomed: "As the guests of the Garden, sitting in section so-and-so, we have the members of the New York Football Giants and their wives. Please stand."

As we rose, the rafters rang with the most deafening booing I have ever heard. I was taken so by surprise that the smile froze on my face, and not until Charlie tugged on my arm did I realize that I was the only one of our group still standing. We decided that only poor sports would leave before the game was over. Besides, we were afraid of another unpleasant demonstration should we stand up again, now that our position had been exposed. So we sat uncomfortably throughout the game, the object of insulting clichés shouted by wiseacres from a safe distance whenever there was a lull in the proceedings.

We lingered until the Garden was nearly empty in order to make our exit as incon-spicuous as possible. As we began to shuffle out, a lone dissident far above us on the top row began to bombard Charlie with unflattering epithets. We ignored him. The affronts con-tinued. What the little fellow lacked in stature, he made up in volume.

"Let me handle this, Charlie," offered Arnie Weinmeister, a soft-spoken, but fearsome tackle of gigantic proportions. Arnie shouted, "Hey, up there!" at the same time taking three or four giant steps toward the vocalizer.

The jeer-leader did not wait to see that Arnie had no intention of real pursuit, but turned and scurried out the nearest exit with an astounding burst of speed.

"We ought to catch that fellow and sign him up as a halfback. He's faster than anybody on the team," cracked Bill Austin.

Jim Duncan smiled. "Yeah, but who could catch him?"

The sting of such incidents was mitigated by a constant trickle of encouraging letters from loyal fans.

Though the scrapbook contains at least one write-up describing every Giant game since 1948, the "bad" games are noticeably less well represented than the good. This inequity stems not from any attempt at whitewashing, but from a dearth of clippings which allude to the un-happier contests. On any ordinary day Charlie often buys and reads all seven New York daily papers; but after an unfortunate game, he resists the temptation.

"I don't mind being knocked when I de-serve it, and there are plenty of times I do," he explains. "But *I* know when I play poorly, and reading some reporter's description of it isn't going to help me improve. I'd probably just get mad at some nice guy who is only doing his job. They have to write what they see—but I don't have to read it."

When one of these bad reviews falls into my hands, I am likely to mutter darkly: "One would think you were the only man on the field today . . ."

To which he replies philosophically, "And reading some of the flattering write-ups of games we won, you might think the same thing. The quarterback receives more than his rightful share of the credit when things go well, so he should be prepared to accept a lion's share of the blame when they don't."

After years of careful consideration (and practical experience) I have arrived at certain conclusions concerning the practice of booing at professional football games. Likely the cus-tom has its roots in ancient Rome, where spectators attending various exhibitions of manly skill and courage commonly expressed disapproval of a gladiator's unsatisfactory per-formance by turning "thumbs down." Happily, today's losers live to play another day. There-fore, since booing neither influences a coach's decision nor spurs a player to greater effective-ness, it serves no practical purpose other than calling attention to the booer—which is probably the whole idea, after all.

Leaning heavily on an overactive imagination and a vague memory of a course in freshman psychology, I have relegated the booers to several categories. Boos come from:

1. The fellow in the company of friends who know little about football and consider him something of an expert. To prove that he does indeed have a full grasp of the subject he sprinkles his enlightened explanations of the proceedings with rousing catcalls emitted at the slightest provocation.

2. His friends.

3. The same fellow in the company of his girl friend.

4. His girl friend.

5. The extrovert who has come to the game alone and wishes to strike up a conversation with his neighbors.

6. His neighbors.

7. The introvert who is browbeaten all week by a domineering employer and, unable to strike back at his boss, transfers his wrath to the players on the field, thereby gaining an outlet for his pent-up emotions. (Psychiatrists might do well to recommend this type of therapy to patients suffering from insecurity and inferiority complexes.)

8. The man sitting on his left.

9. The introvert who is browbeaten by his wife.

10. The man sitting on his right.

11. A category already hinted at in numbers 2, 4, 6, 8, and 10 results in Dr. Conerly's maxim: People sitting next to people who boo, boo too. It seems to be a form of mass hysteria participated in by impressionable people caught up in the spirit of the occasion—a mild form of mob violence.

12. The fellow who has come to the game only to get away from the kids for a few hours. He really doesn't know what is happening and therefore is bored. An occasional good boo helps immeasurably to relieve the monotony.

13. The small man who tried out for the team in high school and was told by the coach, "Son, come back when you grow six inches and gain thirty pounds." He has had no trouble adding the pounds these last ten years, but unfortunately got no taller. He delights in venting his frustration on the king-sized players, all of whom represent the star tackle who stole his girl in high school.

14. The big fellow who was told by his high school coach, "Son, come back when you have lost thirty pounds." Folks still call him "Tubby."

How does Charlie feel about being the object of spectator disapproval? Mr. C. contends that the ticket purchased by the malcontent entitles him to express any opinion he might hold—however loudly.

How do I react? I locate the knavish songbird, place him in one of the foregoing categories, and mentally summon the Royal Executioner.

CARTOON BY GALLAGHER

Reproduced by permission, *Sport* Magazine, © Macfadden-Bartell Corp.

*"I wouldn't ask you men to do anything I wouldn't do myself, and
I'd gouge, kick and cheat to win this one."*

CARTOON BY KRAUS

© 1955 The New Yorker Magazine, Inc.

The complex, violent duties of playing middle linebacker for the pros are spelled out in detail in this article on Joe Schmidt, MLB of the Detroit Lions.

MIDDLE LINEBACKER

Myron Cope

Four broad rumps, fairly bursting through the skintight silver knickers worn by the Detroit Lions, are spread out before him. They're his men—linebacker Joe Schmidt's men—and when the Baltimore Colts' center snaps that ball, those four rumps will lurch ahead. These are Detroit's front-line troops: Darris McCord, 250 pounds; Ray Krouse, 275 pounds; Bob Miller, 255 pounds; Gil Mains, 255 pounds. If they go in low, the way they should, Joe Schmidt won't even see their heads bob up over the horizon of their backsides.

They're dug in a yard or so apart. Beyond them, through the gaps, Joe can see the Baltimore linemen crouching grimly, their upper lips tucked in against their teeth, and beyond them, the Baltimore backs. Joe hates them all with a fury that has possessed him from the moment he set foot on the field.

Joe Schmidt is built that way. Before he got into uniform he neither felt nor looked like a fanatic. When he is in street clothes, his extraordinarily broad shoulders, his size eighteen neck, his kindly eyes, his blond hair and his even manner give him the appearance of a nice old Saint Bernard. But once he puts on that uniform, he becomes Mr. Hyde.

So now, as Joe sets himself for the Baltimore attack, he looks across the line where Johnny Unitas, dirty-faced, is barking signals. Unitas? Hell, he's a sandlotter from Joe's own home town of Pittsburgh. Unitas may be an old pal, and he may be one of the National Football League's best passers, but to Joe Schmidt right now, Unitas is just a miserable busher up from the Bloomfield Rams.

Directly behind Unitas is Alan (The Horse) Ameche. *O.K., you big horse, let's see what you've got,* is Schmidt's reaction. *Let's see what all that beef gets you.*

Nearby, to Ameche's left, is Lenny Moore—tall and sleek, hard to hold and fast as a dash man. On this November Sunday in 1956, the rookie halfback has a blistering rushing average of roughly ten yards per trip. Joe Schmidt is intent on bottling him up. *Try to get that precious step into the clear, Moore. Just try to get it.*

Then there's L. G. Dupre, out in the flat away off to Ameche's right. Chunky Dupre, who runs with his head down, and goes like he's pedaling a bicycle. *What is he up to out there?*

Unitas, Ameche, Moore, Dupre—Joe hates them all, just as he hates any enemy backfield. Can a man really generate so much emotion without any provocation? Joe has always been able to, even as a college kid playing for the University of Pittsburgh back in 1952. That year Pitt went to South Bend to play Notre Dame, and Notre Dame was favored by fourteen points. Before the game Red Dawson, the Pitt coach, left the dressing room and, in effect, turned the team over to Joe Schmidt.

"You guys whip Notre Dame, or so help me, I'll whip you!" ranted Joe. They whipped Notre Dame, 22–19, and after the game one of the Pitt players said, "Hell, we were more scared of Joe than we were of Notre Dame."

Joe wasn't around at the finish to hear the compliment. He'd left the game early in the second half with a brain concussion, after catching a forearm in the head. There was no other way Joe would have left.

Joe Schmidt has always played football at the boiling point, and it is like that now against the Colts. Krouse and Miller, his guards, are playing the Baltimore guards head-to-head, leaving an open path between Joe and the Baltimore center. As middle linebacker, Joe stands about a yard behind the line, directly opposite the ball. It's a good bet that the Baltimore center will burst right at him. Joe has got to protect that path. He also has to cover seven or eight yards of lateral ground—his corner linebackers, Bob Long and Roger Zatkoff, both are three or four yards away from him. Then suppose Unitas throws? Joe is responsible for ten yards behind him.

It's maneuverability that counts here, and Joe has it—the fastest reactions, probably, of any linebacker in the business. As pro linemen go, he is small. He stands 5 feet 11. He weighs only 215 pounds—and not 216—because he's got to have that maneuverability. In the off season he plays handball or squash perhaps four times a week for two or three hours at a time. He eats not one potato, not a single slice of bread and butter. Linemen may run to 275 pounds and more, but the smart ones don't carry a pound more than is good for them.

Linebackers are forever being kicked in the shins, and some of them will wear shin pads when the soreness becomes excruciating. Joe won't. "I'd like to," he has said, "but they'd weigh me down." Those pads are made of a light, fiber-type material, and weigh perhaps a pound, but Joe Schmidt doesn't feel that he can afford to give away even this much against speedsters like Baltimore's Lenny Moore.

It's third down for the Colts on the Detroit 46-yard line, with 5 yards to go for a first down. Unitas can take almost any card from the deck here. He can keep the ball, hand it off, pitch it out or pass it. These alternatives race through Joe Schmidt's angry mind. He is thinking-mad. He is watching that ball in the center's hands, but out of the corners of his eyes he is casing the Baltimore line. He spots a tip-off. A guard is sagging back ever so slightly. When the ball is snapped, he'll pull out of the line to run interference. Unitas has called a wide play—probably a pitchout to Moore.

But *will* it be a pitchout? Joe can't be sure.

He'll tell you, "Some of those offensive linemen, if you watch them hard you can almost tell after three or four plays what they'll do the rest of the game. If a guy's going to come forward, maybe he'll put just a little pressure on his hand. If he's going to pull out, maybe he'll sag back just a little."

However, Joe also will tell you that occasionally these mannerisms are deliberate ruses. You can't be sure about them, and in any case, he says, "You can't be right all the time."

At the Baltimore snapback everybody in Joe's sight explodes. There go the four rumps, surging forward. There's nobody to stop Krouse and Miller, because, sure enough, those Baltimore guards have pulled out, and they're running off to Joe's right. Unitas pivots to pitch out. For the barest fraction of a second, Joe doesn't move an inch. You never know—Unitas could fake that pitchout to Moore and send Ameche roaring up the middle.

It isn't a fake. Unitas lets the ball go. Joe shoots to his right as fast as he can go. If he is an instant too slow, that big Baltimore center—Szymanski is his name—will cut Joe off and be all over him. But Joe gets past this first hurdle.

Lenny Moore has got the ball now and is racing wide. Those two Baltimore guards are forming in front of him. Up in the line, the opposing tackles are having at each other. Joe's partner, right linebacker Roger Zatkoff, is coming up to block Moore's path, but now he has his hands full with the Baltimore end. Detroit's defensive right halfback, out wide, is moving up. He is angling slightly so as to prevent Moore from reaching a clear alley to the sideline.

Moore's hand is forced. He has to cut in. He has those two big guards rolling ahead of him now, and the three of them come thundering around the bend like horses in a Wild West movie chase.

Bob Miller, the Detroit right tackle, isn't out of it yet. Miller may look like just a strong draft horse to the people up in the fiftieth row, but down on the field he is using his head. He didn't get sucked into charging deep into the backfield. He went in shallow, where he might get a shot at the ball carrier. Now, running to his right, he has slipped behind Moore and grabbed a piece of him.

Joe Schmidt doesn't relax for an instant. Maybe Miller will hold Moore fast, so that when Joe crashes into Moore, too, a lot of nice people in the grandstands will say, "Tush, tush, that wasn't necessary." But Joe knows he can't afford to assume that Miller *will* hold Moore.

Miller had a piece of Moore, all right, but it was like having a fistful of water. Moore is free again, still coming around that bend behind those two guards. It's Joe Schmidt's turn now. He has a choice to make, and he has to make it right now.

He can "play the guards"—push them around and get them out of the play, and hope that the safety man will come up to take care of Moore. It's often done that way. But what if Moore slips the safety man? He'd hardly be caught by a motorcyclist.

Then there's the alternative that makes the difference between a great linebacker and an ordinary one. It requires what coaches call "love of contact." When a player has this, they refer to him as "hard-nosed." Joe doesn't hesitate to play it the hard way. Head down, he charges straight into those thundering guards. They meet him head-on. There is a clatter of helmets and a thudding of shoulder pads. Joe splits the guards like wooden soldiers and brings down Moore with a knee-high tackle that seems almost to cut Lenny in two.

The deadly artistry of Schmidt's tackling is obvious to the most casual of spectators, but the finesse that precedes the tackle is less noticeable. Pro football in the last decade has developed into a complex game that demands linemen who are not only brawnier than their predecessors, but also faster and smarter. Finesse is called for on every play, even those that don't appear crucial.

Take an inconsequential-looking play run by the Chicago Bears against Detroit at Wrigley Field last December. Routine though the circumstances were, the play presented Joe Schmidt with what he regards as just about the toughest situation a middle linebacker has to face. It was the so-called draw play, as run by the Bears' Rick Casares, who makes a considerable difference. Casares is big and strong— 6 feet, 2½ inches, and 225 pounds. What's more, he is shifty and smart.

The Bears had the ball on their own 41-yard line—second down and 10 long yards to go. Detroit's defense had every right to expect a pass. Zeke Bratkowski, the Bears' quarterback, took the snap and began fading back. His linemen allowed Detroit's guards to break through, but he saw to it that the guards were bumped to the outside, so that a path was left clear up the middle. Bratkowski faked his pass and deftly slipped the ball to his fullback—Casares—who came charging up the middle toward Joe Schmidt.

Joe hadn't fallen for Bratkowski's fake pass. He always keeps his eye on the ball, and if he happens to lose sight of it, he stays put until he spots it again. So Joe was right there waiting for Casares. Joe had trouble seeing him, though, because Casares was running behind a bodyguard—a 6 foot 4, 245-pound center named Larry Strickland. Joe could knock Strickland down, all right, but then Casares would break to the right or left and be gone.

"I backed up," says Joe, reconstructing his maneuvers. "I wanted Casares to make his move first. I gave him a few yards. I wanted to keep away from Strickland as much as possible. Maybe I bumped him or slid or just played him off."

All the while Joe was looking over Strickland's shoulder, keeping his eye on Casares, and when Casares finally did make his move Joe was there to meet him. Casares had gained 4 yards, but this was a long-yardage situation, and four wasn't enough. Detroit finished on top, 21–13.

It is his faculty for making the right move at the right time that enables Joe to get in on so many tackles as to give the illusion that he is all over the field. Cocaptain of the National Football League champions and Associated Press Lineman of the Year in 1957, he is the paragon of today's pro lineman.

Consider Joe's responsibilities as the player charged with calling defensive signals for Detroit. Talking football one day not long ago at his mother's home in Mt. Oliver, Pennsylvania, a suburb of Pittsburgh, Joe quietly enumerated the functions he frantically dispatches during the approximately thirty seconds that tick off between plays.

"Now don't misunderstand me," he said. "I don't always remember everything there is to do between plays, but I try to remember as much as possible." Altogether, he listed a dozen items that go along with selecting the defensive pattern best suited for the situation at hand.

He must know what yard line the ball is on, and how far it is from the sidelines; what down is coming up, how many yards the opposition has to go for a first down, and how much time remains on the clock. He must further consider which running backs and pass receivers the opposition has in the game, and also which plays it has been favoring.

From the Detroit standpoint, Joe has to know which defensive coverages have been placed at his command by the coaches for this particular game. He must remind his forward linemen of what to watch for, since they cannot see well from their positions. He must make sure that the defensive backs have heard his signals and set up the correct coverage. Lastly, Joe must stop to think what *he* is going to do when the play starts.

"And believe me," said Joe, "many's the time the opposition has gone into a quick snap before I can remember what the devil I *am* supposed to do. This may sound funny as hell, but there are even times when I forget which defense I've called and play a different one."

The mental gymnastics executed by Joe Schmidt and other defensive signal-callers in pro football demand a trial lawyer's quickness. This hardly squares with the stereotyped picture of linemen as doltish creatures performing a strictly muscular job.

"Listen," says Lion defensive coach Buster Ramsey, the rasping Tennessean on whose recommendation Detroit drafted Schmidt six years ago. "We've had linemen who were Phi Beta Kappas or engineering graduates, but were dumb as they come as far as football sense is concerned. Joe Schmidt has a keen football mind. Everybody on the team respects him. And he's got to have that. At times he has to get on their tails and ride them, and they won't take it from a man they don't respect."

Playing middle linebacker is something like standing in a wagon and whipping a team of horses. Joe is one middle linebacker who can really go to the whip. Last year, when the San Francisco 49ers were leading the Lions by the lopsided score of 27–7 in the play-off for the Western Conference championship, Joe pulled out all stops.

"It's too damn bad I got to play with a team of lousy yellow quitters," he raved between plays. "What a crummy bunch of doggers this is."

The Lions came back to win, 31–27.

On guts alone Joe Schmidt commands respect. In one game last season he cracked two ribs while smashing through a massed-up herd of blockers. He made no mention of the injury, and played the remainder of the game. Nothing less is expected of a professional lineman. Says Walt Kiesling, a Pittsburgh Steeler coach, who once played a lot of tackle, "The lineman gets no sympathy."

Least of all can he expect sympathy from his own kind—that is, from the linemen playing on the other side of the line of scrimmage. The men up front employ a hundred and one tricks to make suckers of each other. The deceit begins the instant the ball is snapped. A defensive lineman may submarine, loop, slant, pinch or hold his point. An offensive lineman may pull out, block straight ahead, angle block, scissors block or use a far-shoulder cutoff.

There is a slick maneuver called the "takeoff," which the Cleveland Browns are fond of using. Even the more experienced defensive linemen have difficulty seeing through it.

"Suppose our Bob Miller is playing opposite Cleveland's Herschel Forester," says Joe Schmidt, taking two names more or less at random. "The ball is snapped to the Cleveland quarterback. Abruptly, Forester pulls out of the line and takes off wide. It's a confidence game. If Miller falls for it, he also takes off wide, thinking that's where the play is going. He leaves a nice, fat hole for the ball carrier to romp through."

In pro football so many possibilities confront the lineman that the unwary can be fooled easily. The Baltimore Colts are partial to a trick called the Colt Special that leaves defensive guards and tackles cursing themselves. When the ball is snapped, an offensive lineman will busy his opponent for a costly moment by jostling him. Then a halfback will run smack into the defensive lineman, clearing the way for a big fullback who is carrying the ball.

This is really rubbing it in. "It just hurts a lineman's pride," explains Joe Schmidt, "to have a little halfback hit him."

Nothing does more for the ego of the young player than his first helmet. Jack Wyant, the title character in the novel Jack Be Nimble, *got his while playing sandlot football under the El in the Bronx.*

FIRST HELMET

George Cuomo

I loved football so much I even used to play sandlot football, and in the Bronx, where you had to search between the rocks to find the sand—the big rocks, because the small ones were hidden under the weeds and the crab grass and dandelions. The el was practically right over us, and we had to stop when a train went by because we couldn't hear the signals. The field we played on was almost triangular, so that for half the game the sidelines closed in on you as you moved toward your goal line. We were all in junior high, and nobody had much money, and I don't think we had two complete uniforms among the eleven of us. There'd be a helmet here and a pair of trousers or shoulders pads there, and sometimes a jersey from the five-and-ten, but that was about it. I played in dungarees and a sweatshirt until I was twelve or thirteen, when I traded a kid a couple big rats I caught in the marshes around Bruckner Boulevard for his old helmet. He traded because it was spring, and football season was far away, but his mother wouldn't let him in with the rats, and the next day he wanted his helmet back. I wouldn't give it—if I had a bike or a baseball glove or anything else to trade, I would have given him that instead, but I wasn't going to give him back the helmet. All summer I rubbed oil and saddle soap into it, and the following fall I felt like Sammy Baugh out there, and I didn't even think of the rocks or the ruts anymore—as if the helmet were a Shield of Virtue or something, a magic amulet, and nothing could hurt me then. The helmet had a smell I can still smell. Even when I just think of the smell it brings back everything else, including the faces of some of the kids we played against. We called ourselves the Crotona Crusaders, because we all lived near Crotona Park, and I was captain and played quarterback and called the plays, because I was the smartest and knew the most about football, and since we didn't have a coach I really ran things. We had a pretty good team, beat a lot of older teams. I spent a lot of time working up plays and formations, with diagrams and all, most of which I got out of books from the East Tremont Branch Library. This was before the T-formation was used everywhere and once I got a book by Clark Shaughnessy, and that year I guess we were the only T-formation sandlot team in the country. I never again enjoyed football as much as I did then.

84

BROWN BROTHERS

Its time in glory was brief but for a few seasons after World War I,
little Centre College of Danville, Ky., toured the country
slaying football giants and reveling in the attention. The Colonels were
a publicity man's dream: they had a catchy nickname, a colorful
coach in Uncle Charley Moran, and a great back in Alvin (Bo) McMillin
(standing at left in team picture). McMillin was a surprise All-America
choice in 1921. Centre had two historic games with Harvard,
losing 31–14 in 1920 (see below) and winning 6–0 in "the upset of
the century" in 1921. Harvard was beaten for the first time in
three years when McMillin ran 32 yards on a reverse for the only touchdown.

UPI

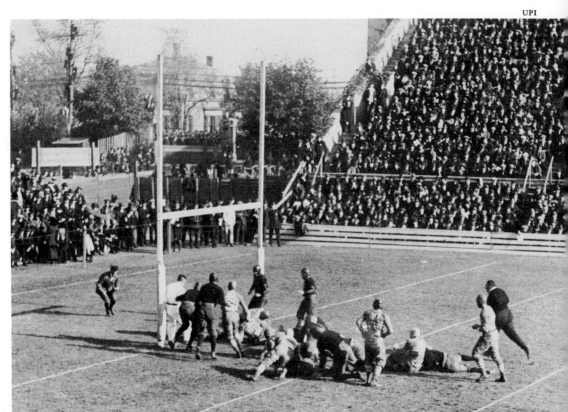

The 1940 National Football League playoff game is remembered as one of the most lopsided major championship events in sports. But the game also marked a major turning point in the development of the offense in football: the Bears, that day, convinced coaches throughout the country that touchdowns came quicker with the new T-formation. The Bears also convinced Sammy Baugh, the great Redskins' passer, that their football method was superior. When asked how he thought the game might have turned out had the Redskins managed to score first, Sammy said, "73 to 7."

BEARS 73, REDSKINS 0

Arthur Daley

The weather was perfect. So were the Bears. In the most fearsome display of power ever seen on any gridiron, the monsters of the Midway won the Ed Thorp Memorial Trophy, symbolic of the world football championship, before 36,034 stunned and deriding fans in Griffith Stadium this balmy afternoon.

It being a Sunday, the Washington Humane Society had the day off. So the Bears had nothing to combat in the play-off except the Redskins, who were pretty feeble opposition indeed. Hence it was that the Chicago Bears scalped the Capital Indians, 73–0, the highest score in the history of the National Football League.

This was simply dreadful. The only question before the house was whether the Bears could score more points when they were on the offensive or when Washington was on the offensive.

Before fifty-six seconds had passed the Bears had a tally. Then, when the second half began, they cut that time down, registering another marker in fifty-four seconds.

There never was anything quite like this. Three weeks ago the Redskins edged out the Bears, 7–3. Today it was something else again. Chicago was a perfect football team that played football of such exquisite class that Washing-

ton could not have won with a brick wall and line of howitzers instead of backs. The Bears would have battered down everything.

By the second half the Redskins showed a marked improvement. Their defense against points after touchdown had reached such perfection that four out of seven were missed. Washington had the misfortune to have to face a team that could have beaten the other nine elevens in the league just as badly.

This was football at its very best. The Bears had the timing for their quick opening plays down to the hundredth of a second. They riddled the Redskins at will with the overwhelming power of their ground game, rocked them with their infrequent passes and smothered them with their defensive power. The blocking was fiendishly accurate and it almost was a physical impossibility for them to make a mistake.

The Bears registered three touchdowns in the first period, one in the second, four in the third, and three in the last. Halas used every eligible man on his squad, thirty-three of them, and fifteen had a share of the scoring.

Halas used Sid Luckman, an Old Blue from Columbia, as his first-half quarterback, and no field general ever called plays more artistically or engineered a touchdown parade in more letter-perfect fashion. But the Lion sat out the second half and still the mastodons from the Midwest rolled.

Ray Flaherty's young men were physically in the game, but that was all. After Bill Osmanski had romped 68 yards for the first touchdown, the 'Skins reached the Bear 26, only to have Bob Masterson's 32-yard field-goal effort fail. That was a blow from which George Preston Marshall's lads never recovered. Had they scored, it might have been different.

The first touchdown was a 75-yard zip to a score. George McAfee picked up 7 yards and then Osmanski, cutting inside Washington's right tackle, went 68 yards more. George Wilson erased two men with the same block to clear the way for the counter.

Then the Bears rolled 80 yards in seventeen plays, the payoff being Luckman's quarterback sneak from the 6-inch line. A moment later Joe Maniaci, the old Fordham Flash, streaked 42 yards for another counter. Jack Manders, Bob Snyder, and Phil Martinovich added the extra points and it was 21–0.

Redskin fans who had watched their heroes win their first seven games of the league season could not believe their eyes. Yet even they were to become convinced that they were watching one of the greatest football teams of all time in action.

The Bears reached the 16 in the second quarter and fumbled. Washington made a gesture by going 63 yards to the 18 on ten successive passes, only to lose the ball on downs. Ray Nolting boomed through with one of the eight Bear pass interceptions and the victors were off to the races. Luckman flipped a 30-yarder to Ken Kavanaugh in the end zone for another counter. Snyder converted.

The third quarter saw the Redskins give up the ghost. Hampton Pool, an end, intercepted Sammy Baugh's lateral flick to Jimmy Johnston on the 16 for a marker. Then the Capital crew tried a fourth-down pass from their 33. It was

batted down. So the Bears took over. Nolting gained 10 yards. But he was just warming up. On the next play he burst through the middle, feinted Baugh into the middle of the Potomac on the 8 and went across standing up.

McAfee intercepted a Roy Zimmerman pass for 35 yards of gorgeous broken-field running for a touchdown and Joe Stydahar split the bars with a placement. The Redskins made an effort to score, reaching the 16, only to lose the ball on downs. Later, Zimmerman's pass was intercepted by Bulldog Turner on the 30. He scored, thanks to a block by Pool, and it was 54–0.

The league champions rumbled 74 yards for their next touchdown in the fourth quarter, Harry Clark going 42 yards on a double reverse for the tally. On this he feinted Frank Filchock into Chesapeake Bay.

The hapless Redskins' Filchock fumbled in the shadow of his goal posts. Jack Torrance, the reformed shot put world record holder, fell on the ball on the 2. So Famiglietti burst across on a quick opener. The last touchdown resulted from a 52-yard drive that was culminated by a 1-yard dance by Clark through the middle.

There was no Redskin hero outside of Flaherty, who had to sit on the bench and absorb it all, too much of a beating for so fine a gentleman and coach. The Bears had thirty-three heroes. Luckman, Nolting, McAfee, Osmanski and Maniaci in the backfield were outstanding. So were Lee Artoe, Stydahar, Danny Fortmann, Turner and Plasman in the line.

The day was gorgeous. The crowd was representative, with high government officials scattered throughout the stands. Everything was under the control of the Magnificent Marshall, except the Bears.

At the end the Redskin band played "Should Auld Acquaintance Be Forgot." If said acquaintance is the Chicago Bears, it should be forgot immediately. At the moment the Bears are the greatest football team of all time.

No other game in football history has been replayed more often—in print and conversation.

OHIO STATE– NOTRE DAME, 1935

Allison Danzig

One of the greatest last-ditch rallies in football history toppled the dreaded Scarlet Scourge of Ohio State from its lofty pinnacle today as 81,000 dumbfounded spectators saw Notre Dame score three touchdowns in less than fifteen minutes to gain an almost miraculous 18–13 victory in the jammed Buckeye Stadium.

Not since the Thundering Herd of Southern California spotted the Ramblers 14 points going into the final period at South Bend in 1931 and won by 16–14 has football provided so magnificent a comeback as this game team of Elmer Layden's staged here in the presence of a crowd that paid a quarter of a million dollars at the gate.

Trailing 13–0 at the end of the third quarter after being manhandled in fearful fashion for the first half by 220-pound Gomer Jones and his giant mates in the Scarlet line, Notre Dame looked to be so hopelessly beaten that no one in the huge throng conceded it the barest ghost of a chance. The fact that the Ramblers had five times threatened to score and been found wanting on each occasion left their adherents with a feeling of the futility of their cause.

And then the incredible happened and happened so fast and furiously, as the lionhearted, blue-shirted players from South Bend became so many swirling, insensate fire-eaters, as to leave the vast assemblage stunned.

In the space of a few minutes, with the stadium clock ticking off the precious remaining moments in the gathering dusk and threatening to save the stampeded home forces from the rout, a team that looked to be irretrievably doomed struck thrice through the air and worked a miracle that brought pandemonium in the Notre Dame stands.

Andy Pilney, the artisan of Notre Dame's victory over Navy with his deadly throwing arm, was the hero of this football battle of the year between two of the mightiest forces in the land. It was Pilney, with his superb passing and his swirling, fearless running from scrimmage and in returning punts, who almost providentially saved the day for the Blue and Gold in a game that was expected to be dominated by Ohio State's sensational sophomore, Joe Williams.

And like the hero that he was, this great-hearted halfback from Chicago, to the consternation of all, was carried off the field on his shield one play short of his goal.

With hardly a minute to go and the score 13–12 in the Buckeyes' favor, Pilney broke loose on a dazzling broken-field run of 32 yards after trying vainly to get off another pass, downing the ball on Ohio State's 19-yard line. The cheers that greeted this last brilliant effort by the Notre Dame back died abruptly as he was seen to lie stretched out just over the sideline.

A stretcher was brought out and Notre Dame's hopes looked to be sunk as he was carried out of the enclosure and placed in an ambulance. But thirty seconds later Wayne Millner was receiving the winning touchdown pass from Bill Shakespeare in the end zone, and the joy of the bedlam-struck Notre Dame cheering section became totally unalloyed when it was learned that Pilney had suffered no more than a torn ligament in his leg.

To appreciate how majestic a role Pilney played in this great triumph over a team that had struck fear to Notre Dame hearts in the first two minutes of play as it intercepted a forward and instantly executed a thrilling lateral pass on the same play, to send Boucher 65 yards for a touchdown, consider his accomplishments.

It was his 28-yard runback of Kabealo's punt, after two beautiful kicks out of bounds by Shakespeare, that started Notre Dame on the road to victory on the last play of the third quarter.

That runback put the ball on Ohio State's 12-yard line and Pilney's pass to Gaul brought it to the 1, from where Millner carried it over. Two minutes after Stilley had failed to add the extra point, Pilney was off to the wars again. From his own 46-yard line he carried and threw the ball 53 yards, hurling three passes to Layden and Zwers for a total of 36 yards, to reach the 1-yard line.

When the Ramblers passed up this scoring opportunity as Millner fumbled on the goal line and Karcher recovered for Ohio State in the end zone for a touchback, a big groan went up from the grandstands.

A minute later it seemed that Notre Dame's hopes were sunk indeed as Jumping Joe Williams, who had scored the Buckeyes' second touchdown at the end of a 50-yard advance, broke loose on a beautiful 23-yard reverse around left end, his only long gain of the day.

With Ohio State in possession of the ball on its 43-yard line and so little time left to play, the Ramblers' plight looked desperate indeed.

But after the Buckeyes' attack had been stopped dead, as it had been all through the second half, save for Williams' end run, Kabealo kicked out of bounds on Notre Dame's 22-yard line and the magnificent Pilney went into action again.

With Ohio State changing from the eight-man line and the seven-man line with a diamond defense that it had been using, and now dropping back men in the futile effort to break up the aerial bombardment, Pilney threw three passes and received one to account for 75 yards in an advance of 78 yards for another touchdown.

His first forward, coming out of a double pass from Layden and protected by a beautiful blocking, went to Fromhart for 37 yards. Next he received a pass from Layden for 9 yards. With the ball on Ohio State's 29-yard line, Pilney threw over center to Fromhart again for 14 yards more, and on the next play he tossed again to Layden, who caught the ball on the goal line, with Kabealo on top of him. It was almost unbelievable. But Notre Dame still needed a point to tie the score.

As Fromhart dropped back for a placement kick the great crowd held its collective breath. It seemed that the outcome of the game hung on this play. When the quarterback's toe dug into the turf and failed to get the ball in the air, a heavy groan went up from the Notre Dame stands, while the tremendously relieved Buckeye followers made the welkin ring with their cheers.

Surely this must be the end for these gamesters from South Bend. Trailing 12–13 and with hardly more than a minute left to play, the Ramblers flatly and indisputably were a licked team. So the happy thousands in the Buckeye stands told themselves. But their feeling of relief instantly gave way to a sense of impending disaster.

Notre Dame kicked off short, hoping to recover the ball, and failed in the stratagem. But the Ramblers, fighting like fury, tackled Beltz so hard on the first scrimmage that he fumbled the ball at midfield and either Pojman or Millner recovered. The Notre Dame followers roared deliriously. Here was a last reprieve, with their team in possession of the ball and time enough left for a last-ditch pass.

The hand on the clock showed less than a minute to play. Pilney, the coolest man in the packed stadium, with its wrought-up thousands, faded back to pass. Finding no receiver uncovered, he ran for it, cut, swirled and fought his way down the field for 32 yards.

This was the end of the game for Pilney.

The end for Ohio State came on the next play as Shakespeare, beautifully protected by the blocking of Mazziotti and Danbom, took his time and passed to Millner in the end zone for the winning touchdown. Notre Dame cautiously kicked off short, Pincura of Ohio State was thrown for a loss by Cronin as he tried to pass, and the game was over.

Thus did Notre Dame turn back one of the most feared squads ever gathered on a college campus. To appreciate the monumental proportions of the feat, one has to realize how decisively the Ramblers were outplayed in the first half.

When the two teams left the field at the end of the second period with the score 13–0, the expectations were that the Buckeyes would let loose in earnest in the second half, unless their coach, Francis (Close the Gates of Mercy) Schmidt, chose to hold down the score. The Buckeyes had scored nine first downs to their opponent's two and gained 118 yards by rushing to Notre Dame's 60.

Ohio State's giant line had tossed the lighter South Bend forwards around in fearful fashion, breaking up the interference and smothering the running plays in their inception and putting such pressure on the passer as to result in interceptions. Notre Dame simply did not have the physical power, it seemed, to stand up against such herculean strength.

The pressure on the Ramblers' passer had led to the Buckeyes' first touchdown as Layden was hurried by the Scarlet's eight-man line and Antenucci intercepted his toss in the air. Instantly the Ohio State fullback, who played an outstanding game in the first half, lateraled the ball to Boucher and the latter, running down the sideline with superb interference, went 65 yards for a score.

The crowd roared in enjoyment. This was a characteristic sample of the tricky, wide-open football that Schmidt taught, and the Ohio State supporters found it good to look upon. From then on, State showed a readiness to shuttle the ball that kept Notre Dame on tenterhooks, and before the end of the first period the Buckeyes put on an exhibition that seemed to forebode dire disaster for the Ramblers.

With three and sometimes four men shuttling the ball in and out and using a split formation that left only the end on the weak side, Ohio State started on a march of 50 yards at the close of the period. Boucher and Antenucci gained almost as they pleased as the South Bend forwards were swept off their feet.

When the celebrated Williams came on the field in the last minute of the period the crowd laughed. As if Notre Dame was not hapless enough already, here was the great game-breaker coming in to add to its distress.

Williams acted as a foil until the ball was brought down to the 3-yard line from the single wing, the short kick and the split formations. Then, at the start of the second period, he shot through Notre Dame's left tackle so hard that the Ramblers slipped off him. The score was 13–0 and it looked as if a rout was in order.

Notre Dame had a chance to score shortly after, when Pilney's 15-yard run from kick formation and beautiful 50-yard punt out of bounds on Ohio State's 1-yard line enabled the Ramblers to gain possession on State's 13, but this opportunity was ruined by Gomer Jones and his rampant mates in the line, as were other Rambler threats on the 37-, 26-, 29- and 9-yard marks. All of these opportunities were created by Pilney and Shakespeare's kicking and Pilney's runbacks, except one gained on a 30-yard run by Millner.

Late in the second period Ohio State started on another march of 40 yards, gained mostly by the amazingly fast Bettridge. Notre Dame stopped that advance. It proved to be last of the game staged by the Buckeyes.

With the second half, the complexion of the contest began to change and it started with the substitution of a second-string line by Notre Dame. Elmer Layden sent in an entirely new set of forwards and they covered themselves with glory.

From there on the Ramblers began to break up State's attack as their own had been broken up in the first half. The Buckeye line began to fade and even the great Gomer Jones, who had been a terror in roving behind the line and jumping up into it to smother plays all along the front, began to lose his speed and finality of tackling.

The play was entirely in Ohio State's half in the third period, thanks to the fine kicking of Shakespeare. Notre Dame was turned back on the Scarlet's 9-yard line when Wojcihovski fumbled on fourth down, with two to go, but shortly after Pilney made his 28-yard runback of a kick to the Buckeyes' 12-yard mark, and from there on his passes ruined what looked like a perfect day for Ohio State and all Columbus.

The crowd, which had been celebrating since last night in jammed hotels and crowded streets with a revelry and riotousness of spirit and color associated with New Year's Eve or

New Orleans' Mardi Gras, filed out of the stadium in abject despair while deliriously happy followers of the still unbeaten Ramblers tore down the goal posts.

The team that Ohio State followers thought invincible had been humbled; their championship dreams had come to an end. And they could lay it all, or mostly all, to the great-hearted halfback from Chicago, Andy Pilney.

The line-up:

Wayne Millner	L.E.	Trevor Rees
Richard Pfefferle	L.T.	Charles Hamrich
John Lauter	L.G.	Inwood Smith
Fred Solari	C.	Gomer Jones
James Martin	R.G.	Gust Zarnas
Frank Kopczak	R.T.	Charles Ream
Martin Peters	R.E.	Merle Wendt
Wallace Fromhart	Q.B.	Stan Pincura
William Shakespeare	L.H.	Frank Boucher
Victor Wojcihovski	R.H.	Dick Heekin
Frank Carideo	F.B.	James McDonald

CARTOON BY FRED BALK

No doubt it would come as something of a surprise to the late Bernard De Voto to find this piece of campus social commentary in a football anthology. But it contains some typically pointed and humorous De Voto opinion about girls, boys—and football—at Northwestern some seasons ago.

THE CO-EDS WERE REAL—
THE BOYS WERE SHADOWS

Bernard De Voto

There was, I found, a neurosis at Northwestern. Also, there was something, at first nebulous and baffling, that set me thinking of Ernest Hocking standing remote above us in Emerson Hall and, in the voice of a lover, setting before us philosophies that had had their moment two thousand years ago, and had gone their way into the limbo of men's hopes. Let me particularize.

It was autumn of 1922 when I went there, and the neurosis was already old. Early that fall the football team and a third of the undergraduates traveled to Urbana for the Illinois game. Insult awaited them there. From store front and lamp post, from fraternity house and trolley car hung banners painted to greet the visitors. "Welcome, sisters," the banners said, and "Northwestern for its pretty girls," and "Hail, Northwestern, the finest girls' school in the Middle West." And many other opprobrious devices. In its recesses of despair the neurosis burned and throbbed. If heaven had been merciful, the girls' school team would have walloped the contemners and exalted the humble, but heaven was realistic. Illinois won

by some incalculable score, and the girls' school went homeward, mourning.

Thereupon the neurosis passed into an active phase. First there were mass meetings, secret, compulsory. Only males could enter them, and if anyone looked like a reporter he was barred at the door. Inside athletes, fraternity officials, professors, deans, Prexy himself danced and bellowed and exhorted. The theme was: there must be more men at Northwestern, and men must be tougher there.

The mass meeting rash lasted for weeks, and meanwhile alumni went out into the sticks resolutely. The campus responded. He who wore a tie was first scorned, then threatened, and finally ducked in the lake. Corduroys and stagged shirts became the uniform of loyalty. Those who could kept a symbolic stubble on their jowls. In the quaint local manner someone declared it proper to "start a tradition," and it was set down in the books as traditional that no Northwestern man took a girl to any athletic contest. To do so would, presumably, interfere with the whole duty of man, to help that team. And again, another spontaneously

92

generated tradition. The athlete was pictured as resenting the softer man's prerogative of spending an evening with a girl; therefore, necking was restricted to certain nights a week, to help that team.

Happily, Tom Robinson's swimming teams gleamed through the darkness. Regularly, methodically, they won Big Ten championships, intercollegiate championships, national championships. So that the neurosis, faced by routine disaster everywhere else, could always allay itself with the waters of the tank. But baseball, basketball, track, wrestling, cross-country and all other diversions gave us only the ignominious ninth or tenth place to which we were accustomed. Football was worst of all. Everywhere the alumni—and the luncheon clubs of Evanston—were active. A stream of hard-muscled lads poured into the campus and out to the field house. But fruitlessly.

My second autumn the team did more disastrously than my first, for then some halfback had run ninety yards to a touchdown against Minnesota, but this year particularly no one ran any distance against anyone. The third autumn was no better, though by now even the commercially-minded downtown campus had caught the neurosis. They went forth to battle, these teams, but they always died. The campus was wholly evangelical. More men and maler men! More men and hairier chests for Northwestern! The corduroys were greasier, the stagged shirts more dissolute. The neurosis had germinated a religion, an exaltation. The student body hardly noticed the weekly martyrdom, so intent, so prayerful were they, looking forward to the day of compensation. Not now, not today, not next week, perhaps not next year, but some time!

Long since, I had understood why I remembered Ernest Hocking in the dimness of Emerson Hall, dealing gently with the vanished idealisms of mankind. For here before me was Heraclitus. It was not today's defeat that counted at Northwestern, not the ignominy of the real, not that which was. No, the neurosis had blotted out ignominy and shame and reality. Only what was to be had any meaning. It was not Being. It was Becoming. This understanding was to make clear to me far more about Northwestern than the football neurosis.

That, indeed, relaxed and for a splendid moment disappeared, as neuroses will. The fourth autumn desperation had its first fruits. The team won a Conference game, and then so vengefully assaulted Notre Dame that Rockne had to send in his first-string backfield to win

the game, and at last reached out and touched the stars. A cloudburst fell on Soldiers' Field the day Michigan came, and somehow, in four inches of water, Northwestern won three to two against a team that would have scored much more if the ground had been dry. The boys burned down an abandoned fraternity house, and cut lengths from the fire hose, and battered a few policemen. Prexy reproved them and they cheered him, seeing his eyelid droop.

Then the skies lightened toward daybreak and the trustees laid the cornerstone of a million dollar stadium, hoping that this would generate the ultimate energy. It did. The next year, by beating the weakest four teams in the Conference while Michigan was beating the strongest four, the team achieved the gold footballs that temporarily sublimated the neurosis. For a moment the flux of things paused in symmetry. For a moment Becoming ceased and Being was achieved. But by that time I was following the clue of Heraclitus through more subtle mysteries of Northwestern.

Being a bachelor and, in years, not much older than the students I taught, I had begun by associating intimately with the undergraduate men. I spent my time at their dormitories and fraternity houses. I went with them to movies and restaurants and speakeasies. I joined their bull sessions and their poker games. For a while. They were likable boys, companionable boys—but only boys. Visits to other colleges showed me that at the other Conference schools boys grew up into men, young men of course, but past adolescence and well past puberty. Maturity was assumed elsewhere, yet I could not find it on our campus. I missed it, and with it most of what had been glamorous in college.

Where were the generous, preposterous, passionate midnight arguments that enlarged the soul? Arguments that reinvented God and recreated the universe a dozen times an evening. Where were the hot lusts for knowledge, sprung from a roommate's air of superiority, or a drowsing professor, or some obscure, probably lascivious allusion in a text? Where were the sparks that set youth championing anarchy or socialism or Rosicrucianism or decadence or astrology? I do not say they were not there, but only that they were not visible. The boys who were not yet young men had driven them under cover. The individual did not appear; the man who experimented with absinthe or table-tapping, who expressed a preference for golf or Sanskrit over homecoming and indulged it without shame, who wore spats because he wanted to or last year's suit because he couldn't afford a new one, who went walking at sunrise because that was his whim or indulged himself with the ladies of the street corner because that was his whim also. There was no individual; or, rather, none was unwary enough to show himself. The tribe had no toleration of individuality.

For all boys were tribal, and Northwestern men were boys. The dreadful Philistinism of adolescence was on them, and overlaying it was a Philistinism more discouraging still. . . . From the first, the women of the campus were a reassurance. Whatever of glamour the men missed, the co-eds had. The men were Philistine, herd-minded, immature. The co-eds were liberal, individual, grown-up. The men had lost entirely the sense of adventure, and in its place had only a formalism that made one's heart gray. The co-eds lived an adventure, and it was a joyful one. Here were enthusiasm and open-mindedness and sophistication and the will to have those intangible accompaniments of college that I have mentioned.

Sophistication! That, I think, was the first, most obvious difference. They seemed so much older than the little boys, so much more of the world. The varied evidence of this was on every hand. I first realized it, I think, when I noticed that if my courses in literature brought up a sexual topic, the men blushed or sniggered while the co-eds treated it as a matter of course. But they were not sophisticated in biological calmness only, but in more worldly ways. They were skeptical. They were tolerant. They were realistic. They were eccentric in that they varied from the norm, whereas the men approached it. They were also gay and delightful and in all things praiseworthy.

Oh, they had their absurdities. Sorority worship is, if possible, even sillier than fraternity awe, and I must confess that these charming girls gabbled like idiots when being true to the star and dagger was talked about. And yet, between the solemnity of a boy telling you why loyalty to Sigma Chi half suffocates him and a girl hymning the immortal loveliness of Kappa Kappa Gamma there is a significant difference. The realistic basis of social importance is never mentioned in the paeons to Sigma Chi. It is frankly conceded in the salutations to Kappa Kappa Gamma, and that is wholesome.

These delightful girls, too, had created at Northwestern as imbecile an "activity" as was ever conceived (save only the Purple Key). I refer to what were called the literary societies, Alethenai, Anonian, Laurean and others. Yet these, too, had a leaven of good sense and realism. No member of Purple Key ever re-

alized that his organization was absurd: no member of Alethenai ever pretended that her organization was literary. With a sanity that redeemed the original absurdity, they all frankly admitted that the literary societies were purely social. That was the tonic realism that the men lacked. That was sophistication, amusement, the worldly sense.

And with these two absurdities, redeemed by their realism, I have exhausted the indictment against Northwestern women. For the rest they were admirable. I remember them as an earnest assurance that youth in the Midland is not wholly Philistine, an assurance that the college is doing its proper work. They had the wit to dress as they liked, which the men did not, and I here acknowledge the charm that resulted. They bowed not down in Rimmon's house, and when they passed the commerce school there was no genuflection. They resisted the regimentation of orthodoxy. They welcomed innovation and individualism. No bunk from the authorities or the alumni imposed upon them. They went the way they had chosen and when a regulation opposed them, ignored it; and when a convention or taboo rose up, laughed it out of sight. Nor did they, as the boys did, regard the faculty as perhaps dull but certainly infallible. . . . For it is the essence of my theme that here, among the women, was everything that Northwestern seemed elsewhere deprived of. They were what youth should be. They were eager and determined and enthusiastic and cool-minded, sane when sanity was desirable, mad when madness was a virtue. For them there was the ancient possibility of wisdom, the ancient possibility of adventurousness and delight in life. They were real; the boys were shadows.

Away, now, from Northwestern, I remember them as incredibly slangy and self-possessed, witty, satirical, underdressed. They tend, in my mind, to become a composite of laughter, bright scarfs and beige stockings. The stockings are, in fact, worth more than perfunctory attention, not alone because they were charming. Those knees, exhibited with such nonchalance, such matter-of-fact carelessness, signified freedom and realism and self-respect. She showed her knees, this composite Northwestern co-ed, and thought nothing of it. No doubt she delighted in them, but not disproportionately. Knees were gay, but life was adventurous. That was the essence; she preserved, and at Northwestern monopolized, the eagerness and arrogance of youth that have immemorially signified college. Currents ran deeply in the earth, tides rose in the sea, and winds were blowing in from beyond the world—and she would find out about them, valuing them more than a cost accounting sheet from Wieboldt Hall or a culture hero of the future who might some day score on Michigan. . . .

If I had a son of college years, would I send him to Northwestern? The answer to such a question may well be: I am a Harvard man. But ignoring that obligation, what I have writ-ten ought to indicate my answer. I would send no son of mine to Northwestern. But a daugh-ter? That, assuredly, is another question. I think of those girls, and of how much of the reality of education they achieve there, in spite of the shadow aforesaid, in spite of the stampede toward commerce, in spite of the careful ortho-doxy that is encouraged. Yes, if I thought well of my daughter, I would send her to North-western.

As partners in one of football's earliest and best passing combinations, quarterback Gus Dorais collaborated with end Knute Rockne in a famous game of pass-and-catch that gave Notre Dame its first victory over Army in 1913. Less well known is their collaboration in a few prizefights in the South Bend-Gary area. Rockne did the fighting; Dorais was his second—and they shared the prize. Dorais and Rockne also shared a dormitory room on the Notre Dame campus and, according to this small confession, collaborated on some profitable hazing schemes.

RADIATOR RENT

Gus Dorais

I knew Knute Rockne not as coach, but as roommate, teammate and fellow conspirator through four undergraduate years at Notre Dame. Any tale of mine, then, about Rock is likely to smell of creosote, for I lived in its aroma throughout those years and suffered the smells of many a batch of hair restorer brewed by Rockne, the budding chemist. None of it ever worked, but that never deterred Rock from stirring up more of his evil-smelling mixtures.

Rock spent those four years trying to get even—which he did and more—for having been mulcted his first week on the campus of a portion of his meager supply of funds by upper-classmen, who convinced him it was proper for incoming freshmen to contribute toward a flower fund for the university president. Though he had little enough money on hand then, or later, either, for that matter, Rock kicked in. However, in the years that followed the tables not only turned—they spun. Many of Rock's enterprising money-raising projects, such as charging green newcomers for the use of one necessity or another, were carried out alone. But he hit upon an idea in our junior year that needed assistance. Before freshmen became too steeped in college ways, I would call on them in Walsh Hall to inquire if the radiator rent had been paid. It never had been, so then it was practice to call 'Rock' in from the hall and

let him start dismantling the radiator. It was always good for a small fee—until school authorities learned about it and put that corporation out of business.

We lived in one of those basement rooms, half below and half above ground, and like every other room in the dormitory at the time, the windows were barred, but not for long. With a bit of professional help we had one window fixed so that it swung open like a door. From then on, the after-hours traffic through that window was greater than the legitimate flow through the main entrance, but whereas the latter was without cost the Rockne-inspired gateway was strictly on a toll basis. From students using it to bring in foodstuffs after hours there was a straight ten per cent fee; from others we took whatever we thought the traffic would bear.

That project almost ended on a night of heavy sleep when neither of us heard a band of late arrivals, nor knew until morning that they had left in our room a pile of such trinkets from South Bend streets as lanterns, sign posts and other similar trivia. As a matter of fact, the prefect who woke students discovered it first and some unpleasant moments followed until finally it blew over with the secret of the profitable window still undiscovered.

This pithy account appeared in the Dundee (Scotland) Courier and Argus, *in 1886, and tells all one needs to know about the game between the football clubs of Arbroath and Bon Accord.*

A DROLL MATCH

Dundee Courier and Argus

This match—the first cup tie—was played at Arbroath on Saturday, when, despite the rain, there was a good turnout of spectators. The match was one of the drollest ever seen here or anywhere else, and baffles description. It was truly "The Massacre of the Innocents," for a more helpless set of innocents never before met the crack club of Forfarshire. Though unable to describe the match, we can give the result, which we hope no one will doubt. Two forty-fives were played. The first result was Arbroath 15, Bon Accord 0; second: Arbroath 21, Bon Accord 0. Grand total: Arbroath 36, Bon Accord 0. Milne, the active goalkeeper of Arbroath, neither touched the ball with hand or foot during the match, but remained under the friendly shelter of an umbrella the whole time.

Anyone who grew up in football's radio age will recall the delight of letting the imagination
reach across the country to a game played 3,000 miles away.

BROADCAST OF THE GAME

Frederick Elbright

Three thousand miles, on the other side of the continent,
and this the hour noon: noon, and a bland sun,
the quiet impersonal sunlight on hibiscus and poinciana leaves,
and the abstract voice out of the amplifier announcing,
"Well, the sun is setting pretty rapidly now . . ."
and the anonymous roar of the crowd cheering,
cheering, already in their evening, at a far place;
the faces, voices never to be gathered again, at a game you'll never see,
and you remembering now, remotely, play by play,
crisp leaves in a coppery sunset, stale taste of rye
and the chilly damp smell of frost moving over the bleachers,
remembering now while the radio voice shouts, "twenty yards!
thirty yards! . . ." and the cheering ascends to frenzied crescendo,
and there is the swift figure running, running into the red sunset,
running into the bloody evening light, and the cries wild,
alto and shrill, mounting in thunderous blare of band:
but the players, the crowd in their evening already dead, hours ago;
and you here in your quiet noon remembering,
but the shadow moving westward. . . .

Behind it all, worshipers, is the Oedipus complex. . . .

FREUD ON THE 50-YARD LINE

Thomas Hornsby Ferril

As I look back over the intellectual caprices of the past quarter-century, I am amazed that neither the Marxists nor the Freudians ever took out after football. There's not a single book on the subject. It is now too late. In Olympian cerebration, Marx and Freud are obsolete; the atom has taken over, and football, for the moment, seems reasonably safe from encroachment, although we may still see a few flurries —cobalt tracers, perhaps, for the study of the parabolas of flat passes—but it won't amount to much because the atom is cut out for graver duties.

If the Marxists had been more alert, they could have made something out of football as brutal capitalistic exploitation of the working class. They might have noted a few strikes for higher pay and a court decision entitling a college football player to workmen's compensation benefits following injury.

But it was the Freudians who made the colossal blunder. You could argue that they overlooked football on the grounds that it was just too big to be noticed, on those Saturday afternoons when the college library was free for their invasion of fiction, drama, poetry, painting, sculpture, music and economics.

Yet why, when the whole town was roaring over their heads, did they pay no attention to the emotional frenzy? Frankly, I think they must have, but the Freudians were notoriously selfish fellows; they wanted everything whole-hog; they were always extremely jealous of anthropologists, and as you look back on their dilemma as far as football was concerned, their dog-in-the-manger attitude was perhaps justified, for no self-respecting Freudian could ever have done a full-dress job on football without cutting some detested anthropologist in on the gravy.

But had the Freudians been less self-centered and had they welcomed a bit of anthropological assistance, just think of the monumental treatises by which the scientific literature of the period might have been enriched, great books wedding the wisdom of *Gesammelte Schriften* with the profundity of *The Golden Bough.*

Let me set down, in nostalgic summary, some of the findings that might have been made, had the Freudians not been sulking in their tents.

Obviously, football is a syndrome of religious rites symbolizing the struggle to preserve the egg of life through the rigors of impending winter. The rites begin at the autumn equinox and culminate on the first day of the New Year

99

with great festivals identified with bowls of plenty; the festivals are associated with flowers such as roses, fruits such as oranges, farm crops such as cotton, and even sun-worship and appeasement of great reptiles such as alligators.

In these rites the egg of life is symbolized by what is called "the oval," an inflated bladder covered with hog skin. The convention of the oval is repeated in the architectural oval-shaped design of the vast outdoor churches in which the services are held every Sabbath in every town and city, also every Sunday in the greater centers of population, where an advanced priesthood performs. These enormous roofless churches dominate every college campus; no other edifice compares in size with them, and they bear witness to the high spiritual development of the culture that produced them.

Literally millions of worshipers attend the Sabbath services in these enormous open-air churches. Subconsciously, these hordes of worshipers are seeking an outlet from sex frustration in anticipation of violent masochism and sadism about to be enacted by a highly trained priesthood of young men. Football obviously arises out of the Oedipus complex. Love of mother dominates the entire ritual. The churches, without exception, are dedicated to Alma Mater, Dear Mother. (Notre Dame and football are synonymous.)

The rites are performed on a rectangular area of green grass oriented to the four directions. The grass, symbolizing summer, is striped with ominous white lines representing the knifing snows of winter. The white stripes are repeated in the ceremonial costumes of the four whistling monitors who control the services through a time period divided into four quarters, symbolizing the four seasons.

The ceremony begins with colorful processions of musicians and semi-nude virgins who move in and out of ritualized patterns. This excites the thousands of worshipers to rise from their seats, shout frenzied poetry in unison, and chant ecstatic anthems through which runs the Oedipus theme of willingness to die for love of mother.

The actual rites, performed by twenty-two young priests of perfect physique, might appear to the uninitiated as a chaotic conflict, concerned only with hurting the oval by kicking it, then endeavoring to rescue and protect the egg.

However, the procedure is highly stylized. On each side there are eleven young men wearing colorful and protective costumes. The group in so-called "possession" of the oval first arrange themselves in an egg-shaped "huddle," as it is called, for a moment of prayerful meditation and whispering of secret numbers to each other.

Then they rearrange themselves with relation to the position of the egg. In a typical "formation" there are seven priests "on the line," seven being a mystical number associated, not, as Jung purists might contend, with the "seven last words," but actually with sublimation of the "seven deadly sins" into "the seven cardinal principles of education."

The central priest crouches over the egg, protecting it with his hands while over his back quarters hovers the "quarterback." The transposition of "back quarters" to "quarterback" is easily explained by the Adler school. To the layman the curious posture assumed by the quarterback as he hovers over the central priest immediately suggests the Cretan origins of Mycenaean animal art, but this popular view is untenable. Actually, of course, the quarterback symbolizes the libido, combining two instincts, namely (a) Eros, which strives for even closer union and (b) the instinct for destruction of anything which lies in the path of Eros. Moreover, the "pleasure-pain" excitement of the hysterical worshipers focuses entirely on the actions of the libido-quarterback. Behind him are three priests representing the male triad.

At a given signal, the egg is passed by sleight-of-hand to one of the triad, who endeavors to move it by bodily force across the white lines of winter. This procedure, up and down the enclosure, continues through the four quarters of the ritual.

At the end of the second quarter, implying the summer solstice, the processions of musicians and semi-nude virgins are resumed. After forming themselves into pictograms representing alphabetical and animal fetishes, the virgins perform a most curious rite requiring far more dexterity than the earlier phallic Maypole rituals from which it seems to be derived. Each of the virgins carries a wand of shining metal which she spins on her fingertips, tosses playfully into the air, and with which she interweaves her body in most intricate gyrations.

The virgins perform another important function throughout the entire service. This concerns the mystical rite of "conversion" following success of one of the young priests in carrying the oval across the last white line of winter. As the moment of conversion approaches, the virgins kneel at the edge of the grass, bury their faces in the earth, then raise their arms to heaven in supplication, praying that "the uprights will be split."

Freud and Breuer in 1896 (*Studien über*

Hysteria), described "conversion" as hysterical symptoms originating through the energy of a mental process being withheld from conscious influence, and this precisely accounts for the behavior of the virgins in the football services.

The foregoing, I confess, scarcely scratches the surface. Space does not permit interpretation of football as related to dreams, or discussion of the great subconscious reservoirs of thwarted American energy that weekly seek expression through vicarious enjoyment of ritualized violence and infliction of pain. To relate football to the Oedipus complex alone would require, as it well deserves, years of patient research by scholarly men such as we find in the Ford Foundation.

I only regret that these studies were not undertaken a quarter-century ago, when the Freudians were in full flower. It's just another instance, so characteristic of our culture, of too little and too late.

CARTOON BY GALLAGHER

Reproduced by permission, *Sport* Magazine, © Macfadden-Bartell Corp.

The letter to Princeton football coach Fritz Crisler, written in the spring of 1934, was in response to a questionnaire the coach had sent to alumni.

LETTER TO COACH CRISLER

F. Scott Fitzgerald

TO FRITZ CRISLER

1307 Park Avenue
Baltimore, Md.

Dear Fritz:

You write me again demanding advice concerning the coming season. I hasten to answer —*again* I insist that using a member of the Board of Trustees at left tackle to replace Charlie ("Asa") Ceppi and Christian ("Dean") Eisenhart would be a mistake. My idea is a backfield composed of Kipke, Eddie Mahan, President Lowell, and anybody we can get for the left side—Pepper Einstein in the center— and then either bring back Light-Horse Harry Lee, or else you will fill in yourself for the last place. Or else shift Kadlic to center and fill in with some member of the 75-pound team.

Failing that, it *is,* as you suggest in your round robin, a question of using a member of the Board of Trustees. Then who? and where? There is "Hack" Kalbaugh. There is the late President Witherspoon—but where is he? There is Harkness Hall, but we can't get it unless we pay for the whole expressage *at this end!*

The best suggestion is probably to put Rollo Rulon Roll-on at full and return to the Haughton system.

Now, Fritz, I realize that you and Tad know more about this thing than I do—nevertheless I want to make my suggestion: all the end men and backfield men and members of the Board of Trustees start off together—then they all reverse their fields, led by some of the most prominent professors and alumni—Albie Booth, Bob Lassiter, etc.—and almost before we know it we are up against the Yale goal—let me see, where was I? I mean the Lehigh goal—anyhow some goal, perhaps our own. Anyhow the main thing is that the C.W.A. is either dead, or else just beginning, and to use again that variation of the "Mexican" shift that I suggested last year will be just disastrous. Why? Even I can follow it! Martineau comes out of the huddle —or topples back into it—he passes to some member of past years' teams—(who won't be named here because of the eligibility rules) and then—well, from there on we go on to practically anything.

But not this year, Fritz Crisler, if you take my advice!

The Team

This profile of George Halas, written the season before the Bears beat the Giants for the 1963 NFL championship, offers a critical look at the strengths and weaknesses of a self-made man—and pro football's most prominent coach.

PAPA BEAR

William Barry Furlong

George Halas, the owner and coach of the Chicago Bears, has all the warmth of breaking bones, a personality as daring as twin beds, and —in the classic dramatic tradition—a strength that is his main weakness: he is a self-made man.

That fact explains, as much as anything else, why he is frugal, hardworking, paternalistic, utterly loyal—and why the juices of humanity seem to have been squeezed from him. The gracious arts seem as practiced in Halas as a pass pattern. He smiles as though it hurts. He pats a man on the back stiffly, like uncooked spaghetti breaking. "The most human thing about him are his failures," says one friend— and he turns from *them* as reflexively as blinking. Yet he has in him the ability to arouse a fantastic loyalty from certain personalities. He is a conscientious man religiously and a generous one privately. And he carries around with him the burden of his own success.

Like all self-made men, Halas immerses himself in his work so completely that he is insulated from reality. "He doesn't realize that other people can't work that 95-hour week," says one friend. This was one of several factors that cost him the services of one of his most loyal employes and friends, Hunk Anderson—who

candidly did not share Halas' compulsion for work—for another coach, Clark Shaughnessy, who carefully offers Halas the impression that he's working at least as hard as the head coach. "Hunk was the type of man who liked to spend some free time at home in Detroit after a game and then come back and work like hell for the rest of the week," says one man who knows him well. "Halas is one of those guys who feels that if you haven't got anything to do, you ought to be down at the office doing it."

And yet this very characteristic was what long insured the Bears' domination of the National Football League. "Nobody else had a tight-knit organization that worked at football 12 months a year," says an old hand in the business. "In those days, football was a three- or four-month a year business." Now everybody works at it 12 months a year and one of Halas' prime edges was lost. (Another was lost when the NFL committed itself fully to free substitution and the platoon system. For until then, Halas built his teams on men who could play both offense and defense and deliver a brutal physical beating to the opposition, particularly late in a game.)

Like all self-made men, Halas believes implicitly in the myths of his own accomplishment, particularly in judging football talent. The Bear tradition of coming up with the great player from a small college—from Ray Nolting to Bulldog Turner to Harlon Hill—has obscured the fact that he once passed up Sammy Baugh in the draft to grab a halfback named Ray Buivid. Or that he is insistent on asserting and reasserting the old myth—i.e., in working with John Adams of Los Angeles State to justify Adams' high draft selection in 1959. ("Adams is the most versatile player who ever came to the Bears," dryly remarks one man familiar with team operations. "So far we've found he can't play six different positions.")

Like all self-made men, Halas believes that Papa knows best. He is paternalistic in the tradition of John D. Rockefeller or Colonel Robert R. McCormick; he believes Western civilization began its decline with the birth of labor unions. To keep the Bears out of the Players Association, he offers them slightly more money during the exhibition season, and engages in a number of small and thoughtful gestures to protect their pride and their reputation. (One example: he refuses to name what players he's cut from the squad so that they can make "adjustments"— either in their home town or with other teams —before the fact becomes public.) But, as with all such employers, some players find his paternalism a trifle smothering. Halas does not allow for—or allow—players who have exalted notions of their own worth. (Some of his finest linemen on the team that became the great Bear squad of 1940–41–42 felt privileged to play for him for $4,000 a year.) And for a long while, he systematically held out money from every paycheck to insure, he claimed, that the player would have enough money to get home after the season. Most players accepted the notion tolerantly but a few were enraged that Halas—but not they themselves—could use their money to operate on during the season. "George has never been able to get used to the idea," says one close acquaintance, "that some men feel competent enough to run their own lives."

Like most self-made men, Halas is not quite aware that the dogmas of his platitudinous past are inadequate to the stormy present. Undeniably, Papa George—a sobriquet curiously fitting —brought a good deal of vision to the early days of pro football. He perceived the opportunity in bringing Red Grange off the campus at the University of Illinois into a pro-football tour that saw the Bears play 10 games in 17 days to help raise pro football from a sandlot attraction to a popular, crowd-pulling spectacle.

He also saw the need—after the Bears played six scoreless ties in 1932—for changing the rules to permit more frequent and more spectacular forward passing, changes which eventually put the pro game far ahead of college football in its appeal and dramatic impact. But he has not been able to adjust his handling of the team to changes in the game. Bill Gleason of Chicago's *American* ("I was the only columnist who ever told him to quit; after all, he wouldn't be out of a job") once approached the difference in a column in which he observed:

"They (Vince Lombardi, Paul Brown, Nick Skorich, Allie Sherman) go after THE man they need for the job. Halas tries to create a man out of the material at hand."

The most dramatic example of how Halas' attitude toward change affects the Bears is in his approach to the key players. "If Halas is— has been—a great coach," says one of his long-time students, "it's because of the way he handled certain kinds of ballplayers." Those were the Old Bears, who played with abandon, with delight, and without money. They took Papa's word as Truth and followed him as compulsively as lemmings going down to the sea. Today, the players are better educated, tutored to a high cynicism by organized recruiting from grade school on up, and aware that success is what the public—not Papa—thinks of them. Therefore, they are likely to do what *they* think is best. Papa doesn't rebel against all this; he's just not up to coping with it. Bill Wade, the current Bear quarterback, is a young man of almost iridescently good habits; he doesn't smoke or drink and tends to blush when people use naughty words. He matches the ideal of what athletes are supposed to be. Unfortunately for Halas, he is also an independent thinker. He will study the most carefully wrought plan for attacking an opponent and then, when he gets in a game, spontaneously try to improve on it. Halas apparently doesn't have it in him to chastise a man like Wade and get him to team discipline. The result: "Wade is running this team," says one member of the Bear family.

The reluctance of the Bear coaching staff to correct Wade in a game has its comic opera aspects. In one exhibition game this season, Wade jettisoned the "game plan," which called for heavy emphasis on running plays, in favor of a passing game laced heavily with the "big bomb"—the long pass. The Bears were stumbling about futilely and coaches on the sidelines were in a ferment over who should tell Wade to go back to the game plan. Nobody did.

Instead, Rudy Bukich was put in at quarterback with orders to run the game plan. He took the Bears 80 yards for a touchdown, moving them briskly along the ground. Wade got the hint and adhered more closely to the game plan after that. "The fact is not simply that Halas didn't do anything about it at the time," says one close observer. "The fact is that he's stuck with this guy and *can't* do anything about it."

For a man who has labored over the flinty, square-jawed image of Man in Control of Destiny, George Halas is a surprisingly sentimental soul. Or, perhaps, he simply has the classic failing of a self-made man: he interprets loyalty as competence. And being unable to discern the difference, he rewards loyalty instead of competence. This has saddled Bear fans with the television commentaries of Red Grange. And it has burdened the Bears with players who cannot do the job. Guard Stan Jones, for instance, was long recognized as possessing a strong straight-ahead charge as well as an inability to pull out and lead the interference on an end sweep. ("This guy can't get out of his own shoes," is the way one member of the Bear family put it.) Yet it was not until this year that Halas seemed to recognize all this and shift Jones' duties to tasks he could perform. Jimmy Dooley, a spread end, possessed a ballet-like agility at grabbing hook passes and dashing out of bounds. But he could not—and cannot —block. ("Some guys are at least clumsy enough to get in the way of somebody from time to time, even if it's their own teammates. Dooley can't even do that.") If a player happens to be both loyal *and* competent, there is literally nothing Halas won't do for him. He has urged players well past their primes to play an extra year or so—and he has made it well worth their while. Once a defensive end who knew he was finished came to Halas to borrow money to buy a half-interest in a business. "Play another year," said Halas, "and buy the *whole* business." These incidents limn the human qualities in the man—qualities often overlooked in the Man of Destiny image—but they do not always help the Bears. In effect, they suggest that while other teams are looking for the best 36 football players they can find, Halas is satisfied with 24 to 30 football players and a half-dozen or so guys he likes.

Many of the characteristics of Halas—his frugality, his stubbornness, his single-mindedness—are the product of his heritage as well as his fight to be somebody. He is of Bohemian ancestry and he grew up in the old Bohemian neighborhood near 18th and Ashland. His parents came from Pilsen, in what is now Czechoslovakia, and his father opened a tailor shop in Chicago. By the time he died, when George was 15, the family owned a building with 18 apartments. George played basketball; he was captain of the team at Illinois. He played baseball; he made it to right field for the New York Yankees but suffered a hip injury and was replaced by a player named Babe Ruth. He played football at Illinois, at Great Lakes (where he was on a Rose Bowl team) and finally for the Staley Starchmakers in Decatur, Illinois. After he brought the Staleys to Chicago in 1921, he found himself not only playing football but writing the publicity, making up the schedules, distributing tickets and passes and coaching the team.

Those were the days when Jim Thorpe played with sheet metal between his shoulder pads, when Halas met his players in the lobby of the Planters Hotel in order to sign them, when the Bears had another owner named Dutch Sternaman. Sternaman was a halfback whose partnership offered Halas an alluring temptation: he didn't have to pay him. For years the two worked together until, as one man very close to Halas recalls, "they were watching each other more closely than they were watching the business." Sternaman didn't agree with Halas' coaching techniques or his strategy and in 1929 their disagreement became so pronounced that the next season Halas was forced to step aside to let a "neutral" man, Ralph Jones from Lake Forest Academy, become the coach. Jones won a league championship with the Bears in 1932 but decided to return to Lake Forest as athletic director (at a salary reported to be $3,500 a year). The Bears themselves lost $18,000 that season and Halas found that Sternaman was willing to sell out for $38,000. Halas went to several people to borrow money—to his mother, to one of his players, Jim McMillen (still a Bear vice-president), to an old school chum, Ralph Brizzolara (still secretary of the organization), to the mother of George Trafton, an historic Bear center, and finally to Charley Bidwill, soon to be owner of the rival Chicago Cardinals. Bidwill not only lent him money but arranged for a bank loan for Halas. "Without Bidwill, Halas couldn't have raised all the money," says one Bear insider, "and I think there was something in the contract that if Halas didn't pay in full, the whole club would revert to Sternaman." Thus but for the grace of Charley Bidwill, it would have been Dutch Sternaman—not George Halas—that would have been up for canonization today.

Of all the accomplishments of these years, the most dazzling and instructive was not on the football field; it was in the newspaper offices. When Halas started running around to see newspapermen, sometimes sitting down to write out what had happened in an effort to get some space, the sports editor of the *Tribune* was Don Maxwell. Today he is editor of the *Tribune* and he is "the man who has more influence on Halas than anybody else." One member of the Bear inner circle points out that "They spend at least two or three nights a week drinking together when both are in town." There is some doubt whether "George is as enthralled with Maxwell as Maxwell is with him but George is not about to let anybody know about it." In any case, Halas' handling of Maxwell and the *Tribune* was pivotal in making him the man—and the image—that he is.

Even in today's light, Maxwell was an exceptional sports editor. His gifts were those of a fine newspaperman, not of an after-dinner speaker. The *Tribune* recognized these gifts, transferred him to the city room, and began moving him steadily up the executive ladder. His successor as sports editor was Arch Ward. At first, Halas got along handsomely with Ward. There are those who feel that the "college all-star game was as much Halas' idea as it was Ward's." (The Bears were the first pro team to play in the all-star game.) By 1939 or 1940, their friendship was so firm that Halas, together with George Marshall of the Washington Redskins, offered Ward the presidency and commissionership of the National Football League at a reported salary of $25,000 a year. Ward turned it down; instead he recommended that the NFL hire Elmer Layden, then football coach of Notre Dame, which it did. The world, as represented by the *Tribune,* seemed good to Halas and so were the sports pages.

Then with Halas in the Navy in World War II, the warmth waned. Ward decided to start a pro football league in direct competition to Halas' league and Ben Lindheimer, operating director of Arlington and Washington park race tracks, was to help him finance it. When Halas returned, he found the *Tribune* sports pages devoted largely to the glories of the All-America conference and racing at Arlington and Washington parks. Now Halas found it useful to build his friendship with Don Maxwell. As it developed, Maxwell couldn't overrule Ward's taste on the sports pages but when Ward died, Halas—through Maxwell—enjoyed an entree on the *Tribune* only a trifle short of that of Colonel McCormick.

Even more remarkable, the other newspapers in town—far from being piqued by the love pact between Halas and the *Tribune*—have stumbled all over themselves to follow the *Tribune's* lead. The manner in which Halas has exploited *all* the papers was dramatized in the way he used them to whiplash and exile the Chicago Cardinals. After the death of Charley Bidwill in 1947, the Cardinals drifted into the influence and control of Walter Wolfner, who married the widow of Bidwill. Wolfner is a man of variable habits, most of which earn him enemies. Halas was among them. "His feud with Wolfner is a tribute to Walter's 'wonderful qualities' as a human being," says one anti-Wolfner man sarcastically. So Halas turned swiftly from helpful cooperation with the Chicago Cardinals to unrelenting enmity. (The late Mrs. Wolfner apparently offered to cancel Halas' debt to her first husband in return for a third-string quarterback named Bobby Layne. Instead Halas peddled him to another team and, according to the Cards' side of the story, specifically inserted in the contract that Layne could not be sold to the Cardinals.) Over the years, the Cardinals found themselves shifted from a two-game-a-season schedule with the Bears—the Bear game in Comiskey Park was for years the only profitable venture for Cardinals at home—to none-a-year. They also found it increasingly difficult to get space on the sports pages before the season opened and the reason was that Halas simply exploited all the publishers in town. For years he had taken part in an Armed Forces exhibition game which had been sponsored at various times by the old *Herald-American* and later the *Sun-Times.* In 1955, Halas suggested that *all* of the papers back the game. He wined and dined the publishers and filled them with tales of their dedication and high purpose. The publishers fell into line with engaging innocence. Soon they had their sports staffs covering the Bears like pollen. In that vital pre-season period when free advertising stimulates season ticket sales, the Bears filled whatever space the newspaper could deliver to pro football; the Cardinals began to wonder if they could even buy space in the papers. For a while they tried to appeal to the publishers' sense of fair play—which suggests much about their judgment—and get them to schedule the Cardinals against the Bears in Soldier Field. Halas went for that idea like cancer of the brain. Eventually, Wolfner caught the hint and moved out of town. It was easier to find a new town than a friendly publisher.

The mesmeric hold that Halas has on the newspapers has helped him cloak incidents that reveal other characteristics. One example is the frugality he exercises in running the Bears. Another is the feud which has torn the coaching staff for a decade.

His parsimonious attitude is so virile in legend that it has taken on a life of its own. It is true that he's frequently lent money to his players—and sometimes to newspapermen —but he expects to get it back, with interest. (On occasion, he has not gotten it back—but he has never complained.)

One player who had borrowed small amounts of money found Halas unwilling to shell out more money, for Halas knew that he was about to cut the player from the squad. "But I need the money to buy my kid milk," wailed the player. Halas considered the problem carefully. Then he said, "What's his address? I'll send him a quart." Halas will meet the salary demands of his top draft choice and then see those a bit lower on the list drift off to the rival American Football League.

Nor does Halas let money slip by him recklessly. One player on a rival NFL team once complained that one of the many reasons he hated playing in Wrigley Field was that Halas would provide only two bars of soap for 36 players. And a man who once put out a television guide recalls the time he proposed to Halas that the guide publish a roster of the players keyed to the telecast of an Armed Forces game. "He wanted $25 for every name that was to appear on the roster," recalls the publisher. Since Halas was also to be the judge of what names went on the roster, the publisher suspected he'd be digging up names of guys who couldn't make the kids' teams that used to play between halves. "So I forgot about *that* project," he says.

The fans themselves see the counting-house talents of Halas in his implacable restoration every autumn of the old box seats once ordered out of Wrigley Field by Phil Wrigley because they were too narrow and uncomfortable. (The wider, more comfortable box seats cut capacity—and revenue—in the box seat area by 20 per cent.) By the time Halas gets finished erecting temporary stands on the east side of Wrigley Field, placing rows of field seats along the sidelines and end zones, and squeezing in standing room, the capacity of Wrigley Field is raised from 36,755 for baseball to more than 49,000 for football. Tex Schramm, general manager of the Dallas Cowboys, once commented that "Halas will sell a ticket anywhere

he can put a chair. Many's the time a player has come out of the game and found some guy in his seat on the bench—and usually the guy has a ticket stub for it."

The feud on the coaching staff is one of those things Halas prefers to ignore. He denies that it exists—"and if Halas says black is white in this town, where do you go?" as one man knowledgeable about the Bear feud puts it. The feud matches Clark Shaughnessy, the craggy, whitemaned defensive coach, against the Old Bear guard, led in recent years by Luke Johnsos. ("If Halas denies there's a feud this time, he may be right because Johnsos isn't fighting back this time," says one of the inner circle.) The feud has roots going back to the 1930's when Shaughnessy was an "advisor" to Halas. Nobody knows quite what started it. "You'd get a million million stories on that," says one observer. But even in the late 1930's, it was bitter enough so that Johnsos and Hunk Anderson would lock Shaughnessy out of team meetings. In the 1940's Shaughnessy departed to serve as head coach at Stanford (and take the team to the Rose Bowl) and of the Los Angeles Rams. Halas brought him back in 1950, just before, as it happened, the Bears were to play the Rams in a playoff for the title in their division of the NFL. The Bears had beaten the Rams twice during the season but now—with Shaughnessy on the Bear sideline—they lost the playoff, 24–14. Shortly thereafter they lost Anderson; his personality was direct and practical while Shaughnessy's leaned to the subtle and theoretical. That seemed to leave Shaughnessy as the man most in Halas' favor. "He's the only guy George really seems to be afraid of," says an acquaintance of both men. "Afraid" is strong and a trifle inaccurate; "dazzled by" appears more accurate. For Shaughnessy has what Halas needs most: an apparent answer for everything. "George is still looking for that pot at the end of the rainbow—the one play or the one player that'll bring him the championship," says a friend. Shaughnessy holds out that hope—and in return enjoys privileges denied the other coaches. "He's the only coach who can come and go as he pleases," says one of the Bear family. He's also the only one who feels free to talk to newsmen. He uses this privilege with great art. After the Bears broke up San Francisco's shotgun offense, 31–0, last year, Shaughnessy lectured brilliantly on how it was accomplished. (There is a general feeling that it was due less to Shaughnessy's defensive strategy than to the great individual effort of linebacker Bill George in continually beating Frank Morze, the San Francisco center, to roam free on sorties into the 49er backfield.) Several weeks later, when the 49ers beat the Bears, 41–31, Shaughnessy couldn't be found by newsmen. When he chooses, Shaughnessy not only offers great insight into defensive technique—he's one of the most ingenious and articulate men in football—but also in how the press can be used for one's own purposes. After one game last season, in which rival pass receivers had eluded defensive back Harlon Hill for touchdowns, Shaughnessy loitered in the anteroom of the Bear clubhouse long enough to say lugubriously, over and over again, that "nobody should make a fine boy like Harlon Hill the goat in this game." It was a virtuoso performance in how to achieve a point in print—the idea that Hill *was* the goat—while appearing to demur the point. At least one bystander watched the performance and predicted that Hill would not long be playing on the Bear defensive team. Later that week, Hill was shifted back to offense. Another example came early this season when Halas was taking more and more control of the defense. In the preseason games he modified it substantially, returning somewhat to standard pro defenses in lieu of the intricate "jitterbugging" that was so much a part of the Shaughnessy defense. Then at the start of the league season Shaughnessy was quoted in one paper as saying the Bears had "the best defensive personnel" they've ever had. It sounded less like a testimonial than a warning—to Halas—that if he failed, the responsibility would be entirely his for not knowing how to use "the best defensive personnel" the Bears have ever had.

There is a feeling that time is growing short for George Halas. And yet he is as vigorous and alert as ever, as parsimonious and paternalistic as ever. He has no master but Father Time and he appears to be holding him at bay. There is no reason to believe that Halas won't—and can't—go on for years as he has in the past: a man whose greatest strength is his greatest weakness—the fact that he's a self-made man.

Football in America was never so unnecessarily rough as it was in the
beginning. After 1888, when the low tackle became legal, the boys
came up with a whole series of bone-wrenching, mass momentum plays.
The hauling, heaving and gouging drew a public
outcry (top). Eventually the rules were changed,
protective helmets were worn (photograph above of
Princeton and Cornell in 1903) and the game was somewhat tamed.

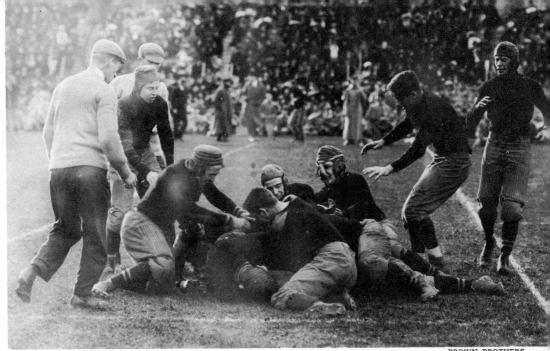

BROWN BROTHERS

Grappling at ground level in the 1906 Army-Navy game at West Point.

Flagrant example of brutal play, modern style, was caught by the camera
during the 1951 Drake-Oklahoma A & M game. Drake's star Negro back,
Johnny Bright, catches a blow from Wilbanks Smith of A & M.
Bright left the game with a broken jaw.

UPI

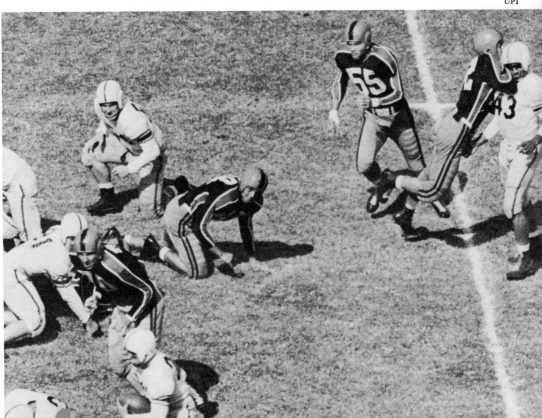

A long short story which expresses the emotion of playing college football as vividly as anything in fact or fiction. The author was a guard at Columbia, who played nearly 60 minutes of every game for three years. As a sophomore he blocked for Sid Luckman; as a senior he blocked for Paul Governali. Now a working novelist, Gallagher says he could never overcome the fear he felt in his first college game.

FIRST GAME

Thomas Gallagher

The Game!

The thought, piercing his sleep ahead of the alarm, sent him flying from the sweaty bed to the window. The Post Office across from the dorms was closed. Must be Saturday, he thought. Or Sunday. But if it were Sunday I'd know. The game'd be over.

He stuck a crazy head of hair out the window and saw the candy man below, stacking his stand near the entrance to the Quad. "Hey Bill! What day is this?"

Bill looked up and smiled. "Let's see," he said, then waited for a bus to pass.

"Come *on*, will you!"

"Saturday, October the Second, Nineteen Hundred and—"

"Okay, okay. Thanks." Jack pulled back in and slammed the window shut. Saturday! he thought, and tried to wet his lips.

He tore into sandals, slacks and a sweater without bothering about socks or underwear and ran a cold washrag over his face. As he slammed out, his alarm went off behind him in the room and followed him down the stairs. He broke into a run. His teammates would know something. Something big. It would probably be in all the newspapers: Big Game Cancelled. Stadium Gutted By Fire. Or maybe:

Navy Team In Train Wreck En Route To New York.

In the cafeteria he slid his tray along the serving rails, helping himself (though he had no appetite) to fruit, milk, cereal, eggs and toast. At the cashier's desk he signed his check and took silverware, starting around a pillar to where the football players sat. He expected changes in their appearance, subtle disclosures of what the night had done to them. But seated carelessly around several tables, they looked too familiar to reveal anything he didn't already know about them.

"What struck you, Jack?" the captain asked, indicating his tangled hair. "Look like you're rarin' to go."

"Yeah," Jack said, flushing, "forgot to comb it."

He prolonged setting his place to have something to do, then sat down and began peeling an orange. Did Kim McCaffery have the stomach to eat? He glanced over and saw him offhandedly munching toast. Something new he's picked up, Jack thought. Back in high school he couldn't eat a *thing* before a game. As for the others, they too were acting as they did every day. For that matter so was he. Was everybody fighting anxiety, then, or was he the one hypocrite among them? He wished it were game time right now. He'd play hard, he'd distinguish himself. But would he, would he still *want* to, six hours from now?

After breakfast he and Kim McCaffery walked back across the campus to the dormitories. In the lobby they sat on a sofa. "Am I tired!" Kim said, yawning.

"Yeah, I know," Jack said, and leaned forward with his elbows on his knees. It hurt a little to breathe.

"Tough night?" Kim said, his grin answering his own question.

Jack resented the grin, the veteran shrewdness of it in someone just as green as he was. Still, it was a relief to agree. "Yeah," he said. "Woke up sweating."

"That's what made us tired."

Us? Then Kim did a little sweating too, Jack thought. I knew it. "Think it's the same with everybody?"

"Must be. I even heard of guys losing weight."

"Losing weight?"

"Sure," Kim said. "Take prize fighters. They make the weight worrying."

"Cut it out!"

"No, honest. A fighter I know told me."

Jack changed his position to get closer. He didn't want to be the only one with imagination about the game, but neither did he want to miss out on something down-to-earth that Kim—if Kim were unimaginative—might have to say about it. In a low voice he said, "Are you worried, Kim?"

"A little, I guess. I mean it isn't like when we played in high school."

"It isn't?" Jack was alarmed. To him high school football had been punishing and real. In fact, aside from a few freshmen games, it was all he had to go by.

"Hell no," Kim said. "The games didn't matter then. They were fun. We just went out and played."

"What about now?"

"Other things go with it now."

"What things, Kim. I mean do you know?"

"Things like the playing field being so much better kept. There being bags of footballs instead of three. Things like that. Not exactly, but things *like* that. Now you've asked me I don't know."

Jack knew what he meant. You couldn't put your finger on what was wrong and say, If not for this I'd be a hell of a player. But something was wrong.

Kim got to his feet. "Wish it were this time

tomorrow. I'd be home now. Come on, you going up?"

In the dorm elevator, a chipper freshman standing behind Jack said, "Good luck today, Jack."

"Thanks."

"You're starting, aren't you?"

"Yeah."

The seven or eight other passengers in the car, having nothing else to do, turned to stare at Jack.

"Hear this Navy team is pretty rough," the boy went on, and when Jack was silent, "Think we'll win?"

Jack, ears red, toes clenched, just shrugged. He wasn't answering the freshman's questions. Someone else was. He was just another passenger, embarrassed by the stupid conversation and not at all sure that he should be forced to listen to it.

When his floor came, he nodded goodbye to Kim (who was grinning again) and stepped off. How could the game not mean the same thing to them both? Why didn't Kim, if something were funny, let him in on the joke? Surely the absurdity of football would appeal to him too. In fact, next to a broken bone, he could think of nothing better suited to his needs.

Entering his room, he balked at the sight of it. Books and papers lay scattered about, the bed was mussed, out of the bottom drawer of his dresser bulged dirty laundry. Even his jacket, the comfortable tan checkered one he'd worn all through freshman year, looked unduly relaxed over the back of a chair—slouchy, like a fickle friend.

Lie down, he thought, do me good. He kicked his sandals off and lay back, trying not to think about the game. No use. He not only thought of it, he saw himself in the center of all the action. He had dreamt all *night* about it, had even been the *hero* of the dream. The hero! If Navy ran up a score and decided to go easy, it would be only fitting if they excluded him from their benevolence. Big hero, eh? he could hear them say. Well, take that. And that!

Can't go through with it, he thought, I can't! He began making up excuses to tell the coaches. Each story sounded reasonable until he imagined himself telling it, whereupon he hastily made up another. If only he had had no athletic ability at all, he might have gone on merely wanting to be a football player. Being on the first team was preventing him from being himself—a tardy spirit, perhaps, but one quite capable of enjoying experience at second hand. I've lost my nerve, he thought, there's nothing to do but go along until I can't stand it anymore. He was always about to reach this point, it seemed; just about to.

At eleven o'clock he got dressed and went downstairs. The squad ate lunch and dinner in a private dining room, and before a game every player had to be there for a coaches' briefing, whether he was hungry or not. Jack walked in and found his teammates eating quietly, like strangers. There was an empty seat at the second table on the right; he took it and politely spread his napkin on his lap. The low-toned talk and watchful looks reminded him of a high school Communion breakfast, everyone conscious of a flame within his breast, trying to shelter it from the eyes of others.

A student waiter clacked down tea, toast, and a small filet. On weekdays he had to wait to be served; now everything was punctual and exact: the scrupulous timing of all great events.

Just then the door swung open and Steve, the head coach, strode in, followed by the assistant coaches. He stopped in the center of the room and turned and waited, a sheet of yellow paper in his left hand, in his right a gold-chained pocket watch the back of which he rubbed with his thumb. A tall, well-proportioned athlete, a man with thirty suits, he had on a frizzy tweed, Scotch grain shoes, a silk Barrymore shirt, and a loosely knotted wine tie—a fabulous producer, a New England-born Italian with a flair for pageantry. He had a tan, always-shaven face with highly developed muscles around the mouth and jaw and a deep raucous voice that carried the whole length of a football field. His nose was enormous and hung from the ridge of his brow like a lobe. When he smiled his brown, close-together eyes looked rabbitlike. Jack did not have to see him, he could smell his cologne.

Talk stopped like candles flicking out. "It's eleven thirty now," he growled. "The bus will leave for the field at twelve. Now I don't mean five to, or ten after. I mean twelve. Anyone late will do laps on Monday.

"We won't warm up till one thirty, so there's no need your rushing to get dressed. Those who want, can take a walk around the field and then get dressed."

He read the second item on the sheet of yellow paper. "Now when you warm up, don't go getting yourselves all sweated up. Jog around, do a few calisthenics and let it go at that. The linemen will go with Blackie, the backs with Red. I'll take the place-kickers. Then at two, we'll walk—remember, I said *walk*—back to the dressing room, and at ten after two everybody but the starting lineup will go to the bench. You men who aren't starting, don't go throwing your helmets all over the sidelines. Make sure they're in front of you. That way, if I call you to go in, you'll have it."

Blackie, the line coach, built on a large scale close to the ground, stood behind Steve with his hands locked in the small of his back, mournfully contemplating his burdensome mid-section. It was his way of showing respect while Steve spoke, and of forcing the players, especially the linemen, to do the same. From time to time his eyes would roll from one of his boys to another in search of an inattentive face. If he found one he would wait until he caught the offender's eye, then send out the same sad message: Shame on you. You'll get yours Monday.

Steve glanced back at the paper and continued. "It's chilly, so get yourselves a blanket and wrap your legs up good. No easier way of tearing a muscle than going into a game cold. And I want to see some life on that bench out there today. Don't just sit there like a bunch of deadheads. Let the men playing know you're there."

A squat Polish boy on the third team struck his fork against his plate and Steve turned and caught him eating. "Stop that eating when I'm talking! Damn fathead. Can't play football, just barely passing your school work, think of nothing but filling your face with food."

The boy looked down turning red, the meat like a wad of tobacco in his mouth. He was one of Blackie's boys, but Blackie barely looked up. Only his eyes rolled. Oh, you fathead, they said with a kind of reverence, how you'll get yours!

"Now men," Steve continued in a lower voice, "I don't have to tell you about this Navy team. They're the same rough team we lost to last year. All right, they lost to Cornell last week, but do you know *how* they lost? The score is 13–7 in their favor and it's their ball on their own 20 with two minutes to play. Instead of bucking for two downs and then kicking out of bounds, they throw a pass! Why, I don't know. Proctor of Cornell intercepted and that's all there was to it. If not for that *one* mistake, we'd be playing an unbeaten team now. Cornell couldn't make a yard through their line all afternoon, and neither could we last year. They're good and you know how a team plays on the rebound. They want this game, and they'll do anything to get it. Not that we can't beat them, because we can. We're in good shape physically, and our passing attack never looked better.

"But it takes more than that, men. It takes hard, rough football. Give it to them from the start. If you do, you'll find they're just like any other team, but if you don't, and think you're in for an easy afternoon, watch out!

"All right, that's all I have to say, except bring those mimeographed sheets with you and hand them in to Doc. Be in the bus and ready to go at twelve."

They were. The plush seats of the bus suggested a longer trip. Jack liked the idea of a long trip between him and the game and leaned back looking out at buildings and at people in the street. He watched a fat woman carrying a bulging shopping bag up a hill against the wind as if he had never seen it done before. It was good to be fat and buy a lot of food and have a stove to cook it in. He remembered in parochial school how he used to promise God something if He did what he asked. Saying it was good to be fat was like that, only this time he didn't know, and didn't *want* to know, what he was asking.

A crowd like an endless caterpillar climbed up out of the subway station as they arrived, and old men and boys, standing on corners and along the streets, waved banners, programs, and ornamental footballs for sale. All eyes gleamed clear with eagerness, and everybody seemed not only to feel the same, but to have forgotten everything in his life that made him different. Girls with their chrysanthemum badges, with their teeth showing and their scrubbed complexions, looked dauntless, free-loving, unbelievably beautiful. They made Jack want to be tender and vulnerable, not rough and ready. He glanced at their boyfriends, so sensibly willing to be spectators, dressed in tweeds and waistcoats, cashmere sweaters—a few already tipsy enough to demand a kiss. What fun they were having!

"There's the team!" someone shouted, and as a blast of music shook the air the crowd swarmed round the bus so thickly that the driver had to plow it through them. Like children surrounding a wagon of wild animals, they wanted to see what it was like to be a football player in a bus before a game. Jack stared at them and was afraid of music. The drums accompanied every movement he made; the trumpets upheld the pounding in his heart. He looked back in wonder at a man on a corner lighting a cigarette: the more prosaic anyone acted, the more unreasonably he admired him. The bus finally got through to the driveway,

where special policemen fenced the people out. Then the team was at the field house, and going en masse to look at the stadium. They filed in from beneath the rafters and ducked under the sideline rope, branching off in different directions on the field. The stands were still almost empty, and Jack thought his teammates looked scrawny in their street clothes. He felt sorry for them, forgetting that he was no better equipped to take punishment. Have no business in a game against a team like Navy, he thought. Coaches must be crazy.

The turf steamed in the sun. White chalky calcium bordered and marked it at right angles, and behind either goal line for ten yards, skew lines were drawn to distinguish the end zone from the rest of the playing field. White wooden goal posts stood out against the green, erect but unimpressive, and with so few people in the stands the many-colored flags fluttered almost pathetically.

Jack went aimlessly along, trying the field with his foot. After the absolute flatness of the practice field, he was amazed at how bellied it appeared from the sidelines; the middle was two or thre feet higher than the sides. Drainage, he thought, they think more of that than whether we play on a hill. He knelt on one knee and ran his hand along the surface, found it wet and cold, the blades not soft, but stiff and sharp. He snapped one out and let the wind take it.

"Sellout," Kim said, lolling over. He turned towards the stands, pointing to a spot in Section 14. "Let's see. Ann and Cliff should be about there. Where's Pris and her girlfriend sitting?"

"Round there somewhere, I guess. Who told you it was a sellout?"

"Talking to an usher. General admission only and he said you should see the line for that."

"Don't worry," Jack said, "the midshipmen marching at the half probably have a *lot* to do with it."

Kim, still turned toward the stands, looked back over his shoulder at Jack. "You sure the girlfriend's a blonde?"

Jack nodded, too amazed to speak. What were they talking about? Was it a joke or was the game actually of secondary importance to Kim? "Come on, there's nothing here," he said, and as they started back he wondered what he had expected to find.

The locker room was crowded when they got back, the air heavy with the smell of dried mud, leather, still-sweaty practice uniforms. The players undressed quietly; a few were apparently trying to remember *how* to undress. They would stand, take off their ties and shirts, and sit down again as though concentrating on what came next. Even those who were undressing un-interruptedly did not act as if they had done it often.

And some, Jack noticed, were very close to being ready, were down to their underwear, and only had to have their ankles taped before putting on their uniforms. They were dull, heavy-headed fools. Whatever Navy might have in store for them, they went right on getting ready.

Jack's locker was open, a new game uniform hanging where he always hung the one he used for practice. It annoyed him to have everything ready and convenient; they did everything but play the game for him. He undressed slowly, without speaking, hanging up each piece as he took it off, folding his underwear for the first time in his life. He slipped his shoulder harness on first, then his hip pads and jersey. He didn't know what made him go on dressing because he kept telling himself to stop. There was no hesitation, his movements were sure, he even asked the boy next to him to help him with his jersey. His voice was calm and matter of fact.

The coaches barged in at twenty-five after one. Steve stalked up and down looking for his starting eleven among the more unreliable third and fourth stringers. He seemed to want to look the men he was counting on square in the eye, as though the outcome of crucial decisions during the game depended on how they looked back at him now. Jack watched from the side of his locker door and when his turn came swung toward Steve with a look that he meant to mean, I'm as worked up as you are. Don't worry about me. Then, for some reason, as Steve moved on, he was reminded of the sand-lot team he had played with as a boy, the Hornets. He could still name every member of that team, and he was suddenly sure that Steve could with the sandlot team of *his* boyhood. Steve must have been a better tackler than his playmates too; he mustn't have wanted to let go of the distinction of being a rock in the line either. Is that why they loved the game so? It was as if the real meaning, the first meaning, of comradeship was born in boys who go out to meet danger together.

"Five minutes, men," Steve said; "take it easy. Start lacing up your shoes and pants. You won't need your helmets, so put them in your lockers. You can get them later. Now don't get excited, take it easy."

Jack zipped his fly and bent over to do his shoes. The hard-rubber cleats clicked against the concrete floor and made him feel off the ground.

"You all know what to do," Steve said. "Backs with Red, linemen with Blackie, place-kickers with me. We'll go out together. The manager has the balls. Just jog around and loosen up. Conserve your strength for the game. All right, let's start walking out. Don't run. Keep together. Run out on the field together."

They walked down the cobblestone path, through a crowd of still-unseated spectators, to the field. The crowd was quiet and respectful, even spellbound. One man forgot about the frankfurter he had in his hand and let the mustard drip; another, whose wife hadn't seen them, surreptitiously motioned to her to stop talking. A few called out encouragements which Jack thought he should acknowledge by smiling or nodding or something, but the majority looked timid and did not say anything until after the team passed. Jack stepped cautiously, looking down at the smooth cobblestones. It was a comfort to have to consider that there was a chance of slipping.

The stadium was three-quarters full, and spectators were still coming in by the hundreds. The team bunched together and waited for the laggers to catch up, then started out. The crowd roared—so raucously that Jack thought something was wrong. First that their uniforms were too gaudy, then that they must look hilariously small to be playing Navy. He put on a burst of speed without knowing it and got out in front of his teammates. The new two-way stretch uniform and resilient turf made him light and free, stronger and faster than ever before, finally doubtful that there was any connection between this entrance and actually playing a game. It was too dangerous to play. With nothing to restrain the full force of his and his opponent's strength, they would seriously injure each other.

But he fell back with the linemen to warm up. They did hip and knee bends, flexed their ankles, wrists, and necks, and occasionally, as if unwinding springs in their stomachs, sprinted ten yards. When they began to sweat they stopped and stood about, hands on hips. Kim jabbed Jack in the shoulder pads. "Don't forget now, Jack," he said, "on the KF78, you go through first." Kim played center and Jack the guard position on his left. They were, in fact, the only two sophomores on the first team.

"I know," Jack said. But up to now it hadn't occurred to him that he might forget his assignments. Suddenly the Navy team was beside the point. "And what about if their weak guard plays in front of me on the F96?" he asked quickly.

"Then you act as pivot and I'll turn him. Damn it, in a situation like that the ball-carrier'll have to *find* the opening." He gave Jack another jab. "How do you feel?"

"Nervous."

"Go over what you do on each play and it won't be so bad."

How do you know? Jack wanted to say. But he came out with, "Wonder where Navy is?"

"Be out in a minute. Service teams always wait'll the last minute. Here they come now."

Jack turned fully expecting to see a hundred men as monstrous as the crowd's hurrah. They jogged out slowly with the sun behind them, like giant shadows of themselves, elongated, faceless, unknown, running in a seemingly endless column. Finally it narrowed, and with the stragglers three trainers floundered out carrying pails, sponges, towels, blankets, and extra helmets. They split up into groups and looked absorbed in warming up, interested only in tracing the movement of their muscles. During lulls their eyes were filled with that contentment which bulls express while grazing.

"Must have six teams, at least," Kim said, "wonder if they all play?" They exchanged anxious glances, as if each knew something fatal about the other and were wondering how to tell him.

"Wish we'd get started," Jack said. But he was losing all desire to be outstanding. He began to try to justify himself for the costly mistakes that he felt sure he was *going* to make, blaming something vague in the past that was not his fault. It haunted him like a hidden deformity.

"We'll be going in a minute," Kim said. "There's no waiting after that. Come on, Steve's waving now."

In the locker room the team squatted hunched up on long benches facing one another without speaking. Sweat dripped off their fingers.

"All right," Steve barked, "everybody but the starting lineup, get your helmets and start out. Go to the bench. You know where to sit."

As the substitutes passed out they crowded round the starting players and gripped their hands and mumbled fierce slogans. Jack kept saying thanks and nodding but wanted them to stop. Saying thanks left no time for his anxiety. A trainer closed the door behind the substitutes, leaving the coaches and eleven players alone. Steve paced back and forth rubbing his watch, his face ravaged by some hidden resolve, his jaw and temples throbbing.

The trainer poked his head back in the doorway. "Two minutes, Steve."

"Navy out?"

"They're coming now."

"All right, men," Steve said, turning to the team. "This is it. There's nothing more to say. We worked four weeks for today, the rest is up to you. The plays and all we gave you don't mean a thing. The team that hits the hardest will win. Coaching can't give you that, men, it's up to you. This Navy team is cocky, and that's the way we want them. Give it to them from the start, and don't let up a minute. You can do it, I know you can." He rubbed his hands together like a wrestler getting ready to enjoy himself. "All right," he rasped, "what do you say?"

He threw out his fist and eleven players jumped up with a roar to grip it and one another's, surrounding him and yelling frenzied resolutions. Jack stared at Kim next to him screaming, "We've got to! We've got to!" and could in no way associate the screams with what he thought of as Kim's voice. Kim was a quivering insane stranger, yet in his terrifying transfiguration Jack saw something encouraging. At last fear existed. He let go a yell himself, then another, but among such profuse affirmations his own embarrassed him. It was as if he were listening self-consciously to his own voice while continuing to be startled by Kim's. He felt confused, in and out of it, and in the end yelled loudest when he knew least what he was saying and why.

The trainer held the door open as they crowded out. In the path they stayed bunched together, the two sophomores, Jack and Kim, encouraging each other all the way. Neither mentioned the rumble in the stands, but the louder it became the more earnestly they jabbed each other's arm or shoulder. At the entrance the team stopped, and Jack looked up at the stands, jammed and flickering with people. Their expectation seemed cruel, but he couldn't take his eyes off them. If he did he would see the starting Navy team huddled on the opposite side of the field.

"Let's go!" the captain said, and they started out. The drummers and trumpeters burst forth; the crowd roared with all its steep, teeming might. It was preposterous, a roar at once defiant and horrified, and it suddenly occurred to Jack that no one had forced him to be a football player. This revelation changed everything, but before he had a chance to think about it a well-known alumnus, a prominent bone specialist with a thin distinguished face, clutched his arm and in a wild outburst of enthusiasm sprinted out on the field with him.

"You can do it, Jack," he screamed, "let's see you go. Fight! Go to it!"

The specialist was wearing a homburg and every time he yelled his false teeth came loose. He kept on running, though, digging his nails into Jack's arm and holding his teeth in with his free hand as he yelled. Jack wanted to break away from him. He could not believe it was happening, yet tried to decide what it meant. If the game could make a bounding Airedale of this man of science, then it *was* momentous; his imagination had been telling him the truth!

Lined up, he had all he could do to stay set and listen for the whistle, and as it blew and he started down the field, he realized that he had neglected to make sure his shoes were tied. The oversight as he ran was like an excuse not to involve himself too deeply in this play. With his shoelaces possibly tripping him, he'd better stay out of it.

The ball backflipped deep into the end zone, where the Navy quarterback nonchalantly downed it for a touchback: Navy's ball on their own twenty, first down, ten to go. They ran into a huddle, the home team into a six-man line defense. In position Jack crouched over on one knee. Sprinting down field had winded him and he did not see how he could go on without a rest. He'd force himself through the first play, he thought, but then the captain would have to call time out. Navy didn't look winded, though, why was that? He looked at their calves, bulging above their white woolen socks, and wished the game were over. The end seemed far off, too good ever to be true.

Navy lined up, his opponent, Red McMann, lurching into position less than two feet away from him. Red had a large square face, smooth and lean, with the cheekbones jutting out. Its unfamiliarity was in Navy's favor, and the odd shape of his helmet was not due simply to a difference in design but to Navy's unorthodox football.

Red stared straight ahead, and Jack did not know whether to feel purposely avoided, or insignificant. But he dug his cleats into the turf and pressed his weight forward for the charge. He could see the ball out of the corner of his eye, and as the Navy center snapped it back he shot his head into Red's midsection, hacking the turf with his cleats. He felt him give gradually, to the left, and knew that the play was not coming his way. Disengaging, he looked up and saw the Navy ball carrier getting round the end, free, galloping down the field like a man

through a blazing forest. Jack thought the crowd was screaming that he, in particular, should catch him, and ran with all his might. But by then the ball carrier had only thirty yards to go and there was no one near him: it was a touchdown, all right, on the very first play of the game. Jack felt humiliated, yet relieved, as though with the chance of winning had passed the responsibility. But he did not want to feel relieved and fought against it.

"Come on," he angrily muttered as Navy lined up for the extra point, "we can stop 'em."

"You bet," others answered.

"We'll stop 'em, all right," the captain said, "let's go."

Navy lined up slowly, making certain there would be no slips. Jack glanced at McMann and couldn't believe his eyes. Red was smiling at him in the friendliest way! He was beginning to speak! "That was a tough break for you fellows. We never expected it."

A little bashfully, Jack smiled back, convinced that under the circumstances it was not a dishonorable thing to do; and though he felt that he could no longer count on his anger now that Red had made it seem unnecessary, he had no regrets. Football was a game, a sport! Only a fanatic would *persist* in being angry.

Just then the Navy center snapped the ball back and Red rammed the steel-rimmed crown of his helmet into Jack's face. The skin on the bridge of Jack's nose came loose; there was a burning sensation as the air hit the flesh beneath; he had to shake his head to clear it. When he stood up the score was 7–0, his hand was bloody where he had unconsciously brought it to his nose, and Navy was casually trotting downfield amidst cheers to line up for the next kickoff. Jack stood stunned by Red's duplicity, by the whole Navy team's seeming indifference to its own brutality. Johnny Haydn, on his team, had been injured on the play. The captain, having called for a time-out, was signalling to the bench for a doctor, sending everybody but the injured tackle to midfield to talk things over.

A doctor went to Haydn, a trainer to the team. The trainer brought towels and a pail of water and a tray of paper cups spilling with water. He sponged each player's face and gave them towels. When he came to Jack he cut the loose skin away from his nose with surgical scissors, greased the flesh with Unguentine, and pasted a Band-aid over it. He was not supposed to say anything about the game but whispered to Jack while working over him that they were to play it regular. Regular, Jack thought, regular! After they had spent all week perfecting a half-dozen defenses? It was like telling him that the coaches were in wild confusion. They should never have agreed to the game in the first place, he thought, it was going to be a rout. He looked over and saw Navy clustering and bobbing in a huddle, saw Red bursting with confidence, energy, well-being. Only the determination not to let such a gross betrayal go unpunished made him want the game to go on.

The doctor decided Haydn couldn't play. He motioned to the bench, and Steve sent two substitute players out to help him in. Jack watched as he limped off, his arms round his teammates' shoulders. He listened to the crowd applaud as they approached the sidelines and, thinking of his responsibility to even things with Red, saw himself getting hurt, only more spectacularly and in a more crucial play; saw himself being carried out on a stretcher, the sublime anguish of a torn cartilage or broken bone; saw the crowd's careful wonder at it all. It was a comforting possibility.

The captain elected to receive and, calling his men into a huddle, told them to use the number one kickoff play. "Kim, let me drive McMann on any play going through us," Jack said as the huddle broke up. "No matter where he plays."

"Did he do that to your nose?" Kim said, and when Jack nodded: "Don't worry, we'll get him."

They lined up. Whoever caught the ball was to start running toward the sideline on the right. This would draw the Navy players out of position and give the linemen a chance to block a path for him up the middle.

The ball soared to the 5-yard line, to the quarterback who caught it on the run. He swerved to his right, drew the Navy men over, then suddenly and without losing stride, reversed his field and arrowed up the center. He almost got through, but near the end of the path a Navy man twisted free and caught him from behind. Nevertheless, they had advanced the ball past midfield on the play, and for the first time they were boisterous as they went into a huddle.

The quarterback called for a quick pass over center from spread formation. If the out-shifted ends drew the Navy secondary out of position, the play couldn't miss. They lined up, and the ends shifted out. The Navy secondary hesitated a moment and then went out to cover them. This left their middle unprotected, all right, but Red McMann, taking advantage of Kim's eagerness to hit him, dived over their heads and rushed the passer so fast that the latter had to throw the ball before he was ready. It wobbled short of its receiver, into the hands of a Navy linebacker, the crowd howling as he started down the field. Jack was on his feet in time to see him go by. Enraged, he forgot everything but that he had to catch him. It was not so much to prevent another touchdown, for which he would be partly to blame, that he ran, but to impress upon Navy the fact that they would simply have to show his team more consideration. Navy was trying to make it a rout without taking into account his team's sincerity; it was harder to take than defeat.

He and four others dumped the linebacker near the 30-yard line. The Navy man bounced up smirking and swaggered back to his team, lobbing the ball to the referee. On the following play, Red McMann and the tackle both smashed into Jack. He wedged his head and shoulders between them, but they had him caught in against their hips, so that when the ball carrier came bucking through, he saw him, but could do nothing about it. They made eight yards, and on the next play they came back through the same hole and made six. This went on for three first downs and Jack didn't know why. They weren't budging *him* any more; someone *else* was being trapped. His jersey was all dirty and wet from sweat, his tongue was dry, he was panting. But he wanted the game to go on and he wanted to hit Red's face hard and over and over again. He wanted to surprise and befuddle him with blows, wanted to see the surprise on his face. Once he went right on charging after the play was over.

"All right," Red bawled, "can't you hear the whistle?"

"What did you say?" Jack asked, suddenly standing, hands on hips.

"I said the whistle blew. Can't you hear?"

"I can hear, all right," Jack said, and when he had his back turned, he grinned. Red was beginning to respect him; he was not so puny after all. He had used the other's greater strength to his own advantage; his movements were quicker; he was more alert. If they couldn't win, he could at least give this clumsy hulk something to remember.

They stopped the Navy advance on their own 10-yard line. The quarter ended. The referee measured off in yard-long strides to set the ball going in the opposite direction from the other end of the field, and in exactly two minutes the whistle blew and the game was on again.

The home team's ball; on the first play they tried an end run and made seven yards. On the next the quarterback called for a buck through center, which meant that Jack had to drive McMann to the left. He lined up and this time did not give the play away, though he had his weight well forward and his heels high. On the signal he charged headfirst with all his strength and hit Red squarely in the face. His spine, like a lance, was from its base straight and firm, and he followed up with his initial charge so quickly and evenly that Red went over on his back. The ball carrier made the three yards they needed for a first down and five besides, and when the teams lined up for the next play Red had blood oozing from his lips and left cheekbone. Jack kept looking at him but he would not look at Jack. In a dull sullen way Red seemed to be licking his wounds while refusing to admit that he had any. You're bleeding, sailor boy, Jack was about to say, but in thinking of saying it he lost the desire to say it.

On the next play they completed a flat pass, advancing to midfield. They followed with an off-tackle play and made six yards, then on a spinner-buck the center aimed the ball wrong and the fullback bobbled it losing them four. They kicked. Navy ran it back thirty yards to their own 40. Four yards on an end run, two on a buck, a kick. A slump followed, during which each team tried to outkick the other. Red and Jack were jarring each other regularly now; it was give and take. Now and then the home team made a spectacular flourish, but the half ended with the score unchanged. Bands struck up as the teams straggled off, and midshipmen began forming on the field to march. Spectators were going for coffee and hot dogs, while announcers, through loudspeakers on either side of the field, announced the scores of other unfinished college games.

In the locker room, Jack and his teammates sat benumbed amid confusion. Everybody on the coaching staff was waving his hands and talking, Steve to the quarterbacks and backfield, his three assistants to the line, while trainers and assistant managers rushed about sponging necks and faces, replacing lost cleats, and bandaging bruised hands. Players nodded at the coaches but were more interested in gulping water; and when pails of quartered oranges and lemons were carried round, they all dug in and cupped them out with their hands, fitting them against their fingers. The cold astringent juice trickled down their jaws and hands and stung their bruises, and they could feel it cool and lively in their stomachs. No longer were the players and coaches clinging to silence and restraint. A sensual, four-footed barbarity broke loose as regrets and curses were spat across the room and the floor became a dump for orange peels, discarded sopping jerseys, torn stockings and dirty bandages.

Wet and dirty, sucking on fruit between heaves for breath, Jack sat taking everything the trainers did for him for granted. His body was telling him what to do and he was doing it. At the same time, as though behind his body's back, he was listening to the coaches. "Jack, their left tackle's fading with the end run," Blackie was saying. "Now we're going to start mousetrapping him. Stay close to the line when you pull out and hit him with your *inside* shoulder. Get that head between him and the ball carrier." He smiled. "Take it easy. Rest. Don't eat too many of those things."

Jack had expected the coaches to harangue the team but now that they were being reasonable he wasn't surprised. With the team tired and bruised and knowing what it was to be jolted, how could they be anything but reasonable? By now his jersey and skivvy shirt stuck coldly to his skin. His stocking was caked with blood where his shin had been nicked, and he began to feel bruises that he did not remember getting. He thought of the hot lathery shower he was going to take when the game was over (all the time remembering it wasn't) and did not see how he would ever get warmed up and start sweating again this second half.

But as the minutes passed and he regained his strength, he recalled how he had outcharged McMann and secretly he became confident. He was no longer a green substitute, for one thing, and he assured himself that Navy was not as invincible as he had imagined. They blundered and were upset when things went against them, and the bruising impacts of the first half were no different from the Tuesday scrimmages against the second team. The thing to do was concentrate on execution. If everybody did what he was supposed to do, they'd win. He remembered the coaches saying the same thing and was surprised to think that they could have known what they were talking about.

"I tell you," Steve was saying, "that touchdown—there was no *reason* for it. Saxon, we told you about that play of theirs all week. All right, you make a mistake, but so does the backer-up and secondary. If any *one* of you boys plays it the way we tell you to, they don't make a yard. But there's nothing we can do about that now. We're going out this half to win and we're not wasting any time about it. It's our choice and we're going to receive. We'll use number three up the middle. Saxon almost broke away with number one last time, so they'll probably be looking for it again."

He broke off, but only long enough, it seemed, to remember that Navy was winning. "I tell you, we should run up a score this half. You can mousetrap their whole line, and with their backers-up playing wide we can throw the quick-45 all afternoon. But you linemen will have to give Genelli better protection. That pass they intercepted was *your* fault, not his."

He stopped again and looked at his watch. "All right, you men who aren't starting, get your helmets and start out. Keep your hoods on and get yourselves a blanket. It's getting cold out there."

Alone with the starting eleven, he tracked back and forth giving instructions as they came to him. "Let's go *inside* their tackles. Jack, if you don't carry that left tackle of theirs clear to the sidelines on mousetraps, there's something wrong with you. He's as clumsy as they come. Paul, throw *short* passes, buttonhooks and quick-45's over center. Then when they close *in* . . ." He lifted his arm suddenly and flipped an imaginary pass off to his right . . . "To the flats, or down behind them, ends crossing. The end run forward, for instance, what happened to that? *Use* it!"

When time came to go, he gripped their hands as they surrounded him, and sent them out. No exhorting this time, and the players did not shout. They knew what they were up against, so their determination was without the impetus of being blind. Nevertheless, Jack thought that Kim, who had been quite insane before the opening kickoff, was now being a little too reasonable; the expression on his face belonged more in a library than in a locker room. You're making a mistake, Kim, he wanted to say, the rest of the game isn't going to be that strategical.

On the way back to the stadium, Jack's chilled muscles ached. He saw Genelli and the captain wrapping and unwrapping their arms around their torsos as they walked, and imitated them. The blood began to circulate, and he did it more vigorously.

Workmen were still clodding mangled patches in the turf but trudged off as soon as they appeared. The team, huddled for the last occult words before battle, trotted out behind the captain to get into position to receive. Navy ran scattering from a huddle and formed a long precise line across the field to kick. Jack thought he detected alacrity in their movements and kept telling himself to be determined. Let Kim in cold blood use artifice; he would with pounding heart use strength. His job was to cut diagonally across the field in time to knock the Navy left end out of bounds. As he leaned

forward waiting for the whistle, he kept the corner of his eye on him, starting over as the kicker teed off on the ball. The end did not see him until the last minute and then threw his arm out for protection. Jack hunched his neck and rammed him with his forehead like a bull, his eyes boring up under rigid eyebrows into the other's ribs. The end fell sprawling with Jack on top of him, and Jack stood up. He went to walk away but the stadium began to capsize, and in an effort to right himself he tried to stand on the sky.

"Who is it?" the captain asked, running over.

"Jack. Probably had the wind knocked out of him."

"You all right, Jack?"

Jack tried to look up and answer but it was as if he were seeing the captain through a wavy mirror, so without looking up he asked what happened.

"You were out for a minute. How do you feel?"

"All right, I guess."

"Well, take it easy, here's the doctor."

Without a word, the doctor broke a gauze-covered, glass tube of spirits of ammonia and put it to Jack's nose. Jack squinted and jerked his head back, then the doctor gave it to him to hold himself. He inhaled the cold rending fumes in long deep draughts that shot up to his brain, and soon everything was bright and clear again.

"How many fingers do I have up, Jack?" the doctor asked, holding up two fingers.

"Two."

"How do you feel?"

"Fine."

"Are you sure?"

"Absolutely."

"Think you'd better have a rest. Few minutes on the bench will do you good."

Jack could have continued playing, but the people in the stands didn't know that; in their confusion as he started off the field they applauded him more than he knew he deserved. He thought of Pris up among them, of her distress and her girlfriend's commiseration, and broke into a brisk trot to let her and everybody else know that he was all right, fine. But they wouldn't let him minimize what had happened; he was just so full of pluck that as he chucked his helmet toward the bench they applauded him all the more.

Steve took him by the arm. "Keep covered and don't drink too much water. How do you feel?"

The last was a personal off-the-record question that put the game, and Steve's relation to his players, in human terms. For the first time since knowing him, Jack was able to conceive of Steve as a man, a lonely man. Up to now he had been more phenomenon than coach, more respected than liked.

"I'm fine, Steve," he said. "There's nothing wrong with me." He wanted to be put right back in; he would make the most impossible tackles, throw the most vicious blocks, kill himself trying. It was the least he could do for lonely old Steve.

"Well, sit down," Steve said. "You'll be going back in a few minutes."

The limbo of the bench broadened his perspective of the game. It was more than the thud and clack of scrimmage, or the way you were always being jarred. It was keeping blankets handy and cups and pails filled with water; it was a line coach telephoning instructions to the bench from a little house atop the stadium; a lanky, white-gloved crewman signalling to the man behind the scoreboard; tumbling cheerleaders; students ushering for extra money. And it was Steve wringing his fedora, wanting desperately to get out and play himself.

The team ran out of a huddle and lined up in single-wing formation. Steve had signalled the quarterback to open up with an end run from the man-in-motion series, so everybody on the bench had his eyes on the wingback, the man-in-motion, Tim Hutchens. As planned, before the signal, Tim spun running toward the fullback who, having by then caught the ball from center, pivoted and laid it out for him as he raced by. Hutchens swooped it in swiftly with his inside arm and hid it behind his outside hip. He was around the end and ten yards down the field before Navy even knew he had the ball. They cut him off after he made twenty yards but he stiff-armed one tackler and hurdled over and slashed through three others for ten more yards before they brought him down. He sprang up with a sparkling smile and ran to tell his teammates what? How easy it was going to be for them to win?

Jack jumped up and cheered as loudly as anyone, but when he sat back down he thought it was pretty rotten of the fellows to make a thirty-yard gain with him on the bench. It was not only like losing friends but like finding out you never meant much to them anyway.

The team shifted into position for the next play immediately. They were on the go, and Navy looked worried. The ball zipped back to Genelli fading back to throw a pass. Both ends raced out, decoying toward the sidelines, the half and fullback toward the flats. The quarterback, meantime, disengaged the man he was blocking and slipped through over center. Genelli feigned throwing to his right, turned suddenly, and let the quarterback have it like a bullet in the chest. The crowd leapt to its feet. There was an open runway for him down the middle with only the safety-man between him and a touchdown. The quarterback was fast, not tricky; a blocker, not a runner. Instead of dodging, he butted the safety with his head. Both the safety's feet left the ground. He jerked forward from the waist, and the slumped, like a man riding a cannonball. The ball carrier's feet finally gave from under him, and both men rolled over on the ground.

The stilled crowd watched as the safety lay rigidly on his back, his legs doubled up against his chest. Jack thought wildly that to straighten them would send parts of the man's stomach flying like shrapnel through his skin. His Navy teammates, coming back from assignments of their own, encountered him in this position, grunting and groaning, his lungs like sucked-in toy balloons. They circled round and watched him—a sudden stranger with a weird affliction.

Fifteen feet away the home team quarterback staggered about like a man outside a saloon. His gyrations looked too ludicrous to be real. He was the buffoon of the tragedy.

The frozen player's legs finally melted to the ground. Slowly the doctor worked them back and forth. The player got up and walked about. A prolonged ovation.

Substitutions were made. The ball went to the same man, Genelli, and again he faded back to throw a pass. But this time it was a fake. He stood with the ball cocked behind his ear as though looking for a receiver, luring the Navy guard in to tackle him. His own quarterback, meantime, hesitated two counts and turned and smashed into the Navy guard's ribs just before the latter was able to make the tackle. Genelli pumped his way through the hole, cutting left as soon as he got by the line of scrimmage. He angled toward the coffin-corner, the Navy secondary racing to head him off. They ran with a cold frenzy, like a mob after a murderer of children. Just as they were about to rip into him he looped a lateral to the fullback, who reversed his field and tore through for a touchdown.

Without waiting to congratulate themselves they lined up for the extra point. Genelli smoothed the turf and made a cross with his finger where he wanted the ball placed. He stood statue-still, his right foot slightly forward, his eyes fixed on the spot. Then, as the ball snapped back, he took a short step with his left foot and swung his right in the smooth swift arc of a pendulum, his eyes always on the belly of the ball. The referee's hands went up as home team rooters gambolled to the proud fury of the drums. The score, 7–7.

Steve ran his eyes along the bench looking for replacements. "Biles, Kursch, Haydn, get your helmets." He came to Jack, stopped, went by, then went back again. "All right, get your helmet."

The four of them crowded together strapping their helmets under their chins.

"Be ready for anything," Steve said, "long passes, reverses, Statue of Liberty, anything. Tell the captain to use a six-man line except in a passing situation. Then go into a five, and you drop back, Jack, and cover over center. Tell the line to play it regular. Biles, hold your ground. Don't follow those reverses. Tell the other end the same thing. They'll come back and go around you if you do. Johnny, watch for mousetraps. If no one takes you, turn in. Don't even cross the line of scrimmage. All right, go ahead. Don't talk. Report to the referee."

The substitutions were made so quickly that no time-out was called. Both captains waved that their teams were ready for the kickoff. The whistle blew. Genelli was too anxious and hit the ball wrong. It bounded through the deployed Navy team to a player on the 30-yard line. He kicked it accidentally and ran and scooped it up. Three home team players smothered him. Navy's ball on their own 30, first down, ten to go. They huddled; lined up. Jack faced Red again. "Well, how nice and clean you look!" Red said. Jack was silent, feeling that Red with his blood-smeared face had a right to criticize him. He was convinced, though, that Red was sorry to see him back. He had given Red a hard time; he would finish him now.

Navy opened with a quick pass that caught the home team off guard. It netted nine yards. Jack was sure they'd come back with a buck and, tensing himself, went at Red with everything he had, only to be sideswiped by the Navy tackle as Red pulled out to protect the passer. Another pass, in the same place, to the same man. Jack saw him catch it, twisting in the air, and fight his way to midfield. Again, he thought. What's the *matter* with them back there. Line can't do *everything*. An end sweep carried Navy eight more yards, a buck six, another pass ten.

"You fellows asked for this, making that touchdown," Red grunted at Jack as they surged back, curiously shoulder to shoulder, after a play. "We just got word to roll up a score."

"You did?" Jack said, furious that his own inadequacy at repartee made it sound like a serious question.

"Yes, we did," Red answered just as seriously. He tapped Jack's shoulder in a friendly way. "And we will."

It was his friendliness that Jack found so convincing, and therefore so infuriating. "You're full of crap!" he said, and turned to find that his team had called a time-out.

"What do you say we hold 'em?" the captain was saying. "Jack, five-man line; drop back on every play. From now on everything's a passing situation. You backers-up, cover the flats. Jack will take care of over center. Let's *hold* 'em this time! Linemen, rush that passer! You're giving him all day to throw the ball. You make a touchdown and then lay down. Damn it, come on. We're gonna beat this team, hear?"

Still fresh from his rest on the bench, Jack went round supporting him. He appealed to the linemen especially. "The home stretch. Let's show 'em what we've got. Make each play the last. It won't be long, come on. Atta boy. Hold 'em." He felt a secret comradeship pass between him and the captain that made him feel older and more responsible than his teammates. He remembered what Red had said about Navy running up a score, but he kept that to himself. The idea of defeat, he thought, was more acceptable to him. It didn't discourage him, as he was afraid it would his teammates, who were too tired and bruised to see the difference between a humiliating defeat and one in which the appearance of a contest was maintained. He felt mature thinking these things; not everyone could appreciate such shades of meaning.

A double reverse around end carried Navy to the home team's 25. Second down and six— sure pass. Jack got set three yards behind the line of scrimmage, his feet wide apart, his outstretched hands like feelers. On the signal two Navy men from different directions crossed in front of him. He dropped back trying to cover them both, jerking one way and then the other, all the while shooting glances toward the passer. The suspense made him want to use his body in a new way, and while, in a sense trying to, it occurred to him that he could not be more committed to stopping the pass even if in his opinion there were still a chance of winning. It was as if in facing defeat he had freed himself of the hundred and one disappointments that must plague any struggle for victory. For the first time since the beginning of the game he felt free of himself, free to join his teammates; he was out on the field, and nowhere else, at last. He had not really wanted the game to be over, he realized now, but had only thought he did. He had been an outsider, trimming the edges of the game, thinking of himself with that compassion which is more fitting in an armchair.

Suddenly, like a monstrous doll from Mars, the ball came tumbling his way. He let it thump against his chest, his eyes bulging, and, as it bounced away, grabbed it, running upright with it out in front of him. He felt like a man frantically looking for a place to lay a red hot platter. Navy hit him from all directions. He hugged the ball desperately and went under. The quarter ended.

He sat dazed and stupid, listening to the good words of his teammates. He was still not positive that he had actually held the ball, had it in his hands. Intercepting a pass was not unusual, but it was for him. How had he managed it? He must have given himself up to his legs and arms, and they must have known what to do.

The final quarter wore on, the ball exchanging hands every few minutes. As if by some secret pact, both teams began to take it easy. Red stopped wasting his breath talking to Jack, and once, when Jack asked him when Navy was going to get around to running up a score, he didn't answer him. During one time-out, Genelli, smudged and tattered, was the only man on the field left standing. A sad overwhelming exhaustion lined his face. Players were sprawled out around him in odd rag doll poses, their spent salty bodies steaming. He looked like the lone survivor of a mighty battle.

"Come on, damn it," he said as the whistle blew, "only five more minutes."

Home team's ball on their own 45, first and ten. They tried a pass. Genelli was rushed and had to run with it. On the ground, out of the play, Jack watched. In Genelli's hands the ball became Aladdin's lamp: the feel of it seemed to give him strength. Zigzagging, he made thirty yards. He became a shining knight, the team a band of loyal ragamuffins.

Fifty thousand feet rumbled in the stands. Minutes to play, and they were deep in Navy's territory. The quarterback, who had the fate of the University in his hands, whose strategy would decide whether the light of truth and knowledge continued to shine within its walls, was in a huddle screaming, "Damn it, shut up! All of you. *I'll* call the play. Single-wing right; end run forward pass. Paul, if no one's open, run with it. Come on, now, on three!"

They shifted into single-wing formation; Genelli started to his right with the ball. He ran toward the sideline, fading back, looking for a receiver. They were all covered. He feinted right and went left, racing straight across to the other sideline. The whole Navy team converged over after him, like checkers swept to one corner of a checkerboard. Three men hit him. Time out. Reeling towards him, Jack heard the captain ask: "You all right, Paul?"

"Sure. You didn't have to call time out."

They all knelt on one knee in a circle. Their chests heaved and strained, and with sticky tongues they tried to wet their crusted lips. In spite of this they gasped encouragement and advice to one another. It was as if they were fighting for their lives, and Jack, ashamed for having entertained the thought of losing, insisted so vehemently that they were still going to win that the others looked at him as if from a distance, though with sympathetic consideration.

Balanced line, Genelli back to try a field goal. On the signal Jack took one step toward McMann and stopped. He wanted to protect Kim, whose snapback to the quarterback absolutely had to be accurate, but he didn't want to lunge at McMann either and leave a hole for the Navy backer-up to run through. So he braced himself and took McMann's charge without giving an inch. He counted three, four to make sure, then looked up and saw the ball floating through the air like a bird with an historic message. The referee hesitated, then raised his hands. Yes, it was good!

The stands exploded as players pounded Genelli's back with brutal fondness and screamed at one another in a desperate effort to convince themselves that they had won. But there was still a minute left to play, and a whole new Navy team was coming in. Jack glanced toward the bench and saw Steve looking down into his hat. He appeared to be reading the label.

Navy caught the kickoff on the ten and ran it back to midfield. Time for maybe two passes. The first was way too long. So was the second. The game was over.

Home team rooters thundered onto the field among the players. Jack, his helmet dangling from his hand, plodded through them. The blood had been drained out of him; he felt scoured and empty, too indifferent to think. The game would perhaps mean something tomorrow; it meant nothing now. What meant something was that he had been in it, not that it was over or that they had won. He had changed in some important way but he didn't know how yet. He didn't have to; the change was waiting for him, like a package to be opened.

COACHES IN
TWO CENTURIES

The modern college football coach
can expect only a few short harassed
years on the job. The profession is
for the young and strong. But there was a
time when coaches lasted as long
as college professors. Two coaches
who became institutions in
their own right were Glenn S.
(Pop) Warner and Amos Alonzo Stagg. Warner,
shown in his Cornell uniform, was a
coach and football innovator
(the double-wing formation) from
the 1890s through the 1930s at
Georgia, Cornell, Pittsburgh, Stanford,
Temple. Stagg (see page 244) first
coached at the University of
Chicago in 1892, was still an
active sideline coach at the College of
the Pacific more than
a half century later.

Glenn Warner

Alonzo Stagg

125

Back at the game's beginning in America, Harper's Weekly *explained why football, of all athletic contests, was the easiest to comprehend.*

FOOTBALL, 1879

Harper's Weekly

Football, if not quite as popular as some other athletic games, nevertheless has many devotees. The meeting of the teams was the great event of the football season and, so far as college sports are concerned, one of the most important of the year. For many years Yale has conquered all opponents at this exciting game, but in 1877 Princeton secured a team that played a drawn game with them. Then the New Jersey lads last year vanquished the New Haven boys after a stubborn fight, and also drew into their net the many smaller colleges that made great efforts in this line.

In the recent contest Yale started out with the intention of retrieving her lost laurels, and in due time sent her men into the field. Their past successes have been gratifying to the college, and they went to the battleground confident of holding their own. Princeton, animated with the victory of last year, never dreamed of failure. The match was played on the grounds of the St. George's Cricket Club, at Hoboken, with fifteen men on each side. The rules governing were those revised at Springfield, Massachusetts, on the 4th of October last. The ground was nearly as perfect as an even, solid, level turf could make it. The extent of the track set apart and

correctly laid down for the contestants was 330 feet in length by 160 feet in width. The goal at each end was composed of two upright posts over twenty feet in height, and placed eighteen feet six inches apart, with a crossbar ten feet from the ground. The game lasted one hour and a half, each side playing forty-five minutes from the goal. To the disgust of both parties, when time was called the victory rested with neither; the contest had proved to be one of those unsatisfactory affairs called a "drawn" game. There were no ceremonies at the finish, if we except a round of cheers given to the Yale team by its opponents. The Princeton men are comparatively happy, however, for the championship yet rests with them. The game had been free from any serious accidents, and football men declared it to be the hardest-fought battle of many seasons.

Of all athletic games football is perhaps the easiest to comprehend, an ability to kick being the only qualification required. A large park or common is best suited to the game, its great advantage being that any number of players may take part, irrespective of age or size. When, however, a match is made, two parties, each containing an equal number of competitors, take the field. Two "goals," consisting each of a couple of upright poles, ten, twelve, or even eighteen feet high, and a crossbar on top, are erected opposite each other at any distance that may be agreed upon, the game being carried on in the intervening space. Two side lines, called goal lines, are drawn from each of the goals. The players are chosen by two captains, who arrange the men in the field, and keep them to their respective sides, and whose duty it is, besides, to see that fair play is carried on. After each captain has posted a trustworthy member of his side at the goal as "keeper," the players on each side are duly placed, and the game is begun by the ball being kicked toward one of the goals from a point midway between each. Whichever side contrives to kick the ball *through* the adversaries' goal reckons either "game," or one toward it; though where the players are equally matched, and the goal well defended, the play may last many hours without a single score being made. After each goal has been made, the players usually change ends, so that no undue advantage be derived from sloping ground, favorable wind, or any other cause that may affect the course of the ball. The latter is generally made of an ox bladder covered with strong leather, India rubber balls being considered inferior.

The rules for playing football differ slightly in different localities, but the following synopsis, divested of all technical terms, will give an excellent idea of the course of the game. Two captains are selected, who toss up for the privilege of giving the ball its first kick. The one who gains this marshals his train, and marches with them to the middle of the space between the bounds, where the opposite party are mustered in a line, ready for the struggle. The ball is then placed on the ground, and the captain gives the first kick toward the opposite bounds. The other party meet it, and return it either by a kick or by carrying it, if preferred, while ten are being counted by their opponents. In some parts of England, among a rougher class, it was the privilege of the latter to make every attempt at throwing down the player who kicked or carried the ball back. This was usually managed by one of the opposite party running rapidly behind, and endeavoring by means of a circular sweep to get a foot inside his leg. This device almost always succeeded, unless it was met by a jump into the air of a peculiar kind, whereby the player contrived to preserve his equilibrium. In this way the game begins. When the exercise becomes violent, the players kick each others' shins without ceremony. Sometimes the game

becomes quite a serious scrimmage, or, as WALLER metrically puts it,

"As when a sort of lusty shepherds try
Their force at football, care of victory
Makes them salute so rudely breast to breast
That their encounter seems too rough for jest."

Football is a most ancient institution in England. It does not appear, however, to have been among the popular exercises before the reign of EDWARD III, and then it was prohibited by a public edict; not, perhaps, from any particular objection to the sport in itself, but because it operated with other favorite amusements to impede the progress of archery. So roughly was it played some three centuries later that the danger attending the pastime caused King JAMES I to say, "From this court I debarre all rough and violent exercises, as the foot-ball, meeter for lameing than making able the users thereof." The rustic youths were accustomed to make use of a blown bladder without the covering of leather by way of a football, putting peas and horsebeans inside, which occasioned a rattling as it was kicked about.

In Scotland it is a time-honored custom to hold a football match on Candlemas Day, the east end of a town against the west, the unmarried men against the married, or one parish against another. The Candlemas Ba', as it is called, brings the whole community out in a high state of excitement. On one occasion, when the sport took place in Jedburgh, the contending parties, after a struggle of two hours in the streets, transferred the contention to the bed of the river Jed, and there fought it out, amid a terrible scene of splash and mud, to the infinite amusement of the multitude looking on from the bridge.

Among the revels which a century back used to mark Shrove Tuesday, in London, football was conspicuous. The London apprentices enjoyed it in Finsbury Fields. At Teddington it was conducted with such animation that careful housekeepers had to protect their windows with hurdles and bushes. There is perhaps no part of the United Kingdom where this Shrove Tuesday sport is kept up with so much energy as in the village of Scone, near Perth, in Scotland. The men of the village assemble at the cross, the married on the one side and the bachelors on the other. A ball is thrown up, and they play from two o'clock until sunset. A person who witnessed the sport in the latter part of the last century thus describes it: "The game was this: he who at any time got the ball into his hands ran with it till overtaken by one of the opposite party. Then, if he could shake himself loose from those that seized him, he ran on; if not, he threw the ball from him, unless it was wrested from him by the other party; but no one was allowed to kick it. The object of the married men was to 'hang' it, that was, to put it three times into a small hole on the moor, which was the 'dool,' or 'limit,' on the one hand. The object of the bachelors was to 'drown' it, or to dip it three times in a deep place in the river, the limit on the other. The party who could effect either of these objects won the game; if neither one, the ball was cut into equal parts at sunset. In the course of the play there was usually some violence between the parties; but it is a proverb in that part of England that 'a' is fair at the ba' o' Scone."

Probably no football player in America ever received more "Gee, whiz" publicity than Red Grange. He was, to quote one of the superlatives, "Jack Dempsey, Babe Ruth, Al Jolson, Paavo Nurmi and Man o' War rolled into one." Now, some 30-odd years after the wild adulation and confusion, comes this excellent story of the cause of it all.

GHOST OF THE GRIDIRON

W. C. Heinz

When I was ten years old I paid ten cents to see Red Grange run with a football. That was the year when, one afternoon a week, after school was out for the day, they used to show us movies in the auditorium, and we would all troop up there clutching our dimes or nickels or pennies in our fists.

The movies were, I suppose, carefully selected for their educational value. They must have shown us, as the weeks went by, films of the Everglades, of Yosemite, of Gettysburg battlefield and of Washington, D.C., but I remember only the one about Grange.

I remember, in fact, only one shot. Grange, the football cradled in one arm, started down the field toward us. As we sat there in the dim, flickering light of the movie projector he grew larger and larger. I can still see the rows and rows of us, with our thin little necks and our bony heads, all looking up at the screen and Grange, enormous now, rushing right at us, and I shall never forget it. That was 33 years ago.

"I haven't any idea what film that might have been," Grange was saying now. "My last year at Illinois was all confusion. I had no privacy. Newsreel men were staying at the fraternity house for two and three days at a time."

He paused. The thought of it seemed to bring pain to his face even at this late date.

"I wasn't able to study or anything," he said. "I thought, and I still do, that they built me up out of all proportion."

Red Grange was the most sensational, the most publicized and, possibly, the most gifted football player and greatest broken-field runner of all time. In high school at Wheaton, Illinois, he averaged five touchdowns a game. In twenty games for the University of Illinois he scored thirty-one touchdowns and ran for 3,637 yards or, as it was translated at the time, two miles and 117 yards. His name and his pseudonyms —The Galloping Ghost and The Wheaton Iceman—became household words, and what he was may have been summarized best by Paul Sann in his book *The Lawless Decade*.

"Red Grange, No. 77, made Jack Dempsey move over," Sann has written. "He put college football ahead of boxing as the Golden Age picked up momentum. He also made some of the ball yards obsolete; they couldn't handle the crowds. He made people buy more radios: how could you wait until Sunday morning to find out what deeds Red Grange had performed on Saturday? He was 'The Galloping Ghost' and he made the sports historians torture their portables without mercy."

Grange is now fifty-five years old, his reddish-brown hair marked with gray, but he was one with Babe Ruth, Dempsey, Bobby Jones and Bill Tilden. I never saw Tilden. I have met Jones. I know Dempsey. I stood beside Ruth when, for the last time, he took off his Yankee uniform on that day when they honored him at the Yankee Stadium and he was just months from death.

"I could carry a football well," Grange was saying now, "but I've met hundreds of people who could do their thing better than I. I mean engineers, and writers, scientists, doctors—whatever.

"I can't take much credit for what I did running with a football, because I don't know what I did. Nobody ever taught me, and I can't teach anyone. You can teach a man how to block or tackle or kick or pass. The ability to run with a ball is something you have or you haven't. If you can't explain it, how can you take any credit for it?"

This was last year and we were sitting in a restaurant in Syracuse, New York. Grange was in town with Lindsey Nelson to do the telecast of the Syracuse-Penn State game. He lives now in Miami, Florida, coming out of there on weekends during the football season to handle the telecasts of the college games on Saturdays and the Chicago Bears' games on Sundays.

He approaches this job as he has approached every job, with honesty and dedication, and, as could be expected, he is good at it. "Grange is a terrific telecaster," Bert Bell, the late commissioner of the National Football League, said. "He describes the most intricate parts of the game without using jargon and he makes it clear to people who aren't even fans."

And, as befits the man who put the pro game on the map and made the whole nation football-conscious, he has been making fans out of people who never followed the game before. Never, perhaps, has any one man done more for the game. And it has, of course, been good to him.

"Football did everything for me," he was saying now, "but what people don't understand is that it hasn't been my whole life. When I was a freshman at Illinois I wasn't even going to go out for football. My fraternity brothers made me do it."

He was three times All-American. Once the Illinois students carried him two miles on their backs. A football jersey, with the number 77 that he made famous and that was retired after him, is enshrined at Champaign. His fellow students wanted him to run for Congress. A Senator from Illinois led him into the White House to shake hands with Calvin Coolidge. This, in its entirety, is what transpired:

"Howdy," Coolidge said. "Where do you live?"

"In Wheaton, Illinois," Grange said.

"Well, young man," Coolidge said, "I wish you luck."

Grange had his luck, but it was coming to him because he did more to popularize professional football than any other player before or since. In his first three years out of school he grossed almost $1,000,000 from football, motion pictures, vaudeville appearances and endorsements, and he could afford to turn down a Florida real estate firm that wanted to pay him $120,000 a year. Seven years ago the Associated Press, in selecting an All-Time All-American team in conjunction with the National Football Hall of Fame, polled one hundred leading sports writers, and Grange received more votes than any other player.

"They talk about the runs I made," he was saying, "but I can't tell you one thing I did on any run. That's the truth. During the depression, though, I took a licking. Finally I got into the insurance business. I almost starved to death for three years, but I never once tried to use my football reputation. I never once opened a University of Illinois yearbook and knowingly called on an alumnus. I think I was as good an insurance man as there was in Chicago. On the football field I had ten other men blocking for me, but I'm more proud of what I did in the insurance business, because I did it alone."

Recently I went down to Miami and visited Grange in the white colonial duplex house where he lives with his wife. They met eighteen years ago on a plane, flying between Chicago and Omaha, on which she was a stewardess, and they were married the following year.

"Without sounding like an amateur psychologist," I said, "I believe you derive more satisfaction from what you did in the insurance business, not only because you did it alone, but also because you know how you did it and, if you had to, you could do it again. You could never find any security in what you did when you ran with a football because it was inspirational and creative, rather than calculated."

"Yes," Grange said. "You could call it that. The sports writers used to try to explain it, and they used to ask me. I couldn't tell them anything."

I have read what many of them wrote, and they had as much trouble trying to corner Grange on paper as his opponents did on the field. On October 31, 1925, Laurence Stallings, the ex-Marine who came out of World War I to write "What Price Glory" and "The Big Parade," sat in the press box at Franklin Field, Philadelphia, and watched Grange take the University of Pennsylvania team apart. When it was all over he worked at his typewriter for a half hour, got up, read what he had written, tore it up and threw it away.

"I can't write it," he said. "It's too big."

Grange had blinding speed, amazing lateral mobility, an exceptional change of pace and a powerful straight-arm. He moved with high knee action but seemed to glide, rather than run, and he was a master at using his blockers. What made him great, however, was his instinctive ability to size up a field and plot a run the way a great general can map not only a battle but a whole campaign.

"The sports writers wrote that I had peripheral vision," Grange was saying. "I didn't even know what the word meant. I had to look it up. They asked me about my change of pace, and I didn't even know that I ran at different speeds. I had a cross-over step, but I couldn't spin. Some ball carriers can spin, but I'd have broken a leg."

Harold Edward Grange was born on June 13, 1903, in Forksville, Pennsylvania, the third of four children. His mother died when he was five, and his sister, Norma, died in her teens. The other sister, Mildred, lives in Binghamton, New York. His brother, Garland, two and a half years younger than Red, was a 165-pound freshman end at Illinois and was later with the Chicago Bears and is now a credit manager for a Florida department store chain. Their father died at the age of 86.

"My father," Grange said, "was the foreman of three lumber camps near Forksville, and if you had known him you'd know why I could never get a swelled head. He stood six-one and weighed 210 pounds, and he was quick as a cat. He had three hundred men under him and he had to be able to lick any one of them. One day he had a fight that lasted four hours."

Grange's father, after the death of his wife, moved the family to Wheaton, Illinois, where he had relatives. Then he sent the two girls back to Pennsylvania to live with their maternal grandparents, and he moved, with his sons, into a five-room apartment over a store where they took turns cooking and keeping house.

"Can you recall," I said, "the first time you ever ran with a football?"

"I think it started," Grange said, "with a game we used to play without a football. Ten or twelve of us would line up in the street, along one curb. One guy would be in the middle of the road and we'd all run to the other side of the street. The kid in the middle would tackle one man, and he'd have to stay out there with him. After awhile everybody'd be out there in the middle except the last kid still running. We had about thirty yards to maneuver in, and I was pretty good at that. Then somebody got a football and we played in vacant lots."

In high school Grange won 16 letters in football, basketball, baseball and track. In track he competed in the 100, 220, low and high hurdles, broad jump and high jump and often won all six events.

The school supplied the uniforms, exclusive of helmets and shoes. Grange bought a second-hand helmet but had to borrow shoes from the other players as they came out of the game. During the first year he never wore a pair of shoes that fit him, but in the last game he caught a kickoff and ran 70 yards for a touchdown. From then on he was a back, and in his sophomore year he scored 15 touchdowns, in his junior year 36—eight in one game—and in his last year 23. Once he was kicked in the head and was incoherent for forty-eight hours.

"I went to Illinois," he was saying, "because some of my friends from Wheaton went there and all the kids in the state wanted to play for Bob Zuppke and because there weren't any athletic scholarships in those days and that was the cheapest place for me to go. In May of my senior year in high school I was there for the Interscholastics, and I'd just got through broad jumping when Zup came over. He said: 'Is your name Grainche?' That's the way he always pronounced my name. I said: 'Yes.' He said: 'Where are you going to college?' I said: 'I don't know.' He put his arm around my shoulders and he said: 'I hope here. You may have a chance to make the team here.' That was the greatest moment I'd known."

That September, Grange arrived at Champaign with a battered secondhand trunk, one suit, a couple of pairs of trousers and a sweater. He had been working for four summers on an ice wagon in Wheaton, and his one luxury now was to pledge Zeta Psi fraternity.

"One day," he was saying, "they lined us pledges up in the living room of the fraternity house. I wanted to go out for basketball and track, but they started to point around the room and say: 'You go out for cheer leader. You go out for football manager. You go out for the band.' When they came to me they said: 'You go out for football.'

"That afternoon I went over to the gym and I was late. I looked out the window, and it looked like they had three hundred freshman candidates out there. I went back to the house and I said to one of the seniors: 'I can't go out for football. I'll never make that team.'

"So he lined me up near the wall, with my head down, and he hit me with this paddle. I could show you that dent in that wall, where my head took a piece of plaster out—this big."

With the thumb and forefinger of his right hand he made a circle roughly the size of a half dollar.

"Do you remember the name of that senior?" I said.

"Johnny Hawks," Grange said. "He was from Goshen, Indiana, and I see him now and then. I say to him: 'Damn you. If it wasn't for you I'd never have gone out for football.' He gets a great boot out of that."

"So what happened when you went out the next day?"

"We had all these athletes from Chicago I'd been reading about. What chance did I have, from a little farm town and a high school with three hundred students? I think they cut about forty that first night, but I happened to win the wind sprints and that got them at least to know my name."

It was a great freshman team. On it with Grange was Earl Britton, who blocked for Grange and did the kicking throughout their college careers, Moon Baker and Frank Wickhorst, who transferred to Northwestern and Annapolis, respectively, where they both made All-America. After one week of practice they played the varsity and were nosed out, 21–19, as Grange scored two touchdowns, one on a 60-yard punt return. From then on they trimmed the varsity regularly, and Zuppke began to give most of his time to the freshmen.

"That number 77," I said to Grange, "became the most famous number in football. Do you remember when you first got it?"

"It was just handed to me my sophomore year," he said. "When you're a sophomore you don't ask for anything. I guess anybody who has a number and does all right with it gets a little superstitious, and I guess that began against Nebraska in my first varsity game."

That game started Grange to national fame. This was 1923, and the previous year Nebraska had beaten Notre Dame and they were to beat "The Four Horsemen" later this same season. In the first quarter Grange sprinted 35 yards for a touchdown. In the second quarter he ran 60 yards for another. In the third period he scored again on a 12-yard burst, and Illinois won, 24–7. The next day, over Walter Eckersall's story in the Chicago *Tribune* the headline read: "Grange Sprints to Fame."

"Is it true that Zuppke bawled you out about that game?" I said.

"Not exactly," Grange said. "In high school we didn't have many plays, but at Illinois we naturally had a lot. In the first quarter Zup said: 'You're learning, and giving the plays away.' I thought: 'I may be learning, but I'm not giving the plays away because I don't know where I'm going myself.'

"After that game, though, I got a letter from a guy in Georgia. He said: 'I know why they didn't throw you on those runs on Saturday. Your number is 77, and I know from experience you can't throw two consecutive sevens. I've been trying a long time.' From then on I looked at it as a good omen."

From the Nebraska game Illinois went to an undefeated season. Against Butler, Grange scored twice. Against Iowa he scored the only touchdown as Illinois won, 9–6. In the first quarter against Northwestern he intercepted a pass and ran it back 90 yards to score the first of his three touchdowns. He made the lone touchdown against Chicago and did the same against Ohio State, this time from 34 yards out, in the last game of the season.

"All Grange can do is run," Fielding Yost, athletic director and coach of Michigan, was quoted as saying.

"All Galli-Curci can do is sing," Zuppke said.

Grange's greatest day came, in fact, his first time out against Michigan, on October 18, 1924, his junior year. On that day the $1,700,000 Illinois Memorial Stadium was dedicated as the Illini met Michigan. The Wolverines were undefeated in twenty games, and for months the nation's football fans had been waiting for this meeting.

There were 67,000 spectators—then the largest crowd ever to see a football game in the Midwest—in the stands as Michigan kicked off. Grange waited on the goal line, with Wally McIlwain, whom Zuppke was to call "the greatest open field blocker of all time" on his right, Harry Hall, the Illinois quarterback on his left, and Britton in front of him. Michigan attempted to kick to McIlwain, but as the ball descended, Grange moved over.

"I've got it," he said to McIlwain.

He caught it on the 5-yard line and McIlwain turned and took out the first Michigan man.

Britton cut down the next one, and Grange was under way. He started to his left, reversed his field to avoid one man and then, cutting back again to the left, ran diagonally across the field through the oncoming Michigan players. At the Michigan 40-yard line he was in the open, and on the 20-yard line, Tod Rockwell, the Michigan safety man, made a futile dive for him. Grange scored standing up, and Michigan never recovered.

In less than twelve minutes Grange scored three more touchdowns, from 67, 56 and 44 yards out, and Zuppke took him out to rest him. In the third period he re-entered the game and circled right end for 15 yards and another touchdown. In the final quarter he passed for another, and Illinois won, 39–14. Against a powerful, seasoned and favored opponent he had handled the ball twenty-one times, gained 402 yards, scored five touchdowns and collaborated in a sixth.

"This was," Coach Amos Alonzo Stagg, of Chicago, later wrote, "the most spectacular single-handed performance ever made in a major game."

"Did Zuppke tell you," I asked Grange now, "that you should have scored another?"

"That's right," Grange said. "After the fourth touchdown we called a time-out, and when Matt Bullock, our trainer, came in with the water I said: 'I'm dog tired. You'd better tell Zup to get me out of here.' When I got to the bench Zup said: 'You should have had five touchdowns. You didn't cut right on that one play.' Nobody could get a swelled head around him."

"And you don't recall," I said, "one feint or cut that you made during one of those runs?"

"I don't remember one thing I ever did on any run I made. I have just one vision of that Michigan game. On the opening kickoff, as I got downfield, I saw that the only man still in front of me was the safety man—Tod Rockwell. I remember thinking: 'I'd better get this guy because after coming all this way I'll sure look like a bum if one guy tackles me.' I can't tell you, though, how I got by him."

Grange says his toughest college game was against Chicago, three weeks later at Stagg Field, where 40,000 spectators filled the stands and, outside the walls, scalpers were getting from $20 to $100 a ticket. In the second period Chicago led, 14–0, when Grange, carrying the ball six times and throwing three completed passes, covered 75 yards for the first score. Chicago then made it 21–7, and Grange made it 21–14, carrying nine times and catching two

passes. In the third period he ran 80 yards through a net of tacklers, and the game ended 21–21.

When Grange started his senior year, Illinois had lost seven regulars by graduation and Harry Hall, its quarterback, because of a broken collarbone. Zuppke shifted Grange to quarterback, and Illinois lost to Nebraska, Iowa and Michigan, and barely beat Butler before, on October 31, 1925, they came into Franklin Field in Philadelphia, to play Pennsylvania.

The previous year Penn had been considered the champion of the East. They had now beaten Brown, Yale and Chicago, among others, and, although Grange's exploits in the Midwest had been widely reported for two years in Eastern papers, most of the 65,000 spectators and the Eastern sports writers—Grantland Rice, Damon Runyon, and Ford Frick, now the Commissioner of Baseball, among them—came to be convinced.

It had rained and snowed for twenty-four hours, with only straw covering the field, and at the kickoff the players stood in mud. Penn kicked off and, on the third play, the first time he carried the ball, Grange went 55 yards to his first touchdown. On the next kickoff he went 55 yards again, to the Penn 25-yard line, and Illinois worked it over from there. In the second period Grange twisted 12 yards for another score, and in the third period he scored for the last time, running 20 yards. Illinois won, 24–2, Grange having carried 363 yards in thirty-six tries in scoring three touchdowns and setting up another.

Two days later, when the train carrying the Illinois team arrived in Champaign, there were 20,000 students, faculty members and townspeople at the station. Once before, Zuppke had had another player impersonate Grange in a float parade in Columbus, Ohio. On still another occasion Grange had swapped coat and hat with a substitute to avoid a crowd. This time he attempted to sneak out of the last car, but he was recognized and carried two miles to his fraternity house.

"Do you remember your feelings during those two miles?" I asked him now.

"I remember I was embarrassed," he said. "You wish people could understand that it takes eleven men to make a football team. Unless they've played it I guess they'll never understand it, but I've never been impressed by individual performances in football, my own or anyone else's. I've seen hundreds of games, especially doing them on television, but I remember only one individual performance. That boy, Dick Moegle of Rice, had a great day in the Cotton Bowl against Alabama just a few years ago."

"That was the game," I said, "when the Alabama player came off the bench and tackled him on one of his runs."

"And that's probably why I remember it," Grange said. "That probably fixed it in my memory, but I remember dozens of fine team performances I've seen."

"Do you remember the last touchdown you scored in college?"

"To tell you the truth, I don't," he said. "It must have been against Ohio State. I can't tell you the score. I can't tell you the score of more than three or four games I ever played in."

I looked it up. His final college touchdown was the last one at Franklin Field. Grange's last college appearance, against Ohio State, attracted 85,500 spectators at Columbus. He was held to 153 yards on the ground but threw one touchdown pass as Illinois won, 14–9. The following afternoon, in the Morrison Hotel in Chicago, he signed with Charles C. (Cash and Carry) Pyle to play with the Chicago Bears and he quit college. Twenty-five years later, however, he was elected to the University's Board of Trustees for a six-year term.

"What kind of a course did you take in college?" I asked him now.

"A general business course," he said. "I had a half year to finish when I quit but I had this chance to make a lot of money and I couldn't figure where having a sheepskin would pull any more people into the football games."

"How were your marks in college?"

"I was an average student. I got B's and C's. I flunked one course—economics—one term, so I took that in the summer at Wheaton College. I'd leave the ice wagon at eleven o'clock and go to class and come back at one o'clock.

"There was so much written about my job on the ice wagon, and so many pictures were taken of me lugging ice, that people thought it was a publicity stunt. It wasn't. I did it for eight summers—starting at five o'clock every morning—for two reasons. The pay was good —$37.50 a week—and I had no money. I didn't even have any decent clothes until my junior year. Also, it kept me in shape. Carrying those blocks of ice up and down stairs six days a week, my legs were always in shape when football season started. Too many football players have to play their legs into shape in the first four or five games."

Grange played professional ball, from 1925 through 1934, with the Bears, the New York Yankees in a rival league that Pyle and he started, and then with the Bears again. He suffered injuries to his left arm and his right knee. This latter immobilized him during the 1928 season, and he was never able to cut again while running. He did, however, make the first All-Pro team, and during his professional career he scored 162 touchdowns and kicked 86 conversions for a total of 1,058 points.

What the statistics do not show, however, is what Grange, more than any other player, did to focus public attention and approval on the professional game. In 1925 the professionals attracted little notice on the sports pages and few paying customers. Interest was so lacking, in fact, that the National Professional Football League did not even hold a championship play-off at the end of the season.

In ten days Grange played five games and changed all this. After only three days of practice with the Bears he made his pro debut against the Chicago Cardinals on Thanksgiving Day, November 26. The game ended 0–0, but 36,000 fans crowded into Wrigley Field, primarily to see Grange. On Sunday, three days later, 28,000 defied a snowstorm at the same field. On Wednesday, freezing weather in St. Louis held the attendance down to 8,000, but on Saturday 40,000 rain-soaked Philadelphia fans watched at Shibe Park. The following day the Bears came into the Polo Grounds against the New York Giants.

It had been raining for almost a week and, although advance sales were almost unknown in pro football, the Giants sold more than 60,000 tickets before Sunday dawned. It turned out to be a beautiful day, and the cautious fans who had not yet purchased their seats stormed the ticket booths. The police on hand sent in riot calls, thousands were turned away and, finally, 73,651 persons were crammed into the park.

"The Giants kept watching Grange in such open-mouthed wonder," Arthur Daley, of the New York *Times,* has since written, "that they completely neglected to keep their eyes peeled on little Joey Sternaman, who did some very unwraithlike running on his own to score most of the points in a 19–7 victory."

It was the beginning of professional football's present popularity and, at the end of those first ten days, Grange got a check for $50,000 for his work. He got another $50,000 when the season closed a month later.

"Can you remember," I asked him now, "the last time you ever carried a football?"

"It was in a game against the Giants in Gilmore Stadium in Hollywood in January of 1935," he said. "It was the last period, and we had a safe lead and I was sitting on the bench. George Halas said to me: 'Would you like to go in, Red?' I said: 'No, thanks.' Everybody knew this was my last year, so he said: 'Go ahead. Why don't you run it just once more?'

"So I went in, and we lined up and they called a play for me. As soon as I got the ball and started to go I knew they had framed it up with the Giants to let me run. That line just opened and I went through and started down the field. The farther I ran the heavier my legs got and the farther those goal posts seemed to move away. I was just thinking: 'When I make that end zone I'm just going to take these things off for the last time.' With that, something hit me from behind and down I went on about the 10-yard line. It was Cecil Irvin, a 230-pound tackle. He was a fine tackle, but he was so slow that, I guess, they never let him in on the plan, but when he caught me from behind I knew I was finished."

Grange, who is 5 feet 11¾ inches, now weighs 200 pounds. In college his weight rose from 172 to 180 pounds, and in his last game with the Bears he weighed 185. On December 15, 1951, he suffered a heart attack, and this motivated him to give up his insurance business and move to Florida where, in addition to their home, he and his wife own a 50-acre orange grove near Orlando, twenty-three lots, on which they are building houses for sale, at Melbourne, and property at Indian Lake, where they plan to build a new home for themselves.

"A heart attack scares you," he said. "You hear about these things, but you always say it can never happen to you. You want to get your estate in order, and I remember that I was embarrassed, too, that everybody could see me when they carried me out of our apartment on a stretcher on the way to the hospital."

"Red," I said, "I'll bet there are some men still around whose greatest claim to fame is that they played with or against you. I imagine there are guys whose proudest boast is that they once tackled you."

"I suppose so," he said. "Once in awhile I'll run into some guy who's had a drink or two, and he'll say: 'I tackled you. Remember? I kicked the hell out of you.' I don't remember, but three things I never argue are religion, politics and sports. I say: 'Sure, I remember. You were great.' If it makes him feel good, it's all right with me. People tell me, or write me, that they saw me do this or that in one game or another. Myself, I don't remember, but I always agree with them."

"Have you ever," I said, "run into a guy who thought he knew everything about football, and didn't know he was talking with you?"

"Yes," he said. "Once, about fifteen years ago, on my way home from work I dropped into a tavern in Chicago for a beer. Two guys next to me and the bartender were having an argument about football. They were arguing about Bronko Nagurski and Carl Brumbaugh. On the Bears, of course, I played in the backfield with both of them, so I didn't want any part of this.

"Sure enough, the first thing you know, they try to bring me into it. The one guy doesn't like Nagurski and he's talking big about him. I happen to think Nagurski was the greatest football player I ever saw and a wonderful guy, and finally one of them says to me: 'Do you know anything about football? Did you ever see Nagurski play?' I said: 'Yes, and I think he was great.' So the other guy says: 'What was so great about him? What do you know about it? Who do you think you are, anyway?'

"I could see it was time to leave, but the guy said: 'No. Wait a minute? What makes you think you know something about it? Who are you?' I reached into my wallet and took out my business card and handed it to him and started for the door. When I got there I looked back. You should have seen his face."

Mrs. Grange had been listening to us talk, and then she had left the room. Now she came back with a small, gold-plated medal that Grange had won in the broad jump that day when he had first met Zuppke.

"A friend of mine just sent that to me," Grange said. "He wrote: 'You gave this to me away back in 1921. I thought you might want it.'

"Just the other day I got a letter from a man in the Midwest who wrote: 'My son just found a gold football and on it is inscribed: "University of Illinois, 1924." It has the initials: "H. G." on it, and I believe it must belong to you.' I was the only H. G. on that squad, so it must have been mine and I guess I gave it to somebody and he lost it. I wrote the man back and said: 'If your son would like it, I'd be happy to have him keep it.'"

"We have a friend," Mrs. Grange said, "who can't understand why Red doesn't keep his souvenirs. He has his trophies in another friend's storage locker in Chicago. The clipping books are nailed up in a box in the garage here, and Red hasn't looked at them in years."

"I've got several of Zuppke's paintings here," Grange said. "In the other room there's that crayon he did of me carrying the ball and some of the others are pastels. I like those, but I don't like to look back. Looking back you can grieve yourself to death. You have to look ahead."

I remembered the night we ate in that restaurant in Syracuse. The place was crowded and, except that two men came up to shake Grange's hand, he was unrecognized. As we stood in line to get our hats and coats Grange nudged me and showed me his hat check. In the middle of the yellow cardboard disk was the number 77.

"Has this ever happened to you before?" I said.

"Never," he said, "as far as I know."

We walked out into the cold night air. A few flakes of snow were falling.

"That jersey with the 77 on it that's preserved at Illinois," I said. "Is that your last-game jersey?"

"I don't know," Grange said. "It was probably a new jersey."

"Do you have any piece of equipment that you wore on the football field?"

"No," he said. "I don't have anything."

The traffic light changed, and we started across the street. "I don't even have an I-sweater," he said.

We walked about three paces.

"You know," Grange said, "I'd kind of like to have an I-sweater now."

Murray Olderman, sports editor of NEA, did this illustration for a Yale
football program cover. It said so much to so many college coaches
and fans that it was used for another Yale program cover a season later.

137

The late Herman Hickman, spinner of Tennessee kinfolk tales, charter member of the Village Green Reading Society, reciter of "Spartacus" for Yale football teams, was once a working guard in college (according to Grantland Rice, the best he had ever seen). Herman had deep respect for those who did the dirty work in the line—and he liked to tell stories about them, too.

BLOCKING FOR BEATTIE FEATHERS

Herman Hickman

As an old football guard, and as an old line coach, I get tired at times of hearing about star backfield men. I have always maintained that if it weren't for the line up front these temperamental backs couldn't make a yard and they really should pay to get in the games.

I think that one of the greatest examples of what fine blocking will do for a great back happened down at Tennessee in 1932. We had a wonderful halfback by the name of Beattie Feathers. He was an All-America for a couple of years at the University of Tennessee, and later on with the Chicago Bears he established a record of 9.9 yards per carry for a single season. The following little incident took place in a Tennessee-Alabama game, which I can assure you is never a picnic.

It was fourth down and goal to go on the Alabama 9-yard line, and they called Beattie Feathers to run the Tennessee single-wing power play off tackle. The wingback and the right end were supposed to obliterate the defensive left tackle, the blocking back and the fullback, going out shoulder to shoulder, were supposed to murder the defensive left end, and both the

guards, pulling to the right with perfect precision, were to turn up the gap, shoulder to shoulder—an irresistible force—and Beattie Feathers was to get a yard lead from the center, take three steps to his right and turn up behind those guards.

Well, nothing could stop this play, but the moving pictures of the game showed that on this occasion a little something had gone wrong. The defensive left tackle leapfrogged right over the top of the wingback and right end and they missed him cold; the blocking back and the full-back, going out shoulder to shoulder to block the defensive left end tripped and fell flat on their faces and didn't even touch him. Then the right guard pulled out to his left, and the left guard pulled out to his right and they met head-on behind the center, knocking themselves out as cold as cucumbers. This is what old guards call "joining the fraternity." You are not supposed to be a real guard until you pull the wrong way. The center got a little jittery and instead of giving Beattie Feathers a yard lead to his right, he snapped the ball back over Beattie's left shoulder. Feathers made a one-handed

138

stab and proceeded to run through the whole Alabama team for a touchdown. He came back to the huddle before the extra point, slapped everybody on the back and said, "Nice blocking boys, nice blocking. Give me blocking like that and I'll go all the way every time."

Of course you have to have line coaches and they have to eat. Some of them, they say, eat better than others—but I wouldn't know about that.

"Would you mind letting us squeeze in a few minutes of football?"

CARTOON BY GALLAGHER

John Victor McNally denies some long-popular tales about his past, introduces a few new ones, and confirms the notion that he is one of pro football's most colorful graduates in this rambling discussion with Gerald Holland.

IS THAT YOU UP THERE, JOHNNY BLOOD?

Gerald Holland

McNally is tall and lean. He has a strong face and untroubled eyes and a good head of iron-gray hair. He looks like a scholar or a poet or a contemplative monk in mufti. In repose, he is a picture of utter relaxation and, moving about, he suggests the effortless coordination of a cat. Ordinarily, he speaks quietly and briefly, as though words were not things to be wasted. On occasion, he is not so frugal with them. In his time, he has drawn street-corner crowds with rousing recitations of Kipling and has silenced soapbox orators with strange but oddly plausible arguments for or against any proposition under discussion.

Candidate John F. Kennedy met him for the first time in Green Bay, during the Wisconsin primary campaign. "Your name," said Senator Kennedy, "was a household word in our home." After the election, President Kennedy greeted McNally again at a White House reception which he attended in the company of his friend Byron White, then deputy attorney general, now a Justice of the Supreme Court.

Before that evening at the White House, McNally had been around a bit. He had taught history and economics at his alma mater, St. John's University in Minnesota. He had entered the University of Minnesota to study for his master's degree at the age of 50. He had started writing a book on economics, a work still in progress. He had read law as a clerk in his uncle's law firm. He had run (unsuccessfully) for sheriff of St. Croix County, Wisconsin, on a platform promising honest wrestling. He had been an Air Force staff sergeant and cryptographer in India and China during World War II. He had done a few things calling for less intellectual challenge. He had tended bar in Shanty Malone's place in San Francisco. He had been a stickman, a croupier, in a gambling house. He had been a seaman, a newspaper stereotyper, a miner, a farmhand, a feed salesman, a floor waxer, a sportswriter, a hotel desk clerk, a pick-and-shovel worker on a WPA project in Los Angeles during the Depression. He had spent a night in jail in Havana for fist-fighting over a matter of principle. He had walked out of a hotel in Atlantic City wearing four shirts and two suits and had settled his bill by mail later on.

In between all this, he had played some football—a lot of extraordinary football—and it was the kind of football he played that led to his election (along with Jim Thorpe, Red Grange, Bronko Nagurski, Cal Hubbard and a dozen others) as a charter member of pro football's Hall of Fame which was dedicated September 7, 1963, at Canton, Ohio, the birthplace of the National Football League.

His full name, as entered in the records at Canton, is John Victor McNally. If it rings no bell, then for John Victor McNally read Johnny Blood—the name he used when he was a household word with the teen-age Kennedy boys, the name of the legendary halfback who scored thirty-seven touchdowns and 224 points during his career with the Green Bay Packers and helped them win four NFL championships. As Johnny Blood, he played all around the pro circuit and served three seasons as player-coach of the Pittsburgh Steelers, the team for which he once signed his friend, Whizzer White.

"I guess you could say," Justice White said recently, "that if it were not for Johnny Blood's persuasiveness, I would not have played professional football. We played together only a year, with the Pittsburgh Steelers, but we have kept in close touch ever since.

"He was a great teammate. A cheerful fellow, friendly off the field. Nothing fazed him. Sometimes, although he was player-coach, he might miss a practice and explain next day that he had been to the library. He was a fine defense man. He was fast. I tried all season to beat him at 100 yards and couldn't. He was a great receiver. He thought there wasn't a ball in the air he couldn't catch. I value him as a friend as much as I admired him as a player."

Don Hutson, a Hall of Fame man and Johnny Blood's teammate with the Packers, has said of him:

"I never saw a fellow who could turn a ball game around as quickly as Johnny Blood. When he came into a game, the whole attitude of the players changed. He had complete confidence in himself. He had tremendous football sense."

A man who has seen all the great backs, from Johnny Blood to Jimmy Taylor of today's Green Bay Packers, said:

"Johnny Blood was one of the last great individualists of the football field when it was still called a gridiron. Like Red Grange, Bo McMillin and Jimmy Conzelman, he had the speed, the change of pace, the swivel hips and the quick eyes to break loose on his own and run through the opposition, whereas today's great backs largely depend on perfect execution of well-drilled blackboard plays laid out by their coaches. Johnny Blood could improvise, make up plays on the spot as the occasion demanded. I don't suppose this always made a hit with his coach, but his performance did."

The exploits of Johnny Blood McNally on and off the field during a professional career that spanned twenty-two seasons were often as wild as they were unpredictable, and yet there was a weird thread of logic running through them. There was the time, for instance, when the Packers were in Los Angeles for a game, and Johnny found himself in need of funds. He approached Coach Curly Lambeau (also a charter member of the Hall of Fame at Canton) in the hotel lobby and stated his case. Lambeau not only refused to advance him 10¢, he said he was retiring to his eighth floor room and locking himself in for the night. If Johnny came to his door, he declared, he would not let him in.

Johnny pondered, pacing the lobby. He reviewed the facts. He had asked and had been refused. But does a man take no for an answer without making certain that the other party fully understands the urgency of the matter? Johnny decided that his coach must be made to listen again. But he had said that he would not open his door. The answer, by all rules of logic, must be found in another method of approach. The door would be locked, but had anything been said about the window?

Johnny hurried to the elevators and rode up to the eighth floor. He found a door leading to a fire escape and then determined that by making his way along a ledge, he could put himself within a mere five or six feet of Coach Lambeau's window. He moved confidently along the ledge until he was in position. He looked down to the courtyard eight floors below. He balanced himself, placing his hands behind him, palms against the wall. He bent his knees slightly and was about to leap when the voice of a teammate rang out from a window two floors below.

"Is that you up there, Johnny Blood?" cried the teammate.

"The same," answered Johnny.

"Dear God in Heaven," shouted the teammate, "what are you going to do, Johnny?"

"Coach wants to see me," Johnny called back. "Told me to drop in and talk over a matter of business." With that he jumped, landed neatly on the window ledge, threw up the half-open window and presented himself to Coach Lambeau who fell back, clutching his heart.

"I thought that perhaps I didn't make myself

clear, Coach," said Johnny, "about that advance I asked for. Now the fact is—"

Curly Lambeau staggered to the chair where his trousers hung. He thrust a hand in a pocket and pulled out a wad of bills.

"Take it, take it!" he cried. "Take it and go. Go where you want, Johnny Blood."

"Thank you, Coach," said Johnny politely. "I knew we could come to an understanding once we talked things over in a calm, reasonable way."

"Just go," groaned Curly. "Go, please go."

Johnny went to the door, turned the lock and opened it.

"Have a good night's sleep, Coach," he said, closing the door behind him.

Although that story is vouched for by Curly Lambeau himself, the legend that has grown up around Johnny Blood is so filled with truths and half-truths and no truth at all that it is necessary to try to grasp a few facts of record and hold fast to them. Throw out the fable that he once stayed up an entire night in a bar and engaged in a toe-to-toe Shakespearean performance with John Barrymore. He never met Barrymore in his life. Nor did he ever heckle a nightclub comedian and then take over the spotlight to put on an impromptu show of his own. To be sure, he did dance a jig on the football field as the band played *Piccolo Pete*. But sportswriters invented scores of other tales, because they knew that Johnny would not bother to deny them.

One truth is that Johnny is not an easy man to catch up with. His home is the house where he was born, in New Richmond, Wisconsin, but he is seldom there long, for he roams the country, visiting old friends, making new ones out of anyone who has something interesting to say, rarely staying in any one place for long. People meeting him for the first time usually want to know exactly how scholarly John McNally became the Johnny Blood of legend, the hell-raisingest, most excitingly colorful player on and off the field that the professional game has ever seen.

He was captured for a little while on the evening of last New Year's Day. That afternoon he had seen the University of Wisconsin lose a thriller to USC in the Rose Bowl. Two days before, he had watched the Packers beat the Giants in New York. He had hoped to witness a complete sweep, professional and collegiate, for the teams representing his home state. Now he sat in the cocktail lounge of the Ambassador Hotel in Los Angeles. He rattled the ice cubes in his empty glass (he rarely drinks before sundown) and called to a passing waiter his standard order for another Scotch and water. "A man," he said, "could die of thirst in a place like this." The waiter looked back and smiled and nodded.

The usual question was asked.

"How did I become Johnny Blood? I think some background should be given here. I was small as a kid in New Richmond. Precocious, I suppose, a quick study. I graduated from high school when I was fourteen. I had been too small to participate in any kind of athletics. Unless you count climbing. I loved to climb things. Trees, telephone poles, the outside of houses. This addiction stayed with me in later life. Once I went to visit a friend in the hospital. It was after visiting hours, and I was turned away on the ground floor. So I went around the back and climbed up to my friend's room on the third floor and went in through the window. My friend seemed to be greatly cheered by the visit. I not only liked to climb up, I liked to climb down. One time when I was playing with Ernie Nevers' Eskimos, I was giving a poetry reading on the street outside our hotel. The team manager came along, took me by the arm, escorted me to my room and locked me in. My room was on the sixth floor. It was child's play for me to go out the window and back down to the street and pick up my recitation at the point where it had been interrupted.

"Getting back to my boyhood, my parents thought I was too young to go away to college at 14. So I stayed home and learned to type and studied commercial subjects. I read a good deal. I remember that it was in those days I first read about Cincinnatus, the Roman general who would farm his land until war came, then would lead his troops to victory and go back to farming again. I made him my hero and, as I grew older, I realized that what Cincinnatus was, was a clutch hitter. I'm a great admirer of clutch hitters."

(Cal Hubbard, the American League's chief of umpires and also a Hall of Fame man, picked an all-time pro team some years ago. He did not pick Johnny Blood, but he said that if he could have had a twelfth player—the equivalent of a clutch hitter in baseball—Johnny Blood would have been his man.)

The waiter set down a fresh Scotch and water.

"When I was seventeen," Johnny went on, "I entered St. John's, a Benedictine college near Collegeville, Minnesota. Suddenly, I started to grow like a weed. I went out for all sports—

football, baseball, track, basketball. I guess I was St. John's first four-letter man. St. John's was a two-year college then, but I stayed on doing some postgraduate study for a year and then decided I wanted to finish up at Notre Dame."

And so you later became known as Johnny Blood, "a vagabond halfback from Notre Dame"? That was in TIME magazine.

"TIME erred. I was neither Johnny Blood nor a halfback at Notre Dame. And I was not yet a vagabond. I went out for the freshman squad —although I was actually a junior—and they put me at tackle. I didn't like that. A tackle's job is to make body contact; a ball carrier's job is to avoid it. I was fast, and I wanted to be a halfback."

What happened when you became eligible for the varsity the following year?

"I wasn't around the following year. I was suspended from Notre Dame in the spring of 1924 for absenting myself from the campus, along with some classmates whose names I refused to reveal. It was just as well that I didn't stay and try out for the varsity. I would have been competing with Don Miller of the Four Horsemen for the right halfback position in that great backfield."

Still, suspension from college is a traumatic experience for a boy. Were you ashamed? Did you feel disgraced? Did you go to the authorities, fall to your knees and beg forgiveness, plead for reinstatement?

"No, I bought a motorcycle. I was just learning to drive it fairly well, when I happened to attend a party in South Bend. There was a girl there, and we got to talking. I told her that I had purchased a motorcycle and was planning a tour of the eastern seaboard. Two of my sisters were sailing for Europe, and I wanted to be in New York to wish them *bon voyage*."

Your devotion to your sisters doubtless impressed the girl at the party. Possibly you were attracted to her as well. Did you see this girl again?

"I did. On the back seat of my motorcycle. She confided to me that she was married to a sailor who was due to sail from Norfolk on a battleship, and she was most anxious to wish him *bon voyage*. So we set out. We spent a night in Chicago sitting on a park bench to conserve funds for fuel. Then we paid a visit to her family in Fort Wayne, Indiana. Her parents approved of the motorcycle tour, without reservation, and so we set off in the general direction of Norfolk."

The girl on the back seat of the motorcycle?

"Correct. We ran out of money at Washington, Pennsylvania. The girl suggested hocking her watch and her wedding ring. I concurred and promised to redeem them later. I did redeem them. Well, at any rate, we got to Norfolk and found her husband's battleship had sailed. The girl was distraught. She had no place to stay, and I was due in New York. So I took her to a YWCA, explained our predicament to a nice lady in charge, and she agreed to let the girl stay until I could send her money to go home on. Which, fortunately, I was able to do."

And you drove off alone to wish your sisters *bon voyage* in New York?

"That's right. Unfortunately, however, my motorcycle broke down several times along the way. I borrowed some money from a cousin in Baltimore and pressed on, but I was unable to reach New York before my sisters' ship sailed. Happily, I had another sister at Radcliffe, so I drove to Boston, called upon her, wished her well and borrowed some money for fuel. At my sister's suggestion, I also wrote home and asked that a small sum be deposited in my checking account, which had been drained completely en route to Washington, Pennsylvania.

"All being well at Radcliffe, I decided to start back to Wisconsin. My motorcycle broke down at Sandusky, Ohio. Luckily, I remembered that the Four Horsemen of Notre Dame had summer jobs in a resort there. I looked up Harry Stuhldreher, reminded him that I had written his poetry for him when we were in Father Carroll's poetry class at Notre Dame and asked him to cash a check. Harry was happy to oblige. I got the motorcycle fixed, and it performed magnificently until I arrived at Amherst Junction, Wisconsin, where it collapsed completely, beyond repair. I abandoned it and caught a freight train for New Richmond. I rode the blinds. Older hoboes will remember the blinds as the space between the coal tender and the baggage car." He raised his voice: "A man could die—." The waiter, standing by, nodded understandingly.

This is all leading up to the story of how John McNally became Johnny Blood?

"It is. Back home again, I decided to go to work. One of my uncles was owner and publisher of the *Minneapolis Tribune*, and another uncle was in charge of the mechanical department. In the company of a former classmate from St. John's, Ralph Hanson, I went to the newspaper and asked for a job. Ralph and I were put to work in the stereotypng department. We hadn't been working long when we read that a professional football league was being formed in Minneapolis and that the East 26th Street Liberties were conducting tryouts. Ralph and I decided to try out, but we agreed that since we both had a year of collegiate eligibility left, we would do well to try out under assumed names."

The waiter put down a glass.

"Check, please," said John McNally. "Well, sir, we tried to think of names, but we couldn't think of any we liked. We were still pondering the problem as we rode out to the ball park where the tryouts were being held. Along the way, we passed a theater. The marquee advertised a Rudolph Valentino picture called *Blood and Sand*. I grabbed Ralph's arm. 'There are our names,' I said. 'I'll be Blood and you be Sand.' "

And that was the start of your professional career?

"I made the team, yes. I had a very good year. The East 26th Street Liberties won the city championship. I then moved on to a team that was being formed at Ironwood, Michigan. From there I jumped to Milwaukee, and then I got an offer to join Ernie Nevers in Duluth. Then I went to Pottsville, Pennsylvania and finally was signed by the Packers. In my negotiations with Curly Lambeau, I asked for $100 a game. He came back with an offer of $110 a game, providing I would initial a clause in the contract forbidding any drinking after Tuesday of each week. I countered with an offer to take the $100 I had proposed and drink through Wednesday. Curly agreed."

Johnny Blood McNally finished his drink and got up. "Excuse me," he said, "I am flying to San Francisco to see Shanty Malone." He waved a hand and was gone.

Months later, Johnny Blood sat at a table in Dinty Moore's restaurant in New York.

"I found Shanty Malone looking very well, still merry-eyed and curly-haired," he said. "I hadn't seen him since 1947. We recalled the old days, starting with the night Shanty knocked on the door of my hotel room, a perfect stranger, and invited me to join him in a drink at a nearby speakeasy. He was a great football fan. Our friendship prospered, and Shanty was there in the clutch when I was caught in San Francisco between seasons without funds. It was then that I went to work for him as a bartender."

Does Shanty still have a bar?

"Oh yes. He has moved several times, but all his places have been pretty much the same as far as atmosphere is concerned. Genteel, in a sort of knock-down-and-drag-out way. Shanty himself is a working philosopher. We discussed some of the great eternal questions, as we had done in the past."

Do you recall any particular eternal question?

Johnny Blood pushed back his plate and ordered some coffee. "Yes. One question we discussed has been on my mind for years. It was posed to me when I was coaching the Pittsburgh Steelers. Just before the start of the season it became necessary for me to cut four men from the squad. I hated to do it. But I told the boys that I had heard of an independent pro team being organized in St. Louis. I suggested that they go there and try out. I persuaded Art Rooney, owner of the Steelers, to advance money enough to get them to St. Louis. Well, the boys went out, worked hard to make the team, but all four failed. They sent me a wire after their release. It read, simply, 'Where to now, Coach?' I didn't know the answer. In the large sense, does anybody?"

Johnny Blood took a sip of coffee and declined a cigarette. He looked around Dinty Moore's restaurant. "This old place," he said, "hasn't changed a bit since the Packers used to eat here back in the '30s."

He was silent for a moment, and then he went on: "I saw a lot of old friends on the Coast. I played golf with Ernie Nevers."

Do you consider Nevers the greatest football player of all time, as some people say?

"Well, Pop Warner said that under his system, Ernie was better than Jim Thorpe. That's pretty high praise, but the peculiarities of the Warner system required the fullback to be the absolute core of the team. He did the signal calling, the passing, the kicking, the spinning and the ball carrying. It was a system that depended utterly on the fullback. Ernie certainly met the test for that position under the Warner system better than anybody else. He certainly was the greatest of the Pop Warner fullbacks, and he was at least the equal of any of the greatest fullbacks of all time.

"Ernie and I talked about the days when we played 60-minute football, the days before the platoon system. We were proud to stay in there for the full distance. If we couldn't stay in there, we felt that we did not measure up. I think present-day players miss that full-time effort, although today's game is better for the spectators. What really created modern football was the platoon system and the slow-motion camera. The camera showed the coaches things they didn't know before. They knew in detail what every man did right and wrong. This helped them to coach more effectively. Now the player knows that the coach is seeing every detail of the action in slow motion and so, playing this part-time football, he is giving his maximum effort every minute. I used to say in the old days that the only thing wrong with pro football was that the stadiums were too small. That turned out to be a pretty good diagnosis in view of the way the game has caught on with the fans. It's a great show. It's dead on the level, you can't fake it, and it's all out there in front of you."

When did you hear that you were picked for the Hall of Fame in Canton?

"Well, I had heard rumors from sportswriters, but the official word came last January when I was visiting Curly Lambeau at his home in Palm Springs, California. We read the news in the Los Angeles papers. We were both very proud that, with Cal Hubbard, Don Hutson, Curly and myself, the Green Bay Packers had four men in the first contingent. I told Curly that I felt my reputation for so-called color probably was what influenced the sportswriters and broadcasters in voting me in as a charter member. Curly was kind. He said I had more than so-called color, and he prayed that the saints would preserve him from any more of that."

What is your own estimate of yourself as a player, Johnny Blood?

"Well, I always figured I was a pretty fair all-round back. I could kick with almost anybody. I wasn't a real good thrower, but in my time I guess I was as good a receiver as there was around—the best, maybe, until Don Hutson came along. Some people said I was the fastest man in the league until Hutson, who was a 9.6 man in college. I could carry weight—I mean the weight of equipment. Lots of great sprinters can't carry weight. I don't know—I was said to be an imaginative signal caller. I called signals for three championship teams. I scored 13 touchdowns for the Packers in 1931, and that was a record for the time. But there were an awful lot of good men. I still say the electors were influenced by the so-called color of the so-called Vagabond Halfback."

Which you weren't, you said.

"I said I wasn't a Vagabond Halfback from Notre Dame. Ollie Kuechle, sports editor of the *Milwaukee Journal,* first called me a vagabond. There's a story connected with that. I was leaving New Richmond to report to the Packers one year and, as sometimes happened, I decided to ride the blinds on a freight-and-passenger train. Now, there was no direct train from New Richmond to Green Bay, but there was a connection at Amherst Junction. The connection got in and left a few minutes before the New Richmond train, unless a wire was received requesting it to wait for passengers. Before taking the freight, I sent such a wire and, when we got to Amherst Junction, the Green Bay train was waiting. I hopped off the blinds of one train and onto the blinds of the other. Along the way, the baggage-car door opened and the baggageman looked out and saw me. He said, 'Is that you, Johnny Blood?' I said yes. He said, 'Did you send that wire telling us to hold for a passenger?' I confessed that I was the party. He shook his head, but he invited me into the car, loaned me his razor and gave me half his lunch.

"Well, Ollie Kuechle heard about the incident. He told Curly he was writing a story about the Packers' Hobo Halfback. Curly was very proud of the Packers, and he asked Ollie if he couldn't avoid suggesting that the team employed hoboes. Ollie thought awhile and then proposed vagabond. Curly thought that sounded much more dignified. And that's the way it came out in the *Journal* and was reprinted all around the league."

Johnny Blood got up from the bench and stretched.

Where to now, Coach?

"I am going to the University of Maine to observe the solar eclipse. Then I plan to visit the baseball shrine in Cooperstown, N.Y., and see what a Hall of Fame looks like."

Before you go, Coach, would you mind a few personal questions?

"No."

You are not married?

"I was married for 10 years. We came to a parting of the ways. But I have nothing but the highest admiration for the state of matrimony."

You move around a good deal. This takes money, Coach.

"Well, I have a competence from a trust fund."

What would you give as your occupation?

"Reading, studying, writing. Meditating. Once meditation was an honorable occupation. Today, it would appear on a police blotter as a form of vagrancy, I suppose."

Could you give just one sample subject of your meditation?

"Moby Dick. I think the whale could think. He could read your mind. Captain Ahab, another hero of mine, did not realize this; so he had the courage of ignorance, comparable, I should say, to the courage of a fullback playing his first season of professional football. He hurls himself against the line. But go back and look at him at the age of 30. He will not be hitting the line with quite the same abandon. For the courage of ignorance, he has substituted the restraint, the caution of a little wisdom."

He strolled away.

Johnny Blood McNally is obviously pleased and certainly very proud to be included in the first band of heroes whose heads have been sculptured and cast in bronze and will be placed on display in the Hall of Fame. In his wanderings up and down the land, meditating as he goes, he probably asks himself from time to time the question a horrified teammate called to him as he perched on a ledge eight floors up many years ago. The answer should come easy, even if he insists that he is the least worthy of the heroes who will look down on the pilgrims at Canton. For just as it was when Coach Curly Lambeau saw the figure come through his hotel window, it is Johnny Blood up there, this time up there to stay.

Hard facts and figures from a Fortune *survey in 1962, reprinted here in part, show that the cost of playing is difficult to build a defense against.*

COLLEGE FOOTBALL HAS BECOME A LOSING BUSINESS

Myles Jackson

In fiscal 1961–62, U.S. college football grossed an estimated $65 million, and the game continues to be the most entertaining and spectacular business enterprise associated with American higher learning. But during the past ten years the economics of college football have become progressively less entertaining to such spectators as university regents and trustees: costs have been going up rapidly and, like other businesses in these times, football is finding out what a profit squeeze feels like. In some cases the squeeze has resulted in outright strangulation.

If football were no more costly than soccer or lacrosse, the prospect of its losing money would be of no great concern: some expenditure on athletics is essential in a balanced university curriculum. As of last season, however, the cost of fielding a three-platoon football team was as high as $760,000 (*Fortune*'s estimate) for schools that operated at big-time levels of competition; the cost was not much less than half that for numerous lesser schools that played football of marketable quality. When sums of this magnitude are involved— they are about double what they were ten

years ago—there has to be a proportionate increase in concern about the possibility of going into the red.

During college football's lusher years, when profits were relatively easy to come by, the argument was sometimes whether amateur college football should be *allowed* to make all the money it did. Nowadays the basic question is whether or not football should be allowed to do what has to be done in order to keep from *losing* all that money. The question is as new as the profit strangle, and in order to answer it, trustees and regents must soon make new and realistic estimates of the real nature of football's contribution to academic life.

They have several options. They may decide to push football even harder as a business. But when operating costs are high, a business has to be run in a businesslike manner, in which case the game should be officially recognized as a business and the players paid like professionals. Developments along this line have already taken place. Another option is to pay the price for a top-ranking team out of the general fund, which is money designed primarily for higher education and which is taxpayers' money in state-supported schools. The college trustees or administrators could also decide that the whole thing is more trouble than it is worth, not to say irrelevant, and drop football altogether. This has happened in the case of eighty-six colleges and universities, mostly small schools, since 1951. The much hashed-over question of football ethics, then, has been superseded by some more pragmatic questions.

There is no doubt that for the majority of colleges there will be a market for college football for some time to come. National Collegiate Athletic Association commercials during televised games this season reported: "Almost 21 million fans set an all-time collegiate record last year, as total attendance increased for the eighth straight season." College-football attendance has in fact increased 18 per cent over 1951. Generally, gross football income has increased along with attendance, rising to last year's $65,000,000 from a national total of about $45 million in 1951. The network-television portion of the total has gone up from $700,000 to $4 million. (The networks, of course, get more than their money's worth out of college football.) New stadiums, and seats added to old ones, have increased capacity by at least 10 per cent; and a growing number of colleges are boosting income by moving from a nine to a ten-game schedule.

Outside the big-city areas, professional football has not really turned out to be the serious competition that many colleges feared. The majority of college games are played in relatively small towns and cities, and this can constitute an economic advantage. In some areas there just isn't much else to do besides go to a football game on a Saturday afternoon; this factor is of more significance to the gate than competition from distant professional teams. For example, at Columbus, around noon on a football Saturday, 12,000 automobiles from out of town begin to stream toward the Ohio State University stadium along streets temporarily turned one-way, as a traffic-control helicopter swings overhead. Even without O.S.U.'s enviable win record, activity of this kind creates an enjoyable presentiment of marvelous events to come. In the small and rather drab prairie town of Norman, Oklahoma (it has one main-street movie theatre), the same effect is generated late Saturday morning as 150 to 200 private airplanes, carrying football customers, begin to land on the grass of the nearby university airport.

But it is apparent that the market will not,

in most cases, be large enough to offset increased costs. The 18 per cent rise in college-football attendance need only be compared with an 84 per cent national increase in student enrollment to indicate a decrease in student interest. The University of Southern California is an example (although not necessarily typical) of how student enthusiasm for the game has flagged. In 1948, 83 per cent of the undergraduates attended U.S.C. home games; last season, student attendance was 51 per cent. The University of Colorado has an undergraduate enrollment of 12,000; for the past few years the student newspaper, presumably representing a cross section of student opinion, has opposed the big-time brand of football Colorado plays. Colorado won the Big Eight championship in 1961. This year there were some 6,600 students who were not enough interested in big-time football to pay $6 for a season ticket book. Because of student pressure at Colorado, football tickets have been separated from the incidental fees that all students pay at registration.

Even though absolute attendance figures are up, the generally acknowledged doubling of costs in a single decade has more than eaten up the additional revenue. In fact, costs may be something more than double if one judges by the comment of Michigan's athletic director, Fritz Crisler, on the occasion of the Big Ten universities' raising allowable ticket prices to a $5 top in 1961. "If ticket prices had increased in proportion to costs, we would have to sell them for $10 to $15."

The net result, according to estimates by N.C.A.A. officials, various athletic administrators, and conference officers, is drenched in red ink. Of the 200-odd schools that were playing anything like marketable football last year, and whose athletic departments had any aspirations of at least breaking even, only thirty to forty were definitely in the black. Of these, the majority were operating on a progressively diminishing margin of profit—or as nonprofit institutions prefer to phrase it, "excess of income over expenditure." At Oklahoma—which during the past few years has not been the power it was when it won twelve conference championships in a row but is still pretty mighty —athletic-department excess of income over expenditure in 1960 (excluding cash reserves) was $3,000. Last year Oklahoma's "excess" was down to $300.

Once a college administration or board of trustees has taken the decision to preserve intercollegiate football in the teeth of rising costs, the next question is whether the school should remain at its current competitive level: the cost factors of marketable college football are closely related to the competitive level at which a school chooses to play. The levels are roughly three: the Big Time, the Middle Time, and the Small Time. The Big Time consists of some eighty-odd teams across the nation that carry the regional stature and the national standing of the Midwest's Big Ten—although, as we shall see, almost any college can qualify for the Big Time, if it is willing to pay the Big Time price. The Middle Time numbers more than 130 schools, typified by such conferences as the Mid-American Conference (Miami of Ohio, Bowling Green, Kent State, etc.), and the Southern Conference (Citadel, Furman, William and Mary, etc.). It includes in its numbers many of the marginal producers for which the moment of decision looms closest. The Small Time—300-odd schools—finds its market at the bottom of the pileup. It has already cut its costs and its pride to fit its revenues, or it has reconciled itself to viewing intercollegiate football as just another expense. Austin College of Sherman, Texas (enrollment 700), was trying to play lower Middle Time ball as a member of the Texas Conference (Abilene Christian, Texas A. & I., etc.) and Austin's 1953 football deficit was more than $33,000. The following year Austin dropped out of the Texas Conference and now plays such Small Time schools as Sewanee and Ouachita of Arkadelphia, Arkansas, at a yearly cost of approximately $14,000.

The alternatives before a college in search of its level are not unfamiliar to business: the school can retreat strategically to the smaller time or it can make the old college try and fight it out in the Big Time market. The latter course involves redoubled efforts—probably hiring a new coach, investing in increased stadium capacity, intensifying recruiting of players, etc. There are still sizable incentives. The successful Big Time school can run its revenues as high as Ohio State's $1,372,000 or Army's $825,675 in 1961. (Total Army football gross from 1952 to 1961 inclusive: $7,546,-000.) As it builds its name and record it has a chance at the big intersectional and post-season bowl games, and at the fees for national telecasting. Fees for national TV run about $135,800 per team per game, and are usually divided among conference members.

The move upward is not to be taken lightly, however. By *Fortune*'s calculations the rock-bottom cost of fielding a team somewhere in the Big Time is $400,000 a year.

The figure itself will come as a surprise to many colleges that are paying it. In gathering material for this article *Fortune* canvassed more than a dozen colleges, including Yale, Brown, Cornell, West Point, Ohio State, Illinois, Northwestern, Oklahoma, Colorado State, Austin College, the University of Southern California, Clemson, Centre College in Kentucky, West Virginia Wesleyan, and Bowling Green, Ohio. Some colleges gilded facts, some distorted them, some did their level best to clarify them, but it is *Fortune*'s conviction that not one really knew how much football was costing.

Football income was recorded to the penny, but expenditures were a blur. Primary football expenses were usually lumped with total athletic-department expenditures. Yale stood almost alone in knowing how much its stadium was costing in yearly operating expense and maintenance; at most of the other schools there was a single entry for athletic plant maintenance, which included the field house, hockey rink, and other buildings as well as the stadium. Ohio State listed nineteen items under "football expenditures"—uniforms, travel, movies, officials, etc.—and the total came to $174,083.63. This did not include football coaches' salaries, or a number of overhead items. In cooperation with *Fortune*, Ohio State athletic-department officials worked out estimated percentages of other costs, including any expenditure that would not exist if there were no football, and such items as the publicity-bureau, ticket-office, and general-administration expenditures directly applicable to football, as well as an estimate of the stadium's yearly operating and maintenance costs. Total football expenditures then turned out to be $760,000. This is something like what it costs to field a team in the very top of the Big Time but well above average for the general Big Time category. The $400,000 figure was arrived at by averaging similar detailed cost estimates from other schools.

The largest single item of football expenditure is the full-ride grant-in-aid, now an accepted fixture at schools that hope to play profitable football. At Ohio State the price for 108 players, including freshmen, amounts to $111,000, which compares with a Big Ten average of about $118,000. (Ohio's all-sports grant total was $219,000, paid for out of athletic-department profits—some of which come from basketball.) The University of Colorado spent over $100,000 on football grants. Oklahoma and U.S.C. together, including some partial grants, averaged over $90,000. If we average all of these and take off about 15 per cent for the sake of being very conservative, we will have a minimum Big Time grant-in-aid estimate of about $90,000.

Sooner or later the ambitious Middle Time school will find itself adding capacity to its stadium. Construction costs vary enormously with stadium design: during the past few years Clemson has increased its stadium capacity from about 25,000 to 45,000 at a cost of $450,-000. Indiana recently built a new 48,000-seat stadium that cost $6,600,000. It is difficult to make anything but a rough estimate of what average costs would amount to in yearly debt-service payments, but the yearly sum being paid by Colorado, which nearly doubled capacity to 41,000 a few years ago, would probably be close to what a new arrival in the Big Time might expect to pay: about $20,000 a year.

The basic construction costs of the older and larger stadiums—like the $2,279,000 Ohio Stadium—were paid off long ago, and the main yearly expense is in operating and maintenance costs. Yale's uniquely detailed records of its bowl maintenance expenses show 1961–62 operating and maintenance expense at $70,000 (excluding property taxes). Illinois spent about $84,000. Ohio State's stadium expense (including $4,000 a year for wooden-seat replacements, and other sums for painting, concrete and plumbing repair, playing field surface maintenance, plus game-day expenses such as wages for ticket takers, car parkers, physicians, post-game cleanup) was an estimated $67,500 for five home games. Oklahoma's estimate of $22,-000 is probably conservative. Although the variation in these sums is considerable, they average out to $60,000, and this is a fairly sound minimum estimate of Big Time stadium operating and maintenance costs alone. If we reduce this sum by a conservative factor of about 15 per cent, to $50,000, and add to it a typical stadium debt-service payment such as Colorado's $20,000, we have at least a working conception of the minimum yearly sum required to operate a recently enlarged stadium in the Big Time: $70,000.

The most elusive cost is player recruiting. A self-study conducted by the Big Ten in 1956 reported that about 95 per cent of all football lettermen in the Big Ten had been "actively recruited." By now the percentage applies to all schools from the Middle Time up. Oklahoma's total recruiting-cost estimate is $14,000. U.S.C.'s is $11,500. Ohio State has an item called "Entertainment," which is connected with recruiting, and is the only listing in that

area: $2,200. This is not so conservative as it might seem, considering the renowned vigor of the Ohio alumni. One of the more accurate estimates is the Colorado item listed under "Recruiting": $23,488. Adding together everything a school might spend in "actively recruiting" 95 per cent of its varsity football players, we can't go wrong in assigning this item the rock-bottom sum of $15,000.

A number of operating expenses are more or less constant across the country: uniforms and equipment cost about $22,000 at Cornell, $21,-700 at Oklahoma, $24,000 at West Point. Training-table cost was $18,000 at U.S.C., $17,500 at Colorado. Ohio State spent $20,600 on motion pictures—there is a camera going at almost every practice session—but this was only Parkinson's Law in action at a rich football school, as photography expenses rose to meet available income. (The Cleveland Browns got along with $15,000 worth of movies.) Motion-picture expense did not often rise above $6,000 at other big schools. Team travel averages $25,000 with one intersectional trip. The average of these sums, plus another $50,000 for training-room supplies and salaries, equipment manager's salary, insurance, extra medical expense, and laundry adds up to what can be termed minimum team operating expenses: $120,000. Add another $3,000 for the marching band. (High-stepping Ohio State spends $19,000 on uniforms and two trips for the 120-piece band—which has ten E-flat cornets, ten tenor horns, ten flügelhorns, and no trombones at all.)

Coaching in the last major item. The minimum range for a Big Time coach is $15,000 to $17,000, but the school probably will have to offer him perquisites equal in value to at least the amount of his salary—e.g., a rent-free house (renovated before he moves in), and perhaps a new car. He will need five to ten assistants at $6,000 to $10,000 each. The total football coaches' salary item at Ohio State was $98,000 last year, $70,000 at Yale; but for a minimum we can drop it to $65,000.

Add to this some $40,000 worth of overhead usually covered in the college administrative budget (news bureau, telephones, office supplies, etc.) and we get our $400,000 as a rock-bottom estimate of how much it costs to play nine or ten football games in the lower fringes of the Big Time.

It is a figure of this magnitude that hangs over the heads of trustees, regents, overseers, and even taxpayers as they ponder the decision of what to do about college football. If a school seems to be in a position to earn $400,000 or more it can go on with the Big Time game. If it can afford to play at this level because deficits are made up out of the general fund—by alumni, endowments, or legislative appropriation—it can also go on. In some cases trustees and administrators who wanted to keep a $400,000 football team operating in the black would need only to take traditional non-football athletic-department expenses off football's back. This course has a certain virtue because it leaves marketable college football where it ought to be—recognized as an out-and-out business proposition, not a benevolent service to other sports.

If all these "ifs" add up to a negative decision, the future need not be so bleak as alumni might think. Colleges playing below the $400,000 level will find themselves in the pleasurable company of other institutions of higher learning that are moving back to amateur football—Small Time, no grants, no worry, no guilt complex, little profit, little loss, and after all is said and done still a fairly rousing game.

New York Giants high-tackle Bronko Nagurski of the Bears in
1934 pro playoff won by New York, 30–13.

BEARS AFTER THE TITLE

Jack Manders boots one of the Bears' 73 points in the 1940 rout of the Redskins at Washington.

Owner-coach George Halas of the Bears
gives his club a lift from the sidelines. Halas won
his first championship in 1933; his most recent
was against the Giants in 1963.

Long before Dink Stover took the train to Yale—and destiny—he fought some telling battles in the process of growing up at Lawrenceville. This selection is from The Varmint, *one of Owen Johnson's best. Stover, a miserable 138 pounds, takes his place alongside Turkey Reiter, Waladoo Bird and Tough McCarty against a rugged Andover team. No one writes boys' fiction like this any more—and the boys (and the game) are minus some wonderful romance.*

STOVER AT LAWRENCEVILLE

Owen Johnson

Saturday came all too soon and with it the arrival of the stocky Andover eleven. Dink dressed and went slowly across the campus—every step seemed an effort. Everywhere was an air of seriousness and apprehension, strangely contrasted to the gay ferment that usually announced a big game. He felt a hundred eyes on him as he went and knew what was in every one's mind. What would happen when Ned Banks would have to retire and he, little Dink Stover, weighing one hundred and thirty-eight, would have to go forth to stand at the end of the line. And because Stover had learned the lesson of football, the sacrifice for an idea, he too felt not fear but a sort of despair that the hopes of the great school would have to rest upon him, little Dink Stover, who weighed only one hundred and thirty-eight pounds.

He went quietly to the Upper, his eyes on the ground like a guilty man, picking his way through the crowds of Fifth Formers, who watched him pass with critical looks, and up the heavy stairs to Garry Cockrell's room, where the team sat quietly listening to the final instructions. He took his seat silently in an obscure corner, studying the stern faces about him, hearing nothing of Mr. Ware's staccato periods, his eyes irresistibly drawn to his captain, wondering how suddenly older he looked and grave.

By his side Ned Banks was listening stolidly and Charlie DeSoto, twisting a paperweight in his nervous fingers, fidgeting on his chair with the longing for the fray.

"That's all," said the low voice of Garry Cockrell. "You know what you have to do. Go down to Charlie's room; I want a few words with Stover."

They went sternly and quickly, Mr. Ware with them. Dink was alone, standing stiff and straight, his heart thumping violently, waiting for his captain to speak.

"How do you feel?"

"I'm ready, sir."

"I don't know when you'll get in the game—probably before the first half is over," said Cockrell slowly. "We're going to put up to you a pretty hard proposition, youngster." He came nearer, laying his hand on Stover's shoulder. "I'm not going to talk nerve to you, young bulldog, I don't need to. I've watched you and I know the stuff that's in you."

"Thank you, sir."

"Not but what you'll need it—more than you've ever needed it before. You've no right in this game."

"I know it, sir."

"Tough McCarty won't be able to help you out much. He's got the toughest man in the line.

Everything's coming at you, my boy, and you've got to stand it off, somehow. Now, listen once more. It's a game for the long head, for the cool head. You've got to outthink every man on the field and you can do it. And remember this: No matter what happens never let up— get your man back of the line if you can, get him 25 yards beyond you, get him on the 1-yard line,—but get him!"

"Yes, sir."

"And now one thing more. There's all sorts of ways you can play the game. You can charge in like a bull and kill yourself off in ten minutes, but that won't do. You can go in and make grandstand plays and get carried off the field, but that won't do. My boy, you've got to last out the game."

"I see, sir."

"Remember there's a bigger thing than yourself you're fighting for, Stover—it's the school, the old school. Now, when you're on the sidelines don't lose any time; watch your men, find out their tricks, see if they look up or change their footing when they start for an end run. Everything is going to count. Now, come on."

They joined the eleven below and presently, in a compact body, went out and through Memorial and the chapel, where suddenly the field appeared and a great roar went up from the school.

"All ready," said the captain.

They broke into a trot and swept up to the cheering mass. Dink remembered seeing the Tennessee Shad, in his shirt sleeves, frantically leading the school and thinking how funny he looked. Then some one pulled a blanket over him and he was camped among the substitutes, peering out at the gridiron where already the two elevens were sweeping back and forth in vigorous signal drill.

He looked eagerly at the Andover eleven. They were big, rangy fellows and their team worked with a precision and machinelike rush that the red and black team did not have.

"Trouble with us is," said the voice of Fatty Harris, at his elbow, "our team's never gotten together. The fellows would rather slug each other than the enemy."

"Gee, that fellow at tackle is a monster," said Dink, picking out McCarty's opponent.

"Look at Turkey Reiter and the Waladoo Bird," continued Fatty Harris. "Bad blood! And there's Tough McCarty and King Lentz. We're not together, I tell you! We're hanging apart!"

"Lord, will they ever begin!" said Dink, blowing on his hands that had suddenly gone limp and clammy.

"We've won the toss," said another voice. "There's a big wind, we'll take sides."

"Andover's kickoff," said Fatty Harris.

Stover sunk his head in his blanket, waiting for the awful moment to end. Then a whistle piped and he raised his head again. The ball had landed short, into the arms of Butcher Stevens, who plunged ahead for a slight gain and went down under a shock of blue jerseys.

Stover felt the warm blood return; the sinking feeling in the pit of his stomach left him. He felt, amazed, a great calm settling over him, as though he had jumped from out of his own body.

"If Flash Condit can once get loose," he said quietly, "he'll score. They ought to try a dash through tackle before the others warm up. Good!"

As if in obedience to his thought Flash Condit came rushing through the line, between end and tackle, but the Andover left halfback, who was alert, caught him and brought him to the ground after a gain of 10 yards.

"Pretty fast, that chap," thought Dink. "Too bad, Flash was almost clear."

"Who tackled him?" asked Fatty Harris.

"Goodhue," came the answer from somewhere. "They say he runs to the 100 in ten and a fifth."

The next try was not so fortunate, the blue line charged quicker and stopped Cheyenne Baxter without a gain. Charlie DeSoto tried a quarterback run and some one broke through between the Waladoo Bird and Turkey Reiter.

"Not together—not together," said the dismal voice of Fatty Harris.

The signal was given for a punt and the ball lifted in the air went soaring down the field on the force of the wind. It was too long a punt for the ends to cover, and the Andover back with a good start came twisting through the territory of Ned Banks who had been blocked off by his opponent.

"Watch that Andover end, Stover," said Mr. Ware. "Study out his methods."

"All right, sir," said Dink, who had watched no one else.

He waited breathless for the first shock of the Andover attack. It came with a rush, compact and solid, and swept back the Lawrenceville left side for a good 8 yards.

"Good-by!" said Harris in a whisper.

Dink began to whistle, moving down the field, watching the backs. Another machinelike advance and another big gain succeeded.

"They'll wake up," said Dink solemnly to himself. "They'll stop 'em in a minute."

But they did not stop. Rush by rush, irresistibly the blue left their own territory and passed the 45-yard line of Lawrenceville. Then a fumble occurred and the ball went again with the gale far out of danger, over the heads of the Andover backs who had misjudged its treacherous course.

"Lucky we've got the wind," said Dink, calm amid the roaring cheers about him. "Gee, that Andover attack's going to be hard to stop. Banks is beginning to limp."

The blue, after a few quick advances, formed and swept out toward Garry Cockrell's end.

"Three yards lost," said Dink grimly. "They won't try him often. Funny they're not onto Banks. Lord, how they can gain through the center of the line. First down again." Substitute and coach, the frantic school, alumni over from Princeton, kept up a constant storm of shouts and entreaties:

"Oh, get together!"

"Throw 'em back!"

"Hold 'em!"

"First down again!"

"Hold 'em, Lawrenceville!"

"Don't let them carry it 70 yards!"

"Get the jump!"

"There they go again!"

"Ten yards around Banks!"

Stover alone, squatting opposite the line of play, moving as it moved, coldly critical, studied each individuality.

"Funny nervous little tricks that Goodhue's got—blows on his hands—does that mean he takes the ball? No, all a bluff. What's he do when he does take it? Quiet and looks at the ground. When he doesn't take it he tries to pretend he does. I'll tuck that away. He's my man. Seems to switch in just as the interference strikes the end about ten feet beyond tackle, running low—Banks is playing too high; better, perhaps, to run in on 'em now and then before they get started. There's going to be trouble there in a minute. The fellows aren't up on their toes yet—what is the matter, anyhow? Tough's getting boxed right along, he ought to play out further, I should think. Hello, someone fumbled again. Who's got it? Looks like Garry. No, they recovered it themselves—no, they didn't. Lord, what a butter-fingered lot—why doesn't he get it? He has—Charlie DeSoto—clear field—can he make it?—he ought to—where's that Goodhue?—looks like a safe lead; he'll make the 20-yard line at least—yes, fully that, if he doesn't stumble—there's that Goodhue now—someone ought to block him off, good work—

that's it—that makes the touchdown—lucky—very lucky!"

Someone hit him a terrific clap on the shoulder. He looked up in surprise to behold Fatty Harris dancing about like a crazed man. The air seemed all arms, hats were rising like startled coveys of birds. Someone flung his arms around him and hugged him. He flung him off almost indignantly. What were they thinking of—that was only one touchdown—four points—what was that against that blue team and the wind at their backs, too. One touchdown wasn't going to win the game.

"Why do they get so excited?" said Dink Stover to John Stover, watching deliberately the ball soaring between the goalposts; "6–0—they think it's all over. Now's the rub."

Mr. Ware passed near him. He was quiet, too, seeing far ahead.

"Better keep warmed up, Stover," he said.

"Biting his nails, that's a funny trick for a master," thought Dink. "He oughtn't to be nervous. That doesn't do any good."

The shouts of exultation were soon hushed; with the advantage of the wind the game quickly assumed a different complexion. Andover had found the weak end and sent play after play at Banks, driving him back for long advances.

"Take off your sweater," said Mr. Ware.

Dink flung it off, running up and down the sidelines, springing from his toes.

"Why don't they take him out?" he thought angrily, with almost a hatred of the fellow who was fighting it out in vain. "Can't they see it? Ten yards more, oh, Lord! This ends it."

With a final rush the Andover interference swung at Banks, brushed him aside and swept over the remaining 15 yards for the touchdown. A minute later the goal was kicked and the elevens again changed sides. The suddenness with which the score had been tied impressed every one—the school team seemed to have no defense against the well-massed attacks of the opponents.

"Holes as big as a house," said Fatty Harris. "Asleep! They're all asleep!"

Dink, pacing up and down, waited the word from Mr. Ware, rebelling because it did not come.

Again the scrimmage began, a short advance from the loosely-knit school eleven, a long punt with the wind and then a quick, businesslike lineup of the blue team and another rush at the vulnerable end.

"Ten yards more; oh, it's giving it away!" said Fatty Harris.

Stover knelt and tried his shoelaces and rising, tightened his belt.

"I'll be out there in a moment," he said to himself.

Another gain at Banks' end and suddenly from the elevens across the field the figure of the captain rose and waved a signal.

"Go in, Stover," said Mr. Ware.

He ran out across the long stretch to where the players were moving restlessly, their clothes flinging out clouds of steam. Back of him something was roaring, cheering for him, perhaps, hoping against hope.

Then he was in the midst of the contestants, Garry Cockrell's arm about his shoulders, whispering something in his ear about keeping cool, breaking up the interference if he couldn't get his man, following up the play. He went to his position, noticing the sullen expressions of his teammates, angry with the consciousness that they were not doing their best. Then taking his stand beyond Tough McCarty, he saw the Andover quarter and the backs turn and study him curiously. He noticed the halfback nearest him, a stocky, close-cropped, red-haired fellow, with brawny arms under his rolled-up jersey, whose duty it would be to send him rolling on the first rush.

"All ready?" cried the voice of the umpire. "First down."

The whistle blew, the two lines strained opposite each other. Stover knew what the play would be—there was no question of that. Fortunately the last two rushes had carried the play well over to his side—the boundary was only 15 yards away. Dink had thought out quickly what he would do. He crept in closer than an end usually plays and at the snap of the ball rushed straight into the starting interference before it could gather dangerous momentum. The back, seeing him thus drawn in, instinctively swerved wide around his interference, forced slightly back. Before he could turn forward his own speed and the necessity of distancing Stover and Condit drove him out of bounds for a 4-yard loss.

"Second down, 9 yards to go!" came the verdict.

"Rather risky going in like that," said Flash Condit, who backed up his side.

"Wanted to force him out of bounds," said Stover.

"Oh—look out for something between tackle and guard now."

"No—they'll try the other side now to get a clean sweep at me," said Stover.

The red-haired halfback disappeared in the opposite side and, well protected, kept his feet for 5 yards.

"Third down, 4 to gain."

"Now for a kick," said Stover, as the Andover end came out opposite him. "What the deuce am I going to do to this coot to mix him up? He looks more as though he'd like to tackle me than to get past." He looked over and caught a glance from the Andover quarter. "I wonder. Why not a fake kick? They've sized me up for green. I'll play it carefully."

At the play, instead of blocking, he jumped back and to one side, escaping the end who dove at his knees. Then, rushing ahead, he stalled off the half and caught the fullback with a tackle that brought him to his feet, rubbing his side.

"Lawrenceville's ball. Time up for first half."

Dink had not thought of the time. Amazed, he scrambled to his feet, half angry at the interruption, and following the team, went over to the room to be talked to by the captain and the coach.

It was a hangdog crowd that gathered there, quailing under the scornful lashing of Garry Cockrell. He spared no one, he omitted no names. Dink, listening, lowered his eyes, ashamed to look upon the face of the team. One or two cried out:

"Oh, I say, Garry!"

"That's too much!"

"Too much, too much, is it?" cried their captain, walking up and down, striking the flat of his hand with the clenched fist. "By heavens, it's nothing to what they're saying of us out there. They're ashamed of us, one and all! Listen to the cheering if you don't believe it! They'll cheer a losing team, a team that is being driven back foot by foot. There's something glorious in that, but a team that stands up to be pushed over, a team that lies down and quits, a team that hasn't one bit of red fighting blood in it, they won't cheer; they're ashamed of you! Now, I'll tell you what's going to happen to you. You're going to be run down the field for just about four touchdowns. Here's Lentz being tossed around by a fellow that weighs 40 pounds less. Why, he's the joke of the game. McCarty hasn't stopped a play, not one! Waladoo's so easy that they rest up walking through him. But that's not the worst, you're playing wide apart as though there wasn't a man within ten miles of you; not one of you is helping out the other. The only time you've taken the ball from them is when a little shaver comes in and uses his head. Now, you're not going to win this game, but by the Almighty you're going out there and going to hold that Andover team!

You've got the wind against you; you've got everything against you; you've got to fight on your own goal line, not once, but twenty times. But you've got to hold 'em; you're going to make good; you're going to wipe out that disgraceful, cowardly first half! You're going out there to stand those fellows off! You're going to make the school cheer for you again as though they believed in you, as though they were proud of you! You're going to do a bigger thing than beat a weaker team! You're going to fight off defeat and show that, if you can't win, you can't be beaten!"

Mr. Ware, in a professional way, passed from one to another with a word of advice: "Play lower, get the jump—don't be drawn in by a fake plunge—watch Goodhue."

But Dink heard nothing; he sat in his corner, clasping and unclasping his hands, suffering with the moments that separated him from the fray. Then all at once he was back on the field, catching the force of the wind that blew the hair about his temples, hearing the halfhearted welcome that went up from the school.

"Hear that cheer!" said Garry Cockrell bitterly.

From Butcher Stevens' boot the ball went twisting and veering down the field. Stover went down, dodging instinctively, hardly knowing what he did. Then as he started to spring at the runner an interferer from behind flung himself on him and sent him sprawling, but not until one arm had caught and checked his man.

McCarty had stopped the runner, when Dink sprang to his feet, wild with the rage of having missed his tackle.

"Steady!" cried the voice of his captain.

He lined up hurriedly, seeing red. The interference started for him, he flung himself at it blindly and was buried under the body of the red-haired half. Powerless to move, humiliatingly held under the sturdy body, the passion of fighting rose in him again. He tried to throw him off, doubling up his fist, waiting until his arm was free.

"Why, you're easy, kid," said a mocking voice. "We'll come again."

The taunt suddenly chilled him. Without knowing how it happened, he laughed.

"That's the last time you get me, old rooster," he said, in a voice that did not belong to him.

He glanced back. Andover had gained 15 yards.

"That comes from losing my head," he said quietly. "That's over."

It had come, the cold consciousness of which Cockrell had spoken, strange as the second wind that surprises the distressed runner.

"I've got to teach that red-haired coot a lesson," he said. "He's a little too confident. I'll shake him up a bit."

The opportunity came on the third play, with another attack on his end. He ran forward a few steps and stood still, leaning a little forward, waiting for the red-haired back who came plunging at him. Suddenly Dink dropped to his knees, the interferer went violently over his back, something struck Stover in the shoulder and his arms closed with the fierce thrill of holding his man.

"Second down, 7 yards to gain," came the welcome sound.

Time was taken out for the red-haired halfback, who had had the wind knocked out of him.

"Now he'll be more respectful," said Dink, and as soon as he caught his eye he grinned. "Red hair—I'll see if I can't get his temper."

Thus checked, and to use the advantage of the wind, Andover elected to kick. The ball went twisting, and, changing its course in the strengthening wind, escaped the clutches of Macnooder and went bounding toward the goal where Charlie DeSoto saved it on the 25-yard line. In an instant the overwhelming disparity of the sides was apparent.

A return kick at best could gain but 25 or 30 yards. From now on they would be on the defensive.

Dink came in to support his traditional enemy, Tough McCarty. The quick, nervous voice of Charlie DeSoto rose in a shriek: "Now, Lawrenceville, get into this, 7–52–3."

Dink swept around for a smash on the opposite tackle, head down, eyes fastened on the back before him, feeling the shock of resistance and the yielding response as he thrust forward, pushing, heaving on, until everything piled up before him. Four yards gained.

A second time they repeated the play, making the first down.

"Time to spring a quick one through us," he thought.

But again DeSoto elected the same play.

"What's he trying to do?" said Dink. "Why doesn't he vary it?"

Someone hauled him out of the tangled pile. It was Tough McCarty.

"Say, our tackle's a stiff one," he said, with his mouth to Stover's ear. "You take his knees; I'll take him above this time."

Their signal came at last. Dink dove, trying to meet the shifting knees and throw him off his balance. The next moment a powerful arm caught him as he left the ground and swept him aside.

"Only a yard," said McCarty. "He got through and smeared the play."

"I know how to get him next time," said Dink.

The play was repeated. This time Stover made a feint and then dove successfully after the big arm had swept fruitlessly past. Flash Condit, darting through the line, was tackled by Goodhue and fell forward for a gain.

"How much?" said Stover, rising joyfully.

"They're measuring."

The distance was tried and found to be 2 feet short of the necessary 5 yards. The risk was too great, a kick was signaled and the ball was Andover's, just inside the center of the field.

"Now, Lawrenceville," cried the captain, "show what you're made of."

The test came quickly, a plunge between McCarty and Lentz yielded 3 yards, a second 4. The Andover attack, with the same precision as before, struck anywhere between the tackles and found holes. Dink, at the bottom of almost every pile, raged at Tough McCarty.

"He's doing nothing, he isn't fighting," he said angrily. "He doesn't know what it is to fight. Why doesn't he break up that interference for me?"

When the attack struck his end now it turned in, slicing off tackle, the runner well screened by close interference that held him up when Stover tackled, dragging him on for the precious yards. Three and four yards at a time, the blue advance rolled its way irresistibly toward the red and black goal. They were inside the 20-yard line now.

Cockrell was pleading with them. Little Charlie DeSoto was running along the line, slapping their backs, calling frantically on them to throw the blue back.

And gradually the line did stiffen, slowly but perceptibly the advance was cut down. Enmities were forgotten with the shadow of the goalposts looming at their backs. Waladoo and Turkey Reiter were fighting side by side, calling to each other. Tough McCarty was hauling Stover out of desperate scrimmages, patting him on the back and calling him "good old Dink." The fighting blood that Garry Cockrell had called upon was at last there—the line had closed and fought together.

And yet they were borne back to their 15-yard line, 2 yards at a time, just losing the fourth down.

Stover at end was trembling like a blooded terrier, on edge for each play, shrieking:

"Oh, Tough, get through—you must get through!"

He was playing by intuition now, no time to plan. He knew just who had the ball and where it was going. Out or in, the attack was concentrating on his end—only McCarty and he could stop it. He was getting his man, but they were dragging him on, fighting now for inches.

"Third down, 1 yard to gain!"

"Watch my end," he shouted to Flash Condit, and hurling himself forward at the starting backs, dove under the knees, and grabbing the legs about him, went down buried under the mass he had upset.

It seemed hours before the crushing bodies were pulled off and someone's arm brought him to his feet and someone hugged him, shouting in his ear:

"You saved it, Dink, you saved it!"

Someone rushed up with a sponge and began dabbing his face.

"What the deuce are they doing that for?" he said angrily.

Then he noticed that an arm was under his and he turned curiously to the face near him. It was Tough McCarty's.

"Whose ball is it?" he said.

"Ours."

He looked to the other side. Garry Cockrell was supporting him.

"What's the matter?" he said, trying to draw his head away from the sponge that was dripping water down his throat.

"Just a little wind knocked out, youngster—coming to?"

"I'm all right."

He walked a few steps along and then took his place. Things were in a daze on the horizon, but not there in the field. Everything else was shut out except his duty there.

Charlie DeSoto's voice rose shrill:

"Now, Lawrenceville, up the field with it. This team's just begun to play. We've got together, boys. Let her rip!"

No longer scattered, but a unit, all differences forgot, fighting for the same idea, the team rose up and crashed through the Andover line, every man in the play, 10—15 yards ahead.

"Again!" came the strident cry.

Without a pause the line sprang into place, formed and swept forward. It was a privilege to be in such a game, to feel the common frenzy, the awakened glance of battle that showed down the line. Dink, side by side with Tough McCarty, thrilled with the same thrill, plunging ahead with the same motion, fighting the same fight; no longer alone and desperate, but nerved with the consciousness of a partner whose gameness matched his own.

For 30 yards they carried the ball down the field, before the stronger Andover team, thrown off its feet by the unexpected frenzy, could rally and stand them off. Then an exchange of punts once more drove them back to their 25-yard line.

A second time the Andover advance set out from the 50-yard line and slowly fought its way to surrender the ball in the shadow of the goal-posts.

Stover played on in a daze, remembering nothing of the confused shock of bodies that had gone before, wondering how much longer he could hold out—to last out the game as the captain had told him. He was groggy, from time to time he felt the sponge's cold touch on his face or heard the voice of Tough McCarty in his ear.

"Good old Dink, die game!"

How he loved McCarty fighting there by his side, whispering to him:

"You and I, Dink! What if he is an old elephant, we'll put him out of the play."

Still, flesh and blood could not last forever. The half must be nearly up.

"Two minutes more time."

"What was that?" he said. groggily to Flash Condit.

"Two minutes more. Hold 'em now!"

It was Andover's ball. He glanced around. They were down near the 25-yard line somewhere. He looked at Tough McCarty, whose frantic head showed against the sky.

"Break it up, Tough," he said, and struggled toward him.

A cry went up, the play was halted.

"He's groggy," he heard voices say, and then came the welcome splash of the sponge.

Slowly his vision cleared to the anxious faces around him.

"Can you last?" said the captain.

"I'm all right," he said gruffly.

"Things cleared up now?"

"Fine!"

McCarty put his arm about him and walked with him.

"Oh, Dink, you will last, won't you?"

"You bet I will, Tough!"

"It's the last stand, old boy!"

"The last."

"Only two minutes more we've got to hold 'em! The last ditch, Dink."

"I'll last."

He looked up and saw the school crouching along the line—tense drawn faces. For the first time he realized they were there, calling on him to stand steadfast.

He went back, meeting the rush that came his way, half-knocked aside, half-getting his man, dragged again until assistance came. De-Soto's stinging hand slapped his back and the sting was good, clearing his brain.

Things came into clear outline once more. He saw down the line and to the end where Garry Cockrell stood.

"Good old captain," he said. "They'll not get by me, not now."

He was in every play it seemed to him, wondering why Andover was always keeping the ball, always coming at his end. Suddenly he had a shock. Over his shoulder were the goalposts, the line he stood on was the line of his own goal.

He gave a hoarse cry and went forward like a madman, parting the interference. Some one else was through; Tough was through; the whole line was through flinging back the runner. He went down clinging to Goodhue, buried under a mass of his own tacklers. Then, through the frenzy, he heard the shrill call of time.

He struggled to his feet. The ball lay scarcely 4 yards away from the glorious goalposts. Then, before the school could sweep them up, panting, exhausted, they gathered in a circle with incredulous, delirious faces, and leaning heavily, wearily on one another gave the cheer for Andover. And the touch of Stover's arm on McCarty's shoulder was like an embrace.

'Hello, Mr. Campbell? Chuck Oakley here. Remember that time you told me
if I ever felt like giving up coaching, you'd always have a place for me
in your company? Well...'

CARTOON BY STEVENSON

Occasionally a single play is so closely identified with a victory that it acquires a reputation of its own. Such a play was KF79, one of the spinner series developed by Lou Little for his single-wing teams at Columbia. KF79 was the play used by Columbia to score its winning touchdown against heavily favored Stanford in the 1934 Rose Bowl game.

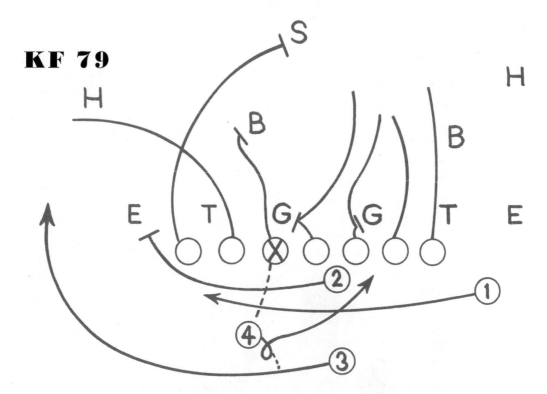

KF 79

By way of explanation: The left halfback (4) receives the ball by direct pass from center as he starts a full spin. He either gives the ball to the fullback (3) who goes by him on a wide end run maneuver, or he fakes handing off to the fullback and completes his full spin with the ball. He may then hand the ball to the right halfback (1), who crosses by him on a reverse run maneuver; or he may fake handing off to the right halfback, keep the ball himself and continue into the line or even fade back for a forward pass. Thus there are four variations

from the same basic play. The blocking changes on each variation. The quarterback (2) must hit the right defensive end with a convincing block from the inside, making him believe the play is coming to the inside and drawing his attention away from the fullback with the ball.

As diagrammed above, KF79 scored the only touchdown in the '34 Rose Bowl game when Cliff Montgomery (4) gave the ball to Al Barabas (3) on the first half of his spin. The deception and blocking were so good that Barabas ran 17 yards untouched for the touchdown.

162

As the erudite sports columnist of the New York Times, *John Kieran occasionally
turned to rhymes about nonscholarly endeavors.*

WHEN THE GUARDS CAME THROUGH

John Kieran

The close of a rainy day;
The edge of a rainy night;
And we at the end of a bruising fray
With a victory in sight.

We huddled and got the call;
The quarterback gave it quick;
And I was to hold the ball,
And Jim was to make the kick.
Down I crouched in my place,
And the pass was fair and true;
But I was flat on my frozen face
And I was just a hospital case
When the guards came through!

Wet to our weary knees,
Mud to our blinking eyes,
Shivering lest we freeze,
Still we could hear the cries:
"Win for the Gold and Blue!"
That's what we tried to do!
But the wickedest crime of modern time
Was the way I was smothered in choking slime
When the guards came through!

Ho! One came in with a crash,
A blundering human tank!
Hi! One came in with a dash,
A touch of swagger and swank,
An air of How-d'ya-do!
And Fancy-meeting-you!
And what became of the bally ball I never really knew,
For the world was ended and I was dead;
They broke my heart and they broke my head
When the guards came through!

Diagrammed and described below is a bit of chicanery by Minnesota that caused a furor in the Big Ten in 1941. The "play," although frowned upon by paid coaches as poor ethics, is still a favorite with sandlot teams and with middle-aging fathers forced to play touch against their sons.

THE "TALKING" PLAY

Al Laney

The most controversial play of the football season, the game-winning play for Minnesota over Northwestern November 1, 1941, and declared to be illegal by Lynn Waldorf, Northwestern coach, who did not see it, is diagrammed on this page. It is reproduced partly from visual memory and partly from the replies to questions asked in the Minnesota dressing room after the game. Infallibility is not claimed, but the diagram is believed to be correct.

This observer, seated in the press box, must confess to being caught napping, as were eleven Northwestern players and 64,464 customers. He looked up from charting the preceding play at the exact moment that Gene Flick, the Minnesota center, scooped up the ball and threw it to Bud Higgins, who ran 41 yards for a touchdown that won the game, 8–7.

A picture of the alignment of the Minnesota players at the moment is clear and vivid still. The positions of the Northwestern men are guesswork, but approximately correct. What happened immediately after the play was set in motion is not vouched for as exact, since twenty-two men were moving rapidly, but it, too, is advanced as approximately correct.

Northwestern, with a touchdown, was leading Minnesota, 7–2, in the third period and

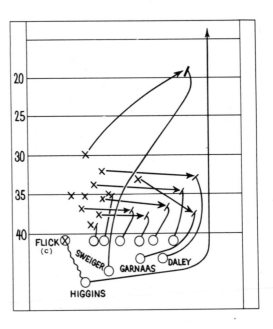

looked the probable winner. A safety had given Minnesota two points in the first period. Northwestern had stopped the Gopher power, the running attack, and appeared likely to collect the substantial reward which that stupendous feat justifies. Minnesota, because of injuries, had been using a backfield composed of two fullbacks and two quarterbacks most of the time and was vulnerable to Otto Graham's passes.

The trick play was set up when Bill DeCorrevant's punt from his own 33, half blocked, rolled out of bounds on the Northwestern 41. On first down, Bob Sweiger, Minnesota fullback, took the ball on a reverse and ran toward the left sideline. He went to his knee just inside. It was essential that time remain in. John Getchell, the referee, returned the ball 15 yards in from the sideline.

Minnesota did not huddle. The linemen casually advanced to the scrimmage line, six of them beyond the ball toward midfield. They stood straight up and assumed listless attitudes. The backs, Higgins, Garnaas, Sweiger and Daley, strolled to their positions in right formation with Higgins as tailback about a yard to the midfield side of the ball.

Sweiger, so the Northwestern players reported, afterward, added to the deception by talking to one of his opponents. Flick, the center, the last to come in from the sideline, also was talking to an opponent as he strolled up. The Northwestern players were standing around waiting to take their defensive positions.

Flick stood to the left of the ball. He did not straddle it. All Minnesota players just stood for a moment, presumably to make the play legal. Suddenly Flick scooped the ball from the ground, turned and threw it to Higgins, who was already in motion. Ten Gophers charged down and to the right and began to block all opponents who came within range.

Higgins turned the flank almost before Northwestern linemen knew the ball was in play. Sweiger, the eleventh Gopher, charged straight down the field, cut to the right and picked up Higgins at about the 20. He had run a shorter distance and was there in time to block the only Northwestern player who had a chance of stopping Higgins short of the end zone. It was the key block. Without it Higgins would have been knocked out of bounds at about the 15.

Waldorf, who admitted he did not see the play because he was looking elsewhere at the time, based his contention of illegality on statements of his observers in the press box who were of the opinion that Minnesota's players did not come to a second's halt before the play started. We wouldn't know about this, but we presume the play to be legal because Getchell, the referee, had had it explained to him before the game and had been told by Garnaas, the Minnesota quarterback, that it was about to be used.

Garnaas told Getchell before the preceding play that the trick was coming up two plays hence. The official judged it to be perfectly legal. On this point, the rule says:

"In all shift or huddle plays, all (eleven) players of the team in possession of the ball must come to an absolute stop and must remain stationary in their positions, without movement of the feet or swaying of the body, head or arms, for a period of at least one second *before the ball is put in play*."

HOW TO WATCH FOOTBALL

John Lardner

The late John Lardner wrote this on the eve of a football season in the 1940s and like most things he wrote, it has lasting humor and pertinence.

This is going to be the most intelligent football season of all time. You have probably seen it coming. For purposes of illustration, we will take a couple of characters named "He" and "She." I would like to add at this point that those are not the real names, and that any resemblance to persons living or dead is just a hellish coincidence.

Modishly dressed in a coonskin coat and a flask of gin, the male football spectator steers his companion out of the vast stadium after the game. The year is 1929, and the conversation runs as follows:

She—"Who won the game?"

He—"What game?"

We now shift the scene to the year 1947. Our characters leave the ball game again with pure intelligence shining through their bifocaled eyes, discoursing as follows:

She—"I thought the key of the play was the double-spinner, line overshifted, defense 5–3–2–1, when the wingback mousetrapped the defensive guard and the 3 back applied that downfield block to Haggerty."

He—"You appear to have overlooked the hip block and the blind-angle block which took out the wing and the end in the left zone of fairly intense resistance while the running guard screened the shovel pass and the center set up the opening in the right flat zone with the holding block which nullified Scabinski."

She—"You said it!"

This love passage, as poignant as anything in *Romeo and Juliet,* is reproduced here merely to show you that the customers are on their toes these days, and, unless the coaches come back strongly with sixteen or eighteen fresh moves, the fans are apt to begin to understand what the game is all about.

The coaches are hard at work. Richard Cresson Harlow of Harvard thought up three new blind-angle blocks while plundering a duck's nest in the Everglades, and Red Blaik of Army has evolved a play where the ball is handled by six different men while the unbalanced wingback makes change for a $20 bill to confuse the defensive end.

Harry Stuhldreher of Wisconsin is thinking of borrowing the business double from bridge and introducing it into his offense, while Frank Leahy of Notre Dame has invented a pass play which baffles himself, though he claims to have the answer on the tip of his tongue. Incidentally, Leahy will keep the tip of his tongue farther back and a little more to the left this season.

Naturally, not even the smartest fan is going to follow all this strategy from start to finish. For those who would like to be somewhere in what we experts call "the know," however, our secretary has compiled a brief glossary of terms, plays, maneuvers which will be popular this year. The coaches have been good enough to take me into their confidence, and I can't get out. All exits are barred by wolfhounds. Here we go:

BLIND-ANGLE BLOCK A block applied from such an angle that the victim does not see it coming. Many blockers use trickery to perfect this play, disguising themselves with blue glasses and whiskers and pretending to be working their way through college.

CONGESTED BLOCK Any city block containing 5,000 or more residents. The Department of Sanitation should watch out for this.

AUCTION BLOCK An old-fashioned block, which has now been replaced in most circles by contract block.

SCREENED PASS A device to keep mosquitoes from rushing the passer.

FLAT ZONE Speaks for itself.

LEFT FLAT ZONE See Flat Zone.

RIGHT FLAT ZONE See Left Flat Zone.

THREE-TWO-ONE DEFENSE A defense employed by clever lawyers in murder cases. Successor of the Unwritten Law.

OVERSHIFT A loose garment worn by Ukrainian peasants.

MOUSETRAP A cunning offensive device, in which the defender is permitted to charge through the line and then is clipped. Sometimes alternated with the Malay Death Trap, in which a pit is dug behind the line and carefully concealed with twigs and loose grass.

The time was when everybody played Notre Dame football. The time is now when practically everybody plays T-formation football. But they do not play the original T-formation football, which goes back to the Nineteenth Century. They play split T, QT, and inverted T. The need for freezing is imperative. A Mr. Clark Shaughnessy, the modern father of T football, had no sooner given me a set of diagrams to study for homework than five variations of his formula broke out, including two new ones of his own. The time I wasted might have been better spent investigating conditions among the starving faro dealers of Passaic, N.J.

This is a perennial evil in football.

Take the Notre Dame system. Like the Roman Empire in its late period, the proud old name covered a multitude of dissensions and cleavages and cracks in the woodwork. I recall the remarks of Mr. James Conzelman, the more or less outspoken coach of Chicago's professional Cardinals, in re Notre Dame football a few years ago.

"To begin with," said Mr. Conzelman, "this talk of single-wings and double-wings perplexes me. I don't know much about it. I just play Notre Dame football, and I don't know much about that.

"I saw a game the other day between a couple of college football teams that are said to play Notre Dame football. I didn't recognize it. For that matter, I don't think Rockne would have recognized it. A lot of strange things are transpiring under the name of Notre Dame football.

"My pro team, playing the only kind of Notre Dame football I understand, which may not be Notre Dame football either, manages to lose as regularly as the next fellows, and as long as my boys rush around the field asking the Chicago Bears for their autographs when we play them, I know they are interested in football, so why worry?"

I have my own opinion of why Mr. Conzelman adopted Notre Dame football, or what he thought was Notre Dame football, in the first place. There was a bond between him and the late Knute Rockne. Mr. Conzelman, aside from being a writer, scientist, orator, and dude, is a musician. So was Rockne. As a youth the great man performed relentlessly upon the flute. Accompanied by Mr. Owen Murphy, another Notre Dame scholar and later a writer of songs for Joe Cook, Mr. Rockne tootled *con brio* to the strains of "All That I Ask of You Is Love," which deposes, in part:

All that I seek to know,
All that I want above,
All that I crave
In this wide, wide world,
All that I ask of you is love.*

If I did not honor the master for these sentiments, I wouldn't bring it up.

You will observe that Notre Dame got out from under the old system just before it crumbled entirely. The fact that her coach, Mr. Frank Leahy, himself a South Bender, ordered T football into operation at the mother temple would seem to indicate that the Code Shaughnessy—the T, in short—could rule supreme for generations. In other forms of endeavor, a given culture is sometimes good for a couple of centuries.

But not in football. Half a dozen coaches are up to new devilment with XT's, KT's, JT's, and —all right, Mr. Bones, it's coming—DT's. They won't let well enough alone. It will be a judgment on them if some day the game is played exclusively on tablecloths with pencils, and all those good green gridirons are given back to the Indians.

O'DEA OF WISCONSIN

Bill Leiser

They said he had moved on to the next world —this man who crashed through with football records never surpassed or equaled in the gridiron history of America and then vanished as completely and mysteriously as Aladdin's Geni.

It was suggested in the *Literary Digest* of March that he must be resting in the unknown soldier's grave.

But Patrick John O'Dea, football's long lost immortal, is very much alive.

Out of the past he came smiling to sit across the dinner table last night. I could hardly believe it. This man, who once punted the length of the field in the air, this greatest dropkicker and placement-kicker the world ever knew, this man who did Red Grange runs as a mere sideline to a more spectacular game.

They said I would never meet him. Of him the *Literary Digest,* March 17, reported: "In 1917 when the Australian army was passing through San Francisco, where he was practicing law, (he) joined the Anzacs without informing even his brother, thus leaving the country as unostentatiously as he came. He has not been heard of since. And (his brother) is certain he is an unknown soldier."

He was the man who could curve a long punted football as a pitcher curves his throws. He could punt 85 yards against your "great" 60-yarders today. The record says he once lifted the football 110 yards in the wind. In an impossible 20-mile cross-field gale he place-kicked half the length of the gridiron, straight through the bars. He once sidestepped Gil Dobie on the run to drop-kick 55 yards for a score. There has been no one like him, before or since, in the game.

And he was supposed to have moved on.

Yet there he sat grinning across the table last night, as healthy a specimen as I have seen in my time. He didn't go to war. He didn't disappear into thin air. He merely took up new work in his own way. And, up in Westwood, off in the northeast corner of California they will be surprised to learn this morning that the Red River statistician they have known for fifteen years as Charles J. Mitchell is actually the long lost Pat O'Dea, one of the greatest athletes of all time.

Everyone who understands anything at all of the history of football knows of Pat O'Dea, the Australian, who came to America in 1896 and, for four years on the University of Wisconsin varsity, displayed a ravishing, kicking, smothering type of football that America never knew before and may never know again.

169

What's in the record books alone will keep his name alive as long as the game is played. There were heroes, great ones, before 1896, and there have been heroes of the gridiron since 1900, but, to those who saw Midwest football at the end of the last century, the names of Jim Thorpe and Red Grange, even, mean little alongside of Wisconsin's Pat O'Dea.

It was his fame that drove him out of sight. He was in San Francisco, in 1917, well known, too well known, perhaps, everywhere. Always he had to talk football. Always he was helping athletes—he even helped the Stanford crew of 1914. But always he was the man who had been great on the football field, and almost never the man who could talk of new work to be done. He didn't like living in what were to him "mere student days of the past."

With the war, his income from the home land was knocked down to nothing. He had an opportunity to start in a new field, off where no one knew him—off where he could be just himself and not the man who had kicked footballs for Wisconsin, so off he went to become Charles J. Mitchell of the Red River Lumber Company of Westwood, and he has been there ever since.

No one knew him there. He simply moved in as a stranger. For fifteen years now, Charles J. Mitchell, a secretary-manager of the Westwood Auto Club (and Chamber of Commerce), a director of the Lassen Volcanic Park Association, a leader in the fight for good new roads that are being obtained, and roads open in winter, in that beautiful section, and a statistician for Red River lumber, has been the kind of fighting, astute, well-liked progressive citizen that makes small towns into bigger cities.

"Probably I was wrong," says the very live and smiling Pat. "Mrs. Mitchell, that is, Mrs. O'Dea, always thought I was. But I wanted to get away from what seemed to me to be all in the past. As Pat O'Dea, I seemed very much just an ex-Wisconsin football player.

"I was very happy as Mitchell for a while. Mitchell was my mother's name and Charley that of a cousin I like. Later, I often found it rather unpleasant not to be the man I actually am. So, if you want to write that I'm going to be Pat O'Dea again, for the rest of my life, write it.

"Perhaps I should never have been anything else."

So there he is, his old identity as one of the biggest of all athletes buried behind a fifteen-year-old Charles Mitchell off among 5000 citizens of Westwood, now come back to life again.

He's the kind of man who, perhaps as you and I, simply can't force a real smile before a camera, but what a swell smile he has. And what a stimulating person with whom to talk. And how he can tell you about football.

And what a life he has had, and is still having.

Almost cut down by sharks, as a boy, when he saved a young girl from drowning.

Transferred from the "polite" Australian game to the rough American football of the nineties, he adapted himself to become the most spectacular and greatest star of his time.

Almost burned to death, in hot water, with his athletic career barely through.

Then driven by fame to comparative obscurity, and vanishing with a world believing him in an unknown soldier's grave and now coming back as the old Pat O'Dea.

But first, about that football. You don't have to ask him to learn what he did in football. The record books show a Pat O'Dea who outdid Red Grange before Red Grange was born.

Let me pick, here and there, from the old clips, just to give an idea of who was Pat O'Dea.

Against Pop Warner's champion Carlisle Indians, 1896, postseason, a night game, and Pat O'Dea's debut. He sent a 50-yard "punted forward pass" to Judge Ike Carroll who, from an "onside" start, was eligible to and able to fall on the ball at the goal and roll over for the score. The Indians, who never saw the football because it went high over the girders holding the lights, refused to believe what had happened.

Against Minnesota, 1897, his first game against the team that had been treating Wisconsin badly. Got cornered, let the ball loose on the run and drop-kicked 40 yards through the bars. Dad Moulton, later a Stanford track coach, then a trainer, dropped his water bucket in amazement on the side line. A flabbergasted Minnesota team, from that moment on, was kicked to death, 39–0.

Against Chicago, a "championship game," dropped over two 40-yard field goals and punted Chicago to submission, 28–0, much as Joe Paglia punted California into helplessness last year.

Against Beloit, 1897, a game that was tough, but one in which O'Dea was supposed to make the team do the work. Team couldn't do it, so O'Dea dropped over two drop kicks, only to get a bawling out from Coach Phil King. (Score, 10–0, field goals counting 5 points each in those days.)

Against Northwestern, 1898, a team supposed to whale the tar out of Wisconsin. O'Dea played with famous "kindergarten" team of those days, which included only one veteran besides Pat. O'Dea had disagreement with alumni representatives, who wanted to bring in more help. Said to have been nettled going into game. Ran two plays, dropped back, took two steps, and let the old drop go 63 yards through the bars, the world record. The ball went over the tops of the uprights, and 20 yards on to hit the fence surrounding the field. The game at the finish, 48–0!

Against Beloit, 1899, opening game, and supposed to be mean. O'Dea kicked four field goals and returned a kickoff 90 yards to the goal.

Against Illinois, 1899, another tough one. Twenty-mile gale blowing across the field. Back on his 55-yard stripe, O'Dea prepared for a place-kick.

"What are you doing?" asked the referee. (It was after a fair catch.)

"What do you think?" asked O'Dea.

"I think you're crazy, if you're trying to score in this wind."

Bill Juneau held the ball. Pat lined up so as to kick almost for the righthand corner of the field. One step and he kicked, with the crowd spellbound. The football sailed directly for the corner for a time, then finally, as the wind caught it, it swerved back to the left, and floated smack through the middle of the uprights on the goal line, 55 yards away—the most impossible stunt ever performed.

Against Yale, 1899, lost 6–0. Asked why Wisconsin lost, O'Dea said because he had missed his man, Richardson of Yale, who made the only score on a long run. Press of the day said two greatest sportsmen of all time were Sir Tom Lipton and Pat O'Dea, men who could take it when they lost. Press alto talked of O'Dea's "Best punting ever seen," and weeks later reported information that O'Dea's center, with an arm in a cast, couldn't pass the ball back 10 yards that day—and also that O'Dea played the game with a broken bone which pierced the skin of a finger on his right hand when he "missed his man."

Against Michigan, 1899, with press commenting freely on proposition that Michigan must stop O'Dea. O'Dea gave them a 35-yard drop-kick score to start with, and a long curve punt, which the Michigan safety dropped, allowing Wisconsin man to pick up for touchdown, all in first half. Later, O'Dea was forced out of the only college game in which he did not play the full sixty minutes. Michigan center, as quoted in the old clips, said, "We could have won if we had gotten O'Dea out sooner."

Against Minnesota, 1899. Two plays, then O'Dea carrying the ball. O'Dea cornered by none other than Gil Dobie. O'Dea bluffed a run and Dobie prepared to block, and O'Dea, sidestepping, drop-kicked over Dobie, 55 yards through the air, through the bars.

That's just a part of it. But you get the idea.

Once, in a tight spot, his little halfback, Paul Trat, had the ball and was in a tangle when a score was needed. O'Dea picked Trat up out of the jam and carried Trat, football and all, over the goal. No, he wasn't so big. A little over 6 feet, weight 170 pounds.

Why, O'Dea was supposed to have signals with his ends. He would inform the ends of which way the punted ball would curve after it started down the field. The ends, therefore, had that much advantage on the safety man, who didn't have the information.

I asked Pat O'Dea if it were true that a punted football could be curved?

"Certainly," he answered. He explained how. But I couldn't repeat in detail.

Oh, yes, O'Dea was a hurdle champ, a crack sprinter and a crew stroke besides. But I haven't space for that.

As for punting, 75 yards was a cinch for him, any time. He sent the ball just high enough to allow ends to get under it. If his first punt went too far for the ends, the next went much higher. He gave them all they could take, though they never could take all he could give.

Therefore, often, he punted for the goal line, and if the ball went over, in those days, the rival team had to kick off in return from its 25-yard line. That would be a signal for a Wisconsin fair catch, and an O'Dea dropkick for points if points were in demand.

That is, if I read my old prints correctly.

I asked Pat if youngsters today could be taught to curve punts either way.

"Surely," he answered.

"I coached at Notre Dame just after I left Wisconsin. Red Salmon learned quickly. He was examined frequently by rivals, who sometimes insisted that it was really I who was in the game kicking. He had red hair and some tried to tear it off, thinking to expose O'Dea with a wig. He kicked as well as I could."

Yet Mr. Pat O'Dea believes that it would be entirely possible to teach a half dozen youngsters on each squad to kick as well as he did, or at least, nearly as well.

He learned, you see, in the Australian game, in which they punt forward passes as well as Americans throw them.

He has had a most unusual life.

He was almost cut to pieces by sharks, when

he saved a young girl from drowning, when he was 16 years old, at Fort Phillip Bay in Australia. (He has the Royal Humane Society certificate for that.)

He almost burned to death of hot water when he once stunned his head in a bath tub. For days there was doubt and once reporters were waiting in the hall for the last word from the doctor. "What are they there for?" asked the deathly sick O'Dea.

"To learn when you're going."

"Go out and make them a bet that they're wasting their time," said Pat. They were.

And now, because of disappearance, he has been suggested as an unknown soldier.

His disappearance was natural enough. Almost every other man who has enjoyed tremendous fame has felt the urge, at times, to get away from it. Pat O'Dea did.

It wasn't exactly the "usual" thing. But there never has been anything usual about Pat O'Dea since, as a boy, he played on amateur Australian game teams before 100,000 persons.

Many in San Francisco will know him, and he'll be seeing them again. Frank Guerena, little coxswain of Stanford's old crew, will know him, for O'Dea helped that crew a great deal.

Former Columbia Park boys will know Pat because, twenty-five years ago, when they wanted to go to Australia, he taught them the Australian kicking game, and they went, and split even on their tour.

Fifteen years ago fame drove him away, and changed his name.

Now he's back, Patrick John O'Dea, no longer football's long lost immortal, but a very vigorous, pleasant, smart young fellow, fifty-five years old, who has new work to be done and who's going to be his old self from here on out while he does it.

The most celebrated offensive combination in modern football was Army's left halfback, Glenn Davis (41), and fullback, Doc Blanchard (35), who played during the years right after World War II. Since Blanchard remained in the service and did not turn pro, and Davis played pro with a crippled knee, it is difficult to measure them against the all-time great runners. But as revealed by this story of their careers at West Point, when they played together they were a caution.

MR. INSIDE AND MR. OUTSIDE

Ed Linn

Looking back across the years, it seems as if the marriage of Doc Blanchard and Glenn Davis must have been made in heaven. The fact is, however, it took a little luck and a lot of war to bring them together. Both made the West Point Class of 1947 the hard way. Glenn came to West Point, originally, in the Class of 1946; Doc started his college career in the University of North Carolina's Class of 1945.

George Trevor of the old New York *Sun* first called them Mr. Inside and Mr. Outside, but they were much more than that. It was not simply a case of a powerful man and a fast man complementing each other; Davis and Blanchard were each complete football players in their own right. Mr. Inside had the speed to hit the ends. A big gainer was a play in which the ball was snapped directly back to Davis, who whipped it out to Blanchard on the flank. Doc did all of Army's kicking-off and punting, and it was a rare kickoff that didn't go into the end zone. Occasionally, he even booted the ball between the goal posts. And when an opposing back did get the chance to run it back, he usually found Doc down there to make the tackle. As a tackler and blocker, he was unmatched in his time. On a team that boasted pass receivers like Davis, Hank Foldberg and Barney Poole, Blanchard was probably the most spectacular receiver of all. He had a remarkable ability to leap up between defenders and grab the ball with one big hand. As pass defenders, Doc and Glenn were both among the very best in the country.

It is a mistake to think of Glenn as a scat back. He could hit inside with surprising power, and, on his broken-field runs, he not only side-stepped hopeful tacklers, he had a wonderful ability to shake them off his hips and shoulders. He could kick, and he was excellent as a passer and a pass receiver. Davis was a good man in all phases of defense and something most people forget, he was a fine blocker. When he joined the Los Angeles Rams after his discharge from the Army, coach Joe Stydahar was amazed to find that Glenn was the best blocker on the whole Ram squad.

"Glenn Davis," coach Red Blaik of Army says today, "could do anything you asked him to do and he could do it better than almost anybody else."

He could indeed. All cadets must take a ten-event physical efficiency test. The record, before Davis took it, was 901½ out of a possible 1,000 points. Glenn's score was 962½.

Glenn could have been one of the country's top sprinters if he hadn't preferred basketball during the winter and baseball in the summer. He wasn't much of a basketball player, but he was an excellent baseball prospect. He covered all the ground in center field and he had a powerful throwing arm. At bat he was shy on power, but he hit around .400 and got a lot of leg doubles. In his entire career at the Academy, he was thrown out stealing only once. The Brooklyn Dodgers trained in the West Point field house during Glenn's plebe year, and Army played both the varsity, such as it was in the war years, and the Montreal farmhands. In one game against Montreal, Glenn beat out a bunt, stole second, stole third, and stole home. Branch Rickey kept an eye on him throughout his college career. After the Army-Duke game in 1946, Rickey drove Glenn back to West Point. "This is my offer," he said, as they cleared the Durham, N.C., city limits. "I'll hand you a blank Dodger contract tomorrow and you can fill in whatever amount you feel is fair."

Glenn rarely competed in track meets—and never practiced—and yet he once went down to Madison Square Garden and beat Ed Conwell over 60 yards. In his final year, he was asked to run against Navy, not the easiest thing to arrange since the ball team was playing Navy the same afternoon. A staff car was assigned to sit behind the screen and pick Glenn up as soon as the game ended; Glenn changed into his track suit en route. The 100-yard men had already been called when the car pulled up. Glenn took a few warm-up sprints, got on his mark and tied the West Point record at 9.7. He then ran the 220 and set a new record at 20.9.

Blanchard went out for track during the spring to keep in shape. He had fooled around with the shot a little in prep school, but he could only get it out about 30 feet when he started. Ralph Davis, Glenn's twin brother and the best shot-putter on the squad, took Doc in hand. In a month he was doing better than 40 feet. Two months later, he won the IC4A Indoor Championship with a heave of 48 feet 3½ inches. In the first of a pair of meets with Navy, he got it up to 49 feet 5 inches, but was just barely beaten by Ralph Davis. In the second meet, he set a West Point record at 51 feet 10¾ inches to beat Davis, who got out over 50 feet himself. And in those days you could count all the 50-foot shot-putters in the world on your fingers. Doc is still without doubt the only shot-putter ever to reach 50 feet in his first season.

Doc did a little sprinting at first, too. "I tried the 100," he will say, if asked, "but I didn't do anything." Actually, he won a Heptagonal meet in 10.3.

Although Glenn and Doc were born only fifteen days apart, it would have been hard for them to have been born farther apart and still remain in the country. Glenn Woodward Davis was born in Claremont, California, not far from Los Angeles. Felix Anthony Blanchard Jr. was born in Bishopville, South Carolina. Mr. Davis, a bank manager, didn't press his twin boys to become athletes; Mr. Blanchard Sr., a country doctor, put a football in Little Doc's crib when he was one day old and set out to make him an even better football player than the old man had been. And the old man had been quite a football player. Felix Blanchard, a 240-pounder with tremendous speed, had played for Clark Shaughnessy at Tulane. When Felix got mad, Shaughnessy used to say, he was as good a fullback as ever lived. Big Doc's plans called for his son to follow his footsteps through St. Stanislaus Prep, in Bay St. Louis, Mississippi, and Tulane University. When Little Doc was enrolled in St. Stanislaus, he was thirteen years old and he weighed 175 pounds. When he graduated four years later, the school paper headlined: BLANCHARD HAS RECORD AS GREATEST FOOTBALL PLAYER IN STANISLAUS' HISTORY, no small praise since Marchy Schwartz, who had gone on to become an All-America at Notre Dame, had also done his bit for the school. But the schoolboy editor wasn't simply giving way to adolescent enthusiasm. Doc Blanchard may not have been known to any football fans beyond the Gulf area, but he headed the prospect list of football-minded colleges all over the country. Red Blaik, up at Dartmouth, had heard about him. Frank Leahy, who had seen him when he was coaching Boston College's Sugar Bowl team in 1940, was after him for Notre Dame. So was practically every big-name coach you could think of.

In 1941, when Blaik moved to West Point, he sent Harry Ellinger, his line coach, down to Bay St. Louis to sound Doc out. Doc told him, quite frankly, that he wasn't the least bit interested. He finally enrolled at North Carolina, instead of Tulane, but only because his father's health had begun to fail. Jim Tatum, Mrs. Blanchard's cousin, had just become head coach at North Carolina, but the main reason Doc went there was that it was close enough to Bishopville to allow Big Doc to come up for the games.

As a freshman at North Carolina, Doc was even more overpowering than he had been at St. Stanislaus. He had already reached his full growth—6 feet 1½ inches, 210 pounds—and he could sprint the 100 in ten seconds flat. He not only murdered opposing freshmen, he kept the North Carolina varsity in a state of shock, too. "Once," according to R. A. White, the frosh trainer, "he knocked out two varsity tacklers on the same play. It got so bad that some of the boys wouldn't even try to tackle him." He was, at eighteen, a living textbook on the Basic Footballer. He blocked ferociously, he tackled viciously, he simply ran right over men who tried to tackle him. Gleen Thistlewaite, who had coached at Northwestern, came away shaking his head. "I've seen all the great fullbacks, including Nagurski," he said. "But this boy will be the greatest."

There was, however, one defensive alignment Doc could not overpower. In 1942, the Army stood astride the future of all healthy eighteen-year-old boys, its arms outstretched, its position unshakable. Blanchard tried to stick around a while by enlisting in the Navy's V-12 unit on the campus. He was turned down for being five pounds heavier than the Navy said a good, healthy sailor ought to be. Tatum tried to sweat the "excess" weight off him in a steam room. "He was all muscle and concrete," Tatum found. "I could only cook off about two pounds." So Doc enlisted in the Army. It turned out to be the biggest naval disaster since the French took on Lord Nelson at Trafalgar. He served a year and a half, ending up as a Pfc. with a chemical warfare outfit at the Air Force base in Clovis, New Mexico. Dr. Blanchard had set out to get his son into West Point, and as an indication of the good Doctor's thoroughness and determination, he got him all three possible appointments—from both of his senators and from his representative. Since Blaik had been interested in Doc almost from the day he took over at the Academy, it can be assumed that some correspondence was exchanged between the athletic department of West Point and the congressional offices. Just to keep things straight, let us say that there is nothing wrong about this; Blaik would be the first to admit that fine football players do not find their way to West Point by accident. They do not find their way to Harvard or State Teachers by accident, either.

Doc accepted his appointment from Senator "Cotton Ed" Smith and reported to Lafayette College in Pennsylvania to study for the validating exams. He passed all right, but before he actually reported to the Academy, Big Doc died.

Pfc. Blanchard was assigned to a Field Artillery unit stationed at West Point. He entrained from Bishopville, under Army orders, and arrived at his Field Artillery headquarters on July 1, 1944. The following morning, he gathered his personal belongings and walked across the Plain to cadet headquarters in what is known as the Central Area, a huge block of grim, tan barracks which house most of the cadets. He was assigned to a company, put under the command of a first classman (senior) and assigned to a room on the top (fourth) floor of the North Area barracks. The rest of the day, he was run in and out of his room to pick up clothing and supplies.

The first six weeks of life at the Academy is known as "Beast Barracks." The first three weeks were spent in intense basic training, with rigid discipline and total regimentation. The last three weeks Doc and his classmates were put through maneuvers at Pine Camp in Watertown, N.Y. He didn't see Glenn Davis at all, for Glenn, as a turnback, had undergone "Beast Barracks" the previous year. Even when the academic year started in September, there was little chance for a really close relationship to develop between the two. Cadets are sorted into companies according to height, and Glenn and Doc were almost four inches apart. They weren't even in the same regiment. Doc was in the Second Regiment, Glenn in the First. The classes were small—ten to a class—and shuffled regularly so that cadets with the same marks in individual subjects were studying together. Although Blanchard and Davis were both low in their graduating class (Davis ranked 305th out of 310, Blanchard 296th), they never, in their entire careers at the Academy, had one class together.

Blanchard had heard of Davis, of course, for Glenn had starred for Army the year before. He was kept so busy, however, that he didn't get to meet Glenn until the football squad was called out the day after Labor Day.

Glenn Davis was born nine minutes after his twin brother Ralph (hence the nickname Junior). At Bonita High he earned 13 letters. In his senior year, he won the Helms Foundation trophy as the best schoolboy back in his area by scoring 236 points, an average of better than three touchdowns per game.

Red Blaik first heard about him early in 1943 through a letter from an old friend, Warner Bentley, who was, of all things, a professor of dramatics at Dartmouth: "Everybody in California," Bentley wrote, "talks about a football player at Bonita High School. . . . They say this kid is the fastest halfback ever seen out there. He's an all-around athlete; baseball, basketball and track as well as football. I thought you might be interested in knowing about this boy. His name is Glenn Davis."

Coast footballers usually stick close to home, but the Pacific Coast Conference was then in the midst of one of those purity campaigns which periodically attack college football. Although Davis received about a dozen feelers, they were made so indirectly and vaguely that it was impossible to tell how solid they were. When Blaik got in touch with the Davises, he found them not only willing but eager to have the boys go to West Point.

It was not too difficult to arrange. "It's true," Glenn now says, "that I told them I wouldn't go unless Ralph went, too. The next thing we knew we both had senatorial appointments." He declines to comment on the popular Coast story that neither he nor Ralph had high school grades accrediting them to West Point.

When the eighteen-year-old twins arrived at the Academy in May, 1943, they were met by Blaik and another officer. Blaik asked them what they would like to see.

"Michie Stadium," said the Davis twins.

Although Blaik knew what he had in Blanchard, he had no idea that Glenn Davis was the football player he turned out to be. He was well acquainted with Glenn's high school record, of course, but he had been around long enough to know that small school hot shots frequently fizzle out in tough college competition. But he had only to see Glenn go through the motions on the first day of practice—plebes were eligible for varsity ball in those war years—to realize that he had something special.

Blaik had decided to jettison his faithful old single wing that year and switch over to the T. Glenn, at 170 pounds, became a strange sort of animal, a triple-threat fullback—later, halfback—out of the T. He scored eight touchdowns and was seventh in the nation in total yardage. And yet, he was to become so coupled in the public mind with Doc Blanchard that these touchdowns—in fact, the whole 1943 season—are invariably forgotten when Glenn's "lifetime" records are cited.

Army had a successful year, everything considered, losing only to Notre Dame and Navy. Notre Dame had observed that Glenn had a habit of holding the ball low and away from his body, and they exploited that weakness for all it was worth. Twice in the first half, the ball was jarred or knocked from his grasp; in the third period, with Notre Dame leading 6–0, tackle Jim White stole the ball right out of Glenn's hands on the Army eight. The Irish

went on to score, and the game was broken wide open.

Even in his bad days, however, Glenn performed far better on the field than in the classroom. West Point is rugged for any plebe; for a boy with Glenn's sub-par academic background, it is brutal. He would come off the practice field at 5:45, shower, dress, and go back to his room to sneak in 30 minutes' worth of study before supper formation. Eating was no relaxation since, as a plebe, he had to sit at a position of attention on the outer edge of the chair. At 7:15, he would be back in his room prepared to study until "lights-out" sounded at 10:30. "I'd fall asleep over the books at eight o'clock," he told Coast writer Al Stump, "and Dick Walterhouse (his roomie and Army's extra-point specialist) would shove me into bed and set the alarm for 4:00. I'd get up in a cold room and spend the time until reveille at 5:50 trying to figure out just one math problem. In class I was too punchy from lack of sleep to hear the prof. . . ."

Math is the sword upon which most plebes die, and Glenn was no exception. By midseason, Lt. Buck Pohl of the math department was giving Junior special tutoring. While the rest of the squad was seeing Philadelphia and New York on the nights of the Pennsylvania and Notre Dame games, Pohl was driving Junior back to the Point for a weekend tutoring session. Blaik finally excused him from practice altogether so he would have extra studying time. Glenn could never quite catch up, though. In December, he flunked out.

Dismissed from the Academy, he went home to Claremont, took a special four-month math course at Pomona College, and was given a chance to try again in 1944.

Why he decided to try again is a mystery. He did not like the grim play-acting of Army life, the privileges of rank, the abuse and the abusing, the ordering and the kow-towing. He wouldn't have to run the gamut of Beast Barracks a second time, but like Blanchard and the rest of his new classmates, he would have to suffer the indignity of being a plebe, of speaking only when spoken to, of "taking a brace" (a widely exaggerated position of attention: shoulders thrown back, chin tucked in, stomach concaved) and submitting himself to the other stern rituals of plebe life.

Glenn, who was so perfectly coordinated that he could pole vault ten feet the first time he ever held a pole in his hand, wasn't even a good marcher. The solemnity of inspection amused him. Tom Lombardo, his quarterback, had the unhappy duty of inspecting Glenn's room, and Glenn would usually make things tough for him by clowning around.

But if he couldn't see the system when he was on the receiving end, he couldn't see it when he got out of plebe class, either. As an upperclassman, he was quite content to leave the plebes unbraced and unbothered. Once, when the West Point track and basketball squads were riding a single bus back from New York, Glenn stood up and told a weary plebe, Bill Yeoman, to take his seat. Yeoman, well aware that plebes did not take seats from upperclassmen, politely balked. "Oh, come on," Davis said, pushing him down. "Sit down."

This is not to say that Davis was necessarily made of finer clay than the average cadet; it is to say only that he was a temperamental misfit at the Military Academy. The adjectives Glenn's friends always use to describe him are "sweet" and "naive." Sweet, naive halfbacks do not necessarily make the best possible officers.

There is a convention that the military personality is rigid and humorless. It is possible that the opposite is true; that, in his training at least, the quality needed above any other is adaptability. One would have thought, for instance, that Blanchard would have found adjustment to the Military Academy far more difficult than Glenn. Davis lived a spartan life by choice. He trained religiously, kept himself in perfect shape, never drank or smoked. (When he came back to coach the JVs, a cigarette company wanted to buy his testimonial. Glenn refused because he was afraid he might disillusion the boys who took him for a model.) Doc, on the other hand, was an easygoing, fun-loving guy who liked nothing better than a night on the town.

And yet it was Blanchard who was able to say something like: "Well, this is the way it is, and this is the way it has always been and this is the way it will always be. There must be a reason for it, but whether there is or not, I asked for it so there's nothing to do but make the best of it."

Mr. Inside, one might say, was always able to keep himself inside the system; Mr. Outside was almost literally an outsider. After graduation, when their application for a special leave adjustment that would have allowed them to play pro football was turned down, Doc put aside his football uniform once and for all and went to work to make himself as good a flier as he could. Glenn never accepted the decision in his heart, never gave up thinking of getting out and, finally, after he had served his tour of

duty, he resigned his commission. Mr. Inside remained inside to the end. Mr. Outside finally got outside. But a lot of football had flown over the goalposts before then.

In 1944, Davis and Blanchard were almost immediately put in the same backfield. Blaik's material was so rich that he was able to anticipate the two-platoon system, not with offensive and defensive units, but with two separate two-way teams. The starting backfield had Doug Kenna, Max Minor, Dale Hall and Bobby Dobbs. The plebe backfield had Blanchard, Davis and Dean Sensanbaugher plus Captain Tom Lombardo. Glenn, who had worn a fullback's number his first year (34), was given a halfback's number, 41. Blanchard was given number 35. For the next three years, 35 and 41 would be the numbers to look for when the Army team was on the field.

The Big Rabble—as the team is known at the Point—rambled. Blaik always started his veteran backfield, with the plebes coming on late in the first quarter or at the start of the second. It really wasn't an athletic contest when the barefoot college boys of 1944—a smattering of V-12s, pre-drafts and rejects—met Army's pair of powerhouses; it was cruel and unusual punishment. In Doc Blanchard they reaped the whirlwind, in Junior Davis they clutched at a gust of wind. Doc stunned them and Junior dazzled them.

Army beat North Carolina, 46–0, Brown, 59–7, Pittsburgh, 69–7, the Coast Guard, 76–0, Villanova, 83–0, Pennsylvania, 62–7, and only Blaik's sense of compassion kept the scores as low as that.

Playing sometimes little more than a quarter, and rarely more than a half, Davis scored three touchdowns against major opponents North Carolina, Brown, Notre Dame, Villanova and Pennsylvania.

After Army had shellacked Notre Dame, 59–0, racking up more points than they had scored against the Irish in the fifteen previous years combined, Allison Danzig of the *New York Times* wrote: "Twenty years after the Four Horsemen rode to lasting fame, the proud pennants of Notre Dame were ripped to tatters and trampled under the thundering caissons of Army yesterday in the worst disaster the Fighting Irish have suffered on a football field."

Blanchard didn't score, but his ferocious play brought forth the usual expressions of awe and wonder. Running interference for Kenna on a punt, he hit "Tree" Adams, Notre Dame's 6-foot, 7-inch tackle, with a blind-angle block that knocked him, quite literally, for a loop.

Adams went up in the air, turned a complete somersault and landed on the back of his neck.

Comment on Doc started at superlatives and went on up to sublime. Clark Shaughnessy said: "Blanchard is the greatest fullback I have ever seen." (And Shaughnessy had coached Bronko Nagurski and Norm Standlee.)

Jack Lavelle said: "Blanchard is the greatest football player I have ever seen."

Notre Dame coach Ed McKeever wired home the message: "Have just seen Superman in the flesh. He wears No. 35 and goes by the name of Blanchard."

The big game was still Navy. The Middies had done a little scrounging around in the marketplace themselves, and they had a sea-worthy football squad. Because of travel limitations, the game was originally supposed to be played at Annapolis, with half the Middies detailed to cheer for Army. At the last minute, the brass got so excited about the game that they put it into Baltimore's Municipal Stadium. Admission was restricted to purchasers of War Bonds residing within a ten-mile radius of the city and 66,639 people, some of whom may have lived 11 miles from the city, showed up.

It was a ball game worth traveling ten miles to see. At the end of three quarters, Army was leading, 9–7, when Davis intercepted a pass on his own 35 and swung on down to the 48.

They gave the ball to Blanchard, and Little Doc did his father proud. They gave it to him for 25 around right end, then they gave it to him for 3 over left tackle. Davis got 3 around right end, then Doc went up the middle for 5 yards and a first down on the 21. Max Minor made a yard, and then it was all Doc again. It was Blanchard for 3, Blanchard for 4, Blanchard for 3 more and a first down on the 10. So they gave it to Blanchard once more and he smashed inside left guard and hit the end zone standing up.

("This is the only man," Herman Hickman said afterwards, "who runs his own interference.")

The next time Army got the ball, it was Glenn's turn. Blaik had designed a weak-side play for him called "The California Special." The ball came to him on a direct shovel from Lombardo, and Glenn cut inside the end and swung to the sideline where, with that extraordinary ability to rev his speed up notch by notch ("Davis' unlimited gearshifts," Blaik called it), he shot by every man who had a crack at him. The final score was 23–7.

After the game, Ed Tatum, Jim's brother, came back to the locker room to congratulate

cousin Felix. "He was there, Ed," Doc said. "I could feel him patting me on the back after each play and saying, 'Hit like your daddy did, son.' "

At the end of the season, Davis was the country's leading scorer with 20 touchdowns; his average per carry was a fantastic 12.4 yards. Blanchard had 9 touchdowns and a 7.1 per-carry average. Both were, of course, almost unanimous All-America choices.

Davis was given the Maxwell Club Trophy, the Walter Camp Award and the Helms Foundation Award. Glenn and Doc ran second and third behind Ohio State's Les Horvath in the voting for the Heisman Trophy.

The following year, in 1945, Army may have had the greatest college team ever assembled. The ends were Barney Poole and Hank Foldberg, the tackles were Tex Coulter and Al Nemetz, the guards captain Johnny Green and Art Gerometta, the center Ug Fuson. Joining Davis and Blanchard in the backfield were Arnold Tucker, up from third string, and Shorty McWilliams, up from Mississippi State.

With Tucker's adept passing forcing the opposition to worry about its anti-aircraft as well as its flanks and center, Blaik had a perfectly balanced attack. It crushed Wake Forest, 54–0, Michigan, 27–7, Duke, 48–13, Villanova, 54–0, Notre Dame, 48–0, Pennsylvania, 61–0, and Navy, 32–13.

In the first half of the Notre Dame game, Glenn scored three times and Doc twice. Then Blaik, as was his custom, retired them for the afternoon. "Heck, Colonel," Davis said, throwing away his helmet in disgust. "I want to play football and you're not giving me a chance."

Blanchard scored twice in the first quarter against Navy and Davis went 49 yards for a third. For sheer, unbridled power, Doc's second score was frightening. Clyde (Smackover) Scott, whom Navy had picked up from Arkansas (the university, not the battleship), had a head-on shot at him in an open field. Doc just ran over him.

Blanchard had 19 touchdowns in the year; Davis had 18. It was Doc's year, however. He beat Glenn out for the Heisman Trophy, and he won both the Maxwell Cup and the Walter Camp Trophy. More than that, he became the first football player ever to win the AAU's Sullivan Award as the outstanding amateur athlete in the country.

In 1946, the brave old Army team began to come apart. Rip Rowan joined Blanchard, Davis and Tucker in the backfield, but the heart of the line—Green, Nemetz and Coulter—had left. In the opening game, against Villanova, Blanchard twisted away from a tackler and, before he could pick up speed again, Penn's 200-pound end, Francis Kane, hit him around the shoulders. Doc's foot sunk into the wet ground. The knee, instead of bending in as he fell, bent out—like a door being yanked against the hinge. Two different sets of ligaments were torn. Normally, such an injury would be expected to put a man out for the season. Apparently, however, Doc's fantastic calf and thigh development acted as a shock absorber, for he came back to face Michigan after missing only two games. He wasn't the same Blanchard—he didn't kick any more and he didn't scrimmage —but he was back.

The Michigan game was a day of reckoning. The men were beginning to stream home from the wars, and, more important perhaps, fewer boys were being drafted. Michigan, under Fritz Crisler, was coming fast. Bob Chappuis, Bump Elliot, Jack Weisenburger and Paul White were in the backfield; Len Ford and Bob Mann were at the ends. (Throughout the era of Blanchard and Davis, there had always been the feeling, even on the part of the most faithful rooter, that the true ability of the Army team could never accurately be gauged, since the opposition was so underprivileged.) On the fourth play of the game, Tucker suffered a shoulder separation plus a sprained elbow and wrist on his passing arm. He kept the injury to himself and stayed in the game, but with Tucker and Blanchard both under anaesthetic, the wheel swung around and pointed to Junior. With Army trailing, 7–0, he took the ball on Michigan's 41, snuck through guard and ran right into a small patrol of tacklers. Junior didn't surrender. He shook off three successive tacklers as he cut to his right, and, suddenly and astonishingly, he was running free down the sidelines. At the 15-yard line, he was blocked in against the sideline by Paul White, but there never was a ball carrier harder to build a fence around than Glenn Davis. In a typical Davis maneuver, he faked in toward the middle of the field and, in almost the same split second, accelerated his speed and squeezed through on the sideline. White had moved with him on the fake, and that was all the help Glenn needed.

With the half coming to a close, Tucker called a pass play from the Michigan 23, on fourth and 18. The left side of the Michigan line broke through and roughed Davis up just as he was taking Tucker's hand-off. The ball squirted loose and bounced away. Two Michigan linemen dived for it and missed. Davis, running back and to his right, grabbed it on a big hop and, in the same motion, jumped turned and threw to the right corner of the end zone. He couldn't have dropped it better if he had been standing there on a ladder. Bob Folsom, a second-string end, made the catch, with a little jump off his full stride. Army was ahead, but not for long. Michigan took the second-half kickoff and marched for the tying score.

In the fourth quarter, Doc Blanchard, who had been pushed around all afternoon, came to life. He leaped high in the air at midfield to pluck a Davis pass away from a pack of drooling Wolverines. He began to get that short yardage through the line. With the ball on the 18, Mr. Inside and Mr. Outside switched roles. Glenn slammed up the middle for 3, Blanchard went wide for 8. From the 7-yard line, Doc went around left end and headed for the corner. He was hit twice on the 3-yard line but, bad leg or no, he carried both tacklers into the end zone. Final score: Army 20, Michigan 13.

Army lost the battle of statistics, but won the game. It was the big answer on Blanchard and Davis. The line didn't do it for them, the blocking didn't do it for them. They did it themselves. Davis had run 105 yards and completed seven out of eight passes for 168 yards. It was, Red Blaik believes, Glenn's greatest game.

Notre Dame, with Frank Leahy and Johnny Lujack back from the wars, finally stopped them. No game ever provoked more interest. "If Yankee Stadium had a million seats," athletic director Biff Jones said, "we would still fill it for this game." Unfortunately, it turned out to be a dull game—a scoreless tie. Army's string of twenty-five successive victories was broken.

In the Navy game, Blanchard looked like his old armor-clad self for the first time since his injury. It was just as well that he did. He exploded 53 yards for one touchdown, and caught a Davis pass—on a stop-start pattern—for another. Davis had scored earlier on a dazzling 14-yard run. But Navy, given absolutely no chance to extend Army, took complete charge of the second half and brought the score to 21–18. With a minute and a half to go, they had the ball on the Army 3, and it seemed almost certain that the fabulous careers of Davis and Blanchard would end on a stunning note of defeat. Navy had three cracks at the winning touchdown, but Army held. In three years, the Blanchard-Davis clubs had won 27 games and tied one. They had never known defeat.

In the banquet halls where the late Herman Hickman cut such a large, popular figure this parody of "What Is A Boy?" was a sentimental favorite with fathers and sons. It was written by Hickman's aide-de-camp at Yale, Charley Loftus, and after each reading he and Herman always had a flood of requests for reprints. Once again. . .

WHAT IS A FOOTBALL PLAYER?

Charles Loftus

Between the innocence of boyhood and the dignity of man, we find a sturdy creature called a football player. Football players come in assorted weights, heights, jersey colors and numbers, but all football players have the same creed: to play every second of every minute of every period of every game to the best of their ability.

Football players are found everywhere—underneath, on top of, running around, jumping over, passing by, twisting from or driving through the enemy. Teammates rib them, officials penalize them, students cheer them, kid brothers idolize them, coaches criticize them, college girls adore them, alumni tolerate them and mothers worry about them. A football player is courage in cleats, hope in a helmet, pride in pads, and the best of young manhood in moleskins.

When your team is behind, a football player is incompetent, careless, indecisive, lazy, uncoordinated and stupid. Just when your team threatens to turn the tide of battle, he misses a block, fumbles the ball, drops a pass, jumps off side, falls down, runs the wrong way, or completely forgets his assignment.

A football player is a composite—he eats like Notre Dame, but, more often than not, plays like Grand Canyon High. To an opponent publicity man, he has the speed of a gazelle, the strength of an ox, the size of an elephant, the cunning of a fox, the agility of an adagio dancer, the quickness of a cat, and the ability of Red Grange, Glenn Davis, Bronco Nagurski and Jim Thorpe—combined.

To his own coach he has, for press purposes, the stability of mush, the fleetness of a snail, the mentality of a mule, is held together by adhesive tape, baling wire, sponge rubber, and has about as much chance of playing on Saturday as would his own grandfather.

To an alumnus a football player is someone who will never kick as well, run as far, block as viciously, tackle as hard, fight as fiercely, give as little ground, score as many points, or generate nearly the same amount of spirit as did those particular players of his own yesteryear.

A football player likes game films, trips away from home, practice sessions without pads, hot showers, long runs, whirlpool baths, recovered fumbles, points after touchdowns, and the quiet satisfaction which comes from being a part of a perfectly executed play. He is not much for wind sprints, sitting on the bench, rainy days, after-game compliments, ankle wraps, scouting reports or calisthentics.

No one else looks forward so much to September or so little to December. Nobody gets so much pleasure out of knocking down, hauling out, or just plain bringing down the enemy. Nobody else can cram into one mind assignments for an end run, an off-tackle slant, a jump pass, a quarterback sneak, a dive play, punt protection, kickoff returns, a buck lateral, goal line stands, or a spinner cycle designed to result in a touchdown every time it is tried.

A football player is a wonderful creature—you can criticize him, but you can't discourage him. You can defeat his team but you can't make him quit. You can get him out of a game, but you can't get him out of football. Might as well admit it—be you alumnus, coach, or fan—he is your personal representative on the field, your symbol of fair and hard play. He may not be an All-America, but he is an example of the American way. He is judged, not for his race, not for his religion, not for his social standing, not for his finances, but by the democratic yardstick of how well he blocks, tackles, and sacrifices individual glory for the overall success of his team.

He is a hard-working, untiring, determined kid doing the very best he can for his school or college. And when you come out of a stadium, grousing and feeling upset that your team has lost, he can make you feel mighty ashamed with just two sincerely spoken words—"We tried!"

OVERLEAF:

Army in the mid-1940s and Oklahoma a decade later dominated the college football scene with long victory streaks.
Army's stretched through 32 games; Oklahoma won 47 in a row.
Both of these giants were finally brought down in stunning upsets.
Some of the dramatic details of their falls are spelled out in the Sunday sports sections that follow.

The New York Times.

SUNDAY, OCTOBER 26, 1947. L S

COLUMBIA TOPS ARMY, 21-20, ENDING CADET STREAK AT 32; PENN DOWNS NAVY, 21-0; CORNELL AND DARTMOUTH WIN

As Unbeaten Army Finally Bowed to Columbia at Baker Field Yesterday

Kusserow of the Lions maneuvering to get away a pass in the second quarter of the game. In the play are his teammates Rossides (21) and Swiacki, who is blocking Kellum (85) of the Cadets.
The New York Times by Sam...

LIONS SCORE UPSET

Army Has 20-7 Lead at Half-Time, but Bows to Columbia Rally

AERIALS SINK THE CADETS

Swiacki Brilliant as Receiver—Yablonski's Kick Decides—Kusserow Counts Twice

By LOUIS EFFRAT

Columbia 21, Army 20!

A typographical error? No—a thousand times no—and the 35,000 fans at Baker Field yesterday will attest to the authenticity of Columbia's greatest gridiron achievement: a totally unexpected victory that overshadowed even the magnificent Rose Bowl conquest of Jan. 1, 1934, when the Lions beat Stanford.

After thirty-two straight games in which Army had not known defeat, Earl Blaik's cadets appeared to be en route to another triumph yesterday. They battered Columbia almost at will throughout a lopsided first half and enjoyed a 20-7 margin at the intermission. Up to that point the Lions had had no ground attack to speak of and most of their gains overhead were made possible because of spectacular catches rather than by the passing of Gene Rossides.

True, the West Point offense, overpowering though it was, lacked smoothness, but it still was potent enough to grind out the yardage. Army's speedy backs, operating behind so rugged a line, had it ...

QUAKERS HIT HARD

Flash Full Power to Score Twice in Last Quarter Against Navy

PENN IN LONG MARCHES

Goes 42, 55 and 50 Yards Before 78,205 Spectators in Franklin Field

By ALLISON DANZIG
Special to The New York Times.

PHILADELPHIA, Oct. 25—Amid the crash of Army and Illinois, Pennsylvania maintained its place among the football elect with a convincing demonstration of its superiority over Navy today. The final score was 21 to 0.

Held to seven points going into the final quarter, the big, powerful Red and Blue eleven broke the shackles of the Midshipmen's stubborn defense as 78,205 spectators looked on at Franklin Field in summer heat.

In seven plays Penn went fifty-five yards to end the tension of a tight game at the start of the fourth period. Then, for good measure, it struck fifty yards through the air in seven more plays for a third touchdown, with the clock showing eight seconds left to play.

Penn Proves Supreme

From start to finish this was Penn's ball game, and again it was Skippy Minisi who was chief artisan of the victory. As a year ago, although he did not have a hand in any of the scoring ...

MICHIGAN TOPPLES

Stymie Triumphs to Regain World Money-Winning Lead

Cornell's Rally Subdues Princeton by 28 to 21

DARTMOUTH STOPS

HARVARD, 14 TO 13

MINNESOTA, 13 TO 6

By ROSCOE McGOWEN
Special to The New York Times.

By WALTER W. RUCH
Special to The New York Times.

GOLGATE BATTLES BROWN TO 13-13 TIE

By LINCOLN A. WERDEN
Special to The New York Times.

Raiders Score in Final Period but Late Bid to Break Deadlock Fails

TROJANS CONQUER CALIFORNIA, 39-14

Doll Runs Kick-Off 95 Yards to Score for Bowl-Bound Southern California

By The Associated Press.

ILLINOIS CHECKED BY PURDUE, 14 TO 7

DeMoss' Passes Chief Factor in Snapping String of Ten Games Without Defeat

By The Associated Press.

NOTRE DAME TRIPS IOWA ELEVEN, 21-0

Scatback Scampers by Sitko and Brennan Highlight Game at South Bend

By The Associated Press.

Pitt Upsets Ohio State by 12-0; Fumbles Ruin Buckeyes' Chances

Set All-Time Mark

Harvard Ropes Fail

Ground Plays Set Up Passes

Continued on Page 2, Column 3

Continued on Page 8, Column 3

Continued on Page 6, Column 1

Continued on Page 5, Column 5

Continued on Page 5, Column 2

Continued on Page 4, Column 4

Continued on Page 4, Column 2

Continued on Page 5, Column 4

Continued on Page 2, Column 1

Continued on Page 5, Column 1

Continued on Page 3, Column 3

Football Scores

COLLEGES

East

East

Section

3

SPORTS

TWELVE PAGES   □

MARINE

AUTOMOTIVE

NEW YORK

Herald Tribune

SUNDAY, NOVEMBER 17, 1957

SPORTS

WEATHER

MAIL ORDER—BRIDGE

TWELVE PAGES

Section

3

Irish Stop Oklahoma, 7-0; Yale Wins

Army, Dartmouth, Brown and Penn Triumph

PENN VS. COLUMBIA—Aerial game of different type is used by Jack Hanlon (17) as he dives over players for Penn touchdown in second period at Baker Field. Pennsylvania won, 28 to 6.

Associated Press

Notre Dame Ends String At 47 Games

Lynch Goes Over In Last Period

NORMAN, Okla. Nov. 16 (P) —Oklahoma's all-time record of 47 straight football victories was shattered today by an underdog Notre Dame team that marched 80 yards in the closing minutes for the all-important touchdown and a 7-0 triumph.

Oklahoma, 18-point favorite, couldn't move against the rockwall Notre Dame line and the Sooners saw another of its national records broken—scoring in 123 consecutive games.

The defeat was only the ninth for Oklahoma coach Bud Wilkinson since he became head coach at Oklahoma in 1947 and virtually ended any chance for the Sooners getting a third straight national championship.

Although the partisan, sellout crowd of 62,000 came out for a Roman holiday, they were stunned into silence as the Sooners were unable to pull their usual last-quarter winning touchdowns—a Wilkinson team trademark.

Cheer, Cheer for Irish

As the game ended when Oklahoma's desperation passing drive was cut off by an intercepted aerial off the crowd as one and suddenly gave the Notre Dame team a rousing cheer.

It was a far cry from last

Ohio State Jolts Iowa, 17-13, And Clinches Big Ten Title

By Walter Lister Jr.

His next one looked good for a|Iowa won today, the Hawkeyes

YALE VS. PRINCETON—Mike Cavallon (left) gathers in pass from Dick Winter-

Herald Tribune photo by Ted Kell

46,000 See Elis Upset Tiger, 20-13

Cavallon Scores On 3 TD Passes

By Jesse Abramson

PRINCETON, N. J., Nov. 16.—Mike Cavallon, a stalwart 6 foot 4, 200-pound end not hitherto renowned as a pass catcher, perpetrated an historic hat trick for Yale in its eighteenth meeting with Princeton before a full house of 46,-000 in Palmer Stadium today.

The senior from Winnetka, Ill. snared all three touchdown passes as the sure-handed Elis, brilliantly directed by Dick Winterbauer, whipped the favored Tigers, 20 to 13, in this ancient series.

On back-to-back victories over Princeton for the first time since 1945-'46. Jordan Olivar's Bulldogs inflicted the first Ivy League defeat on the Tigers and placed their championship hopes in jeopardy.

Ivy Title Game

With Dartmouth squeezing out a 20-19 victory over Cornell, the Ivy League crown will be settled here next week between Princeton and the Hanover Indians.

Yale, the clean-sweep Ivy winner last year but out of the running now, had no other interest than to do Princeton in as the first step toward the consolation Big Three prize. This the Elis succeeded in do-

Tops Tulane, 20-14

By Bill Wallace

WEST POINT, N.Y., Nov. 16 —A fired-up Tulane team that had lost six of its last eight games led Army by a point late into the fourth quarter here today. The Cadets then staged a devastating 74-yard touchdown drive, led by halfback Bob Anderson, that won the game, 20 to 14, before 21,125.

Continued on page 2, column 4

Jacobs' Colt Sets Jamaica Stakes Mark

Promised Land, a homebred from the stable of Mrs. Ethel D. Jacobs, raced to a new stakes record and came within two-fifths of a second of the track mark in winning the eighth renewal of the Roamer Handicap before a crowd of 37,802 at Jamaica yesterday.

Continued on page 3, column 3

Penn Pounds Columbia As Riepl Romps, 28 to 6

By Irving T. Marsh

Frank Riepl, Pennsylvania's heavy-duty back, proved yesterday that the indispensable man does exist after all.

Continued on page 2, column 3

Wins, 20-19, Over Cornell

Army put the ball in play 12 times and managed scoring drives, two of which came when Tulane was leading.

The Green Wave from New Orleans accomplished their two touchdowns on long home-run plays, a 61-yard and sweep by Claude (Boo) Mason plus a 66-yard punt return by Dick Pettibon. Mason's run opened the scoring at 7:35 of the first period.

Big Green Leads In Ivy League

By Sid Grey

HANOVER, N.H., Nov. 16 — Captain Joe Palermo, in his last game at Memorial Field here, kicked the extra point with 2 minutes 45 seconds to go and booted Dartmouth into the Ivy League lead today by virtue of a 20-to-19 victory over Cornell.

Continued on page 4, column 4

Rangers Pin 4-2 Loss on Canadiens

MONTREAL, Nov. 16 (CP) — Two goals by Dave Creighton, his first of the season, carried the New York Rangers to a 4-to-2 victory tonight over the Montreal Canadiens and put the New Yorkers into first place behind league-leading Montreal in the National Hockey League.

Continued on page 3, column 2

Colorado Routs Nebraska, 27-0

LINCOLN, Neb., Nov. 16 (AP) — Colorado, driving hard to post a respectable Big Eight conference showing, sent four different backs across the goal today to defeat Nebraska, 27 to 0. The Buffs, now 2-3 in conference play, handed Nebraska its eighth loss in nine games.

Nebraska		0	0	0	0	— 0
Colorado		13	7	0	7	— 27

Colorado: Touchdowns — Stransky (2, plunge); Cook (1, run). Point after touchdown — Dowler (2); Cook (1, run). Cannon — Indorf 2, Cook.

Brown Thwarts Harvard For 3d Ivy Victory, 33-6

By Tommy Holmes

CAMBRIDGE, Mass., Nov. 16 — Brown arrived late for today's battle of Ivy League also-rans at Harvard Stadium. The Bruins broke down en route from Providence, and the game started half an hour behind the 1:30 schedule. But all of the 17,000 spectators in this old football park saw the opening kick-off, setting a collegiate record.

Continued on page 2, column 4

Williams Still Unbeaten, Dumps Amherst, 39-14

By Harold Rosenthal

WILLIAMSTOWN, Mass., Nov. 16 — Williams crushed Amherst this afternoon, and rode the crest of a 39 to 14 victory to its first unbeaten season in 40 years. With it, the once-tied "purple staged a successful defense of its Little Three crown before 8,000, the largest crowd ever to jam into Weston Field.

Continued on page 2, column 4

College, School Results

College Football
South

College Football
East

Mid-West

South

From 1905, when the two clubs were formed, until the early 1920s, the Massillon Tigers and Canton Bulldogs attracted most of the top-notch college players who wanted to make a buck and keep their football reputations alive. In fact, for a dozen or more years Massillon and Canton were professional football. In 1916 both teams had combed the East and Midwest for talent and Massillon had come up with Dorais and Rockne of Notre Dame, while Canton boasted Jim Thorpe, the famed Carlisle Indian. As if the bloodthirsty rivalry between the two Ohio towns was not enough, fans, players, club officials bet heavily on the games. Often the results of the games produced a civic outrage—such as the one following the 1916 game when Massillon's halfback Briggs took a pass from quarterback Dorais and dove over the goal line and into the crowd and . . . well, this article in the Massillon Independent *tells what happened, or what might have happened.*

DID CANTON WIN?

The Massillon Independent

According to a decision handed down by Referee Ed Conner, of Cleveland, in the Courtland Hotel, Canton, Sunday evening, following his stopping of a football game between the professional elevens of Canton and Massillon at League park, Canton, in the afternoon, after a 20 minute dispute on the field over a play which Massillon claimed was a touchdown and Canton a touchback, Massillon was beaten 6–0.

But no matter if Referee Conner's decision did give Canton the game it will not convince hundreds of spectators that Massillon was not entitled to a tie score and by rules of fair play and sportsmanship should have been given credit for a touchdown, which both the umpire and head linesman claim was legally made.

The play which resulted in the game being called eight minutes before its completion happened in the fourth quarter. Massillon had possession of the ball on Canton's 11-yard line. Quarterback Dorais and Left Halfback Briggs executed a successful forward pass and, with the ball tucked under his arm, Briggs started for Canton's goal. He had only about three yards to go before he came in contact with the crowd which was standing on the edge of the field. With the ball clutched tightly in his arms he dived into the crowd for what seemed to be a

perfectly legal touchdown but a few moments later one of the Canton men emerged from the crowd carrying the ball.

Briggs came on the field declaring that after he was in the crowd someone kicked the ball from his possession giving the Canton man a chance to recover it. Canton claimed a touchback had been made and Massillon claimed a touchdown. The argument which followed lasted until dark and finally Referee Conner called the game, saying he would make a decision later on when alone with the officials.

Both Umpire Cosgrove and Head Linesman Jones said that the last time they saw the ball it was in possession of Massillon and that the Tigers had scored a legal touchdown.

Regardless of what the other officials had said and claiming he did not see the play, Referee Conner later made the decision which, according to his ruling, gave the game to Canton. Referee Conner, in the past, has always proved a capable official but his decision Sunday did not seem to local fans to be fair and just.

The fact that he did not permit the game to be finished but allowed the time to be wasted by useless arguing resulted in a storm of protests from the spectators. A lot could have happened in eight minutes. Can a referee legally call it a game if he does not allow it to be finished? Many are of the opinion that if he called the game before time was actually up, without the agreement of both captains, there is no game and the only decision he could make would be to rule it no game and call all bets off.

There was a large amount of money up on the game and local fans say it does not seem fair that those who bet should have to lose their money because of the fault of the Canton management in not keeping the crowd a safe distance from the playing field. Briggs said Sunday evening, that he would be willing to sign an affidavit that the ball was kicked out of his hands after he had crossed Canton's goal line.

There were at least 8,000 people jammed into the park Sunday and with all this crowd there was not one policeman or deputy sheriff on the field to keep order. The crowd surged out on the field early in the game and hindered the playing of both teams. It was the crowd that kept Massillon from making at least two touchdowns on forward passes. It was probably the largest crowd that has ever witnessed a football game in this vicinity and the Canton management should have made ample arrangements to take care of the spectators but it was not done. It was a perfectly good game of football, one of the best ever staged hereabouts, but the poor handling of affairs left a bad taste in the mouths of many of the fans who paid good money to see the game and probably saw one or two plays.

Even though Referee Conner gives Canton the game and according to the rules, his decision is final, Massillon outplayed and outclassed Canton in all departments of the game. The east enders, loaded to the gunwales for the big game, could do little against the fierce playing of the Tigers who were in to win.

Although there was not a Massillon boy on the team, the wearers of the orange and black fought just as hard to bring victory to Massillon as if they had lived here. They put up a clean game and were for Massillon always. It was not a question of making any money with them. They were brought here to play football and they played the best they knew how, which was considerably better than Canton did.

Statistics of the game clearly show that Canton was outclassed, although the red and white machine gathered together by Manager Cusack during the last week did outweigh the Tigers. Massillon made nine first downs to Canton's three, completed eight successful forward passes to none for Canton, and had five uncompleted forwards to Canton's three. Massillon intercepted two forwards, while Canton intercepted one. Canton was penalized 35 yards to Massillon's 5, and Massillon punted nine times to Canton's ten. This very clearly shows which city had the best team.

Canton loaded up with Butler, of Wisconsin; Abel, of Colgate, and Smith, the Negro from the Michigan Aggies, at tackle; Lambert, of Wabash at quarter. Davis at guard, was also a new man. This gave Canton a heavy line, but at that, the Tigers' rush line outplayed the east enders.

The wonderful catching of forward passes by Rockne, Massillon's clever left end, and his great defensive playing was the bright spot in the big game. Dorais' throwing of the forward pass was another feature and the Dorais-Rockne combination made Canton feel pretty shaky toward the end of the game. Fleming, Hogan, and Briggs were three other players who starred for Massillon. Briggs certainly played a great game in the last quarter and was on the verge of tears when Massillon was refused a touchdown.

Canton expected Thorpe, the noted Indian athlete, to perform many great deeds of valor, but outside of his kicking the redskin did not do anything noteworthy. He made all of Canton's points on a dropkick and a goal from placement. His punting was exceptionally good but he made only two good gains. Wagner, Canton's left end, and former Pittsburgh University star, played a great defensive game as did Smith, the colored tackle. Outside of the playing of these three men Canton has nothing to boast of.

LINEUPS

Massillon		*Canton*
Rockne	le	Gardner
Jones	lt	Abel
Cole	lg	Edwards
McGuire	c	Waldsmith
Portman	rg	Davis
Southern	rt	Butler
Kagy	re	Wagner
Dorais	qb	Lambert
Finnegan	lhb	Thorpe
Fleming	rhb	Fisher
Hogan	fb	Julian

When this was called "The Best Football Game Ever Played" in the January 5, 1959
issue of Sports Illustrated *there were arguments—but not too many—about the superlative.*
Best, or one of the best . . . those who saw it will never forget it.

SUDDEN DEATH AT
YANKEE STADIUM

Tex Maule

Never has there been a game like this one. When there are so many high points, it is not easy to pick the highest. But for the 60,000 and more fans who packed Yankee Stadium last Sunday for the third week in a row, the moment they will never forget—the moment with which they will eternally bore their grandchildren—came when, with less than ten seconds to play and the clock remorselessly moving, the Baltimore Colts kicked a field goal which put the professional football championship in a 17–17 tie and necessitated a historic sudden-death overtime period. Although it was far from apparent at the time, this was the end of the line for the fabulous New York Giants, eastern titleholders by virtue of three stunning victories over a great Cleveland team (the last a bruising extra game to settle the tie in which they finished their regular season), and the heroes of one of the most courageous comebacks in the memory of the oldest fans.

This was also a game in which a seemingly irretrievable loss was twice defied. It was a game which had everything. And when it was all over, the best football team in the world had won the world's championship.

The Baltimore Colts needed all their varied and impressive talent to get the 17–17 tie at the end of the regular four quarters. Then, for eight and one quarter minutes of the sudden-death extra period, in which victory would go to the first team to score, all of the pressure and all of the frenzy of an entire season of play was concentrated on the misty football field at Yankee Stadium. The fans kept up a steady, high roar. Tension grew and grew until it was nearly unbearable. But on the field itself, where the two teams now staked the pro championship and a personal winners' share of $4,700 against a losers' share of $3,100 on each play, coldly precise football prevailed. With each team playing as well as it was possible for it to play, the better team finally won. The Baltimore Colts, ticking off the yards with sure strength under the magnificent direction of Quarterback Johnny Unitas, scored the touchdown which brought sudden death to New York and the first championship to hungry Baltimore.

This game, unbelievably, managed to top all the heroics of the spectacular Giant victories which had led up to it. The Colts won because they are a superbly well armed football team. They spent the first half picking at the small flaws in the Giant defense, doing it surely and competently under the guidance of Unitas. The Giant line, which had put destructive pressure on Cleveland quarterbacks for two successive weeks, found it much more difficult to reach Unitas. Andy Robustelli, the fine Giant end, was blocked beautifully by Jim Parker, a second-year tackle with the Colts. Unitas, a tall, thin man who looks a little stooped in his uniform, took his time throwing, and when he threw, the passes were flat and hard as a frozen rope, and on target. He varied the Baltimore attack from time to time by sending Alan Ameche thumping into the Giant line.

The Giant defense, unable to overpower the Colts as it had the Browns, shifted and changed and tried tricks, and Unitas, more often than not, switched his signal at the last possible second to take advantage of Giant weaknesses. Once, in the first quarter, when the New Yorkers tried to cover the very fast Lenny Moore with one man, Unitas waited coolly while Moore sprinted down the sideline, then whipped a long, flat pass which Moore caught on the Giant 40 and carried to the 25.

Then the Giant defense blocked a field goal attempt which followed, and Charley Conerly, the 37-year-old Giant quarterback who played one of the finest games of his long career, caught the Colt linebackers coming in on him too recklessly. He underhanded a quick pitchout to Frank Gifford, and Gifford went 38 yards to the Colts' 31; a couple of plays later the Giants led 3–0 on a 36-yard field goal by Pat Summerall.

In the second quarter, with the probing and testing over, the Colts asserted a clear superiority. They had gone into the game reasonably sure that their running would work inside the Giant tackles, and sure, too, that the quick, accurate passes of Unitas to receivers like Moore and Ray Berry could be completed. The first quarter reinforced that opinion and the second quarter implemented it. A Giant fumble recovered on the Giant 20 by Gene Lipscomb, the 288-pound Colt Tackle, set up the first touchdown. Unitas punctured the Giant line with Ameche and Moore and sent Moore outside end once when the Giant center clogged up, and then Ameche scored from the 2 and it all looked very easy.

It looked easy on the next Colt foray, too.

This one started on the Baltimore 14 and moved inevitably downfield. The Colt backs, following the quick, vicious thrust of the big line, went 5 and 6 yards at a time, the plays ending in a quick-settling swirl of dust as the Giant line, swept back in a flashing surge of white Colt uniforms, then slipped the blocks to make the belated tackles. Unitas passed twice to Berry, the second time for 15 yards and the second Colt touchdown. The Giants, now 11 points behind, looked well whipped.

The feeling of the game changed suddenly and dramatically late in the third quarter on the one accomplishment which most often reverses the trend in a football game—the denial of a sure touchdown. The Colts had moved almost contemptuously to the Giant 3-yard line. After the half the Baltimore team, which had manhandled the New York defense to gain on the ground for most of the first half, switched to passing. Unitas, given marvelous blocking by the Colt offensive line, picked apart the Giant defensive secondary with his wonderful passes, thrown so accurately that often Colt receivers snatched the ball from between two Giant defenders who were only a half step out of position. When this irresistible passing attack carried them to the Giant 3-yard line, first down and goal to go, even the most optimistic Giant fans in the stands must have given up.

But the Giant defense, which, more than anything else, brought this team to the championship game, again coped with crisis and stopped Baltimore cold.

Now, for the rest of this quarter and most of the fourth, the Colts were surprisingly limp. The Giant stand keyed their collapse, but an odd play which set up the first Giant touchdown underlined it and so demoralized the Baltimore team that for some time it was nearly ineffectual. Conerly, quick to capitalize on the letdown, sent Kyle Rote, who usually spends his afternoon catching short passes, rocketing far downfield. Rote, starting down the left sideline, cut sharply to his right, and Conerly's pass intersected his course at the Colt 40. Rote carried on down to the 25 and ran into a two-man tackle which made him fumble. There was a paralyzed second when a little group of Colt and Giant players watched the ball bounding free without making a move, then the still life broke into violent motion and Giant Halfback Alex Webster picked up the fumble and carried it to the Colt 1-yard line. Mel Triplett hurdled in for a touchdown and the Giants, fans and all, were back in the game. The crowd, which had been desperately yelling, "Go-o-o-o-o, Giants," roared as if the Giants had taken the lead. And the Giants did, quickly.

The Colt offense, until now clean and quick and precise, began to dodder. The protection which had allowed Unitas to wait and wait and wait before he threw, broke down, and Robustelli and Dick Modzelewski ran through weak blocks to dump the Colt quarterback for long losses. The Giants, on the other hand, were operating with the assurance of experience and a long intimacy with the uses of adversity.

They took the lead on the second play of the fourth quarter. Conerly, who had been throwing to Rote and Gifford, suddenly switched targets. He zeroed in on End Bob Schnelker once for 17 yards and repeated on the next play for 46 more and a first down on the Baltimore 15. Then he befuddled the Colt secondary with Schnelker and threw to Gifford on the right sideline, and Gifford ran through a spaghetti-arm tackle on the 5 to score, sending the Giants into a 17–14 lead.

The Colts now seemed as thoroughly beaten as the Giants had been at the half. Unitas' protection, so solid early in the game, leaked woefully. Only a Giant fumble slowed the New York attack, and when the Giants punted to the Colts with barely two minutes left in the game, not even the most optimistic of the twenty-odd thousand Colt fans who came from Baltimore would have bet on victory.

Baltimore started from its 14, and the hero of this sequence was, of all the fine players on the field this warm winter day, the most unlikely. He has a bad back and one leg is shorter than the other so that he wears mud cleats on that shoe to equalize them. His eyes are so bad that he must wear contact lenses when he plays. He is not very fast and, although he was a good college end, he was far from a great one. On this march, he caught three passes in a row for a total of 62 yards, the last one for 22 yards to the New York 13-yard line. His name is Ray Berry, and he has the surest hands in professional football. He caught the three passes with two Giant defenders guarding him each time. He caught 12 passes for 178 yards in this football game, and without him the Colts would surely have lost.

After Berry had picked the ball out of the hands of two Giant defenders on the New York 13-yard line, Steve Myhra kicked a 20-yard field goal with seven seconds left to play for a 17–17 tie which sent the game into the sudden-death overtime period. The teams rested for three minutes, flipped a coin to see which would kick and which receive, and the Giants won and took the kickoff.

The tremendous tension held the crowd in massing excitement. But the Giants, the fine fervor of their rally gone, could not respond to this last challenge. They were forced to punt, and the Colts took over on their own 20. Unitas, mixing runs and passes carefully and throwing the ball wonderfully true under this pressure, moved them downfield surely. The big maneuver sent Ameche up the middle on a trap play which broke him through the overanxious Giant line for 23 yards to the Giant 20. From there Unitas threw to the ubiquitous Berry for a first down on the New York 8, and three plays later Baltimore scored to end the game. Just before the touchdown a deliriously happy Baltimore football fan raced onto the field during a time-out and sailed 80 yards, bound for the Baltimore huddle, before the police secondary intercepted him and hauled him to the sideline. He was grinning with idiot glee, and the whole city of Baltimore sympathized with him. One Baltimore fan, listening on his auto radio, ran into a telephone pole when Myhra kicked the tying field goal, and 30,000 others waited to greet the returning heroes.

Berry, a thin, tired-looking youngster still dazed with the victory, seemed to speak for the team and for fans everywhere after the game.

"It's the greatest thing that ever happened," he said.

"Now, because you guys won such a great victory last Saturday, before we look at the movies of the game we're going to run off a couple of Mickey Mouses."

CARTOON BY STEVENSON

© The New Yorker Magazine, Inc.

"We needed that yard, Bascomb!"

CARTOON BY GALLAGHER

© the Curtis Publishing Company

High school football in Martins Ferry, Ohio, and rival towns in The Valley is a way of life—and a way to get ahead in the outside world.

RULE ONE: WIN OR ELSE

John R. McDermott

All dressed out in their best bibs and wind-breakers, the members of the Martins Ferry Lions Club stared vacantly down at the bare bones of their fried chicken dinner. Up on the speaker's dais, the new football coach of Martins Ferry High, Bob Wion, was winding up his maiden speech. "So you see," he explained, "my job is not really to win football games. It's to make better citizens out of each and every one of your boys. If we don't win a game all season—and still accomplish that—I'll be happy."

From the chilly stillness in the room boomed an impatient, bass denial—in the form of a shouted obscenity—from one of the members. It broke up the meeting. When all the guffaws and knee-slapping stopped, so did Wion. He muttered his purple-faced thanks and sat down. As the after-dinner smoke cleared, one chari-table diner approached Wion and said, "Don't feel too bad about what happened, Coach. Remember one thing—we're with you, win or tie."

What Wion discovered after being thrown to the Lions was what every other coach of the Ohio Valley Athletic Conference already knew. It is all right for a coach to build solid American character. But if these good citizens lose their game on Friday night, the coach would be well advised not to show his face in town on Saturday. "A losing coach doesn't walk down the street the next day," says one. "He walks down the alleys."

The parents put such a premium on winning football games for hardboiled, practical rea-sons. "Football," says one of them, "is trans-portation out of here." Last year football trans-ported four Martins Ferry starters via football scholarships to West Virginia, Tennessee, Indi-ana and the Air Force Academy. Gene Minder, a millworker and father of two Ferry High tackles, explains: "I told my two boys that if they wanted to amount to something better than their dad they would have to play football. I wasn't lucky enough to play ball. In them days you went down to the stadium and asked for a uniform. They had one size—big. If you wasn't big enough they would just laugh. I kept going down there and they kept laughing. I swore my boys would wear those uniforms. So I raised them on love and spaghetti."

Most parents flavor the pasta and affection recipe with stiff discipline. In mill towns like Martins Ferry this is likely to take violent forms. Wion received an urgent phone call one night from his 225-pound star fullback who ex-plained frantically that he had arrived home three minutes after the 10 p.m. training curfew. "Coach, talk to my Pop, will you?" the player pleaded. "He's bouncing me off the walls down here."

The players themselves dispense their own discipline. At Martins Ferry the team holds trials for players who have broken the code. The team's own sense of justice never fails to astonish Wion. They were perfectly willing to take a boy back on the squad after he had spent a year in the state reformatory, but voted thumbs down on a player who had skipped practice four nights in a row. One boy, accused of getting home a full 10 seconds after curfew, got off with a warning from the team captain that "10 seconds leads to 20 seconds and pretty soon you're out for a half hour. If it happens again, Bobby, we'll—uh—take care of you, see?"

What the players and parents miss, the teachers catch. Though they are lionized by their fellow students, the players know better than to cut up in classes. Sturdy instructors like Ferry High's Latin teacher, Miss Heloise Knapp (fiftyish, 5 feet 10 inches, 190 pounds), can drag a linebacker out of class by his ear faster than he can red dog an enemy quarterback. "I've got players," said Wion, "who can call signals better in Latin than they can in English."

While football provides for the players' futures it also performs a very real service for the town. In Martins Ferry, population 12,000, it provides 8,000 people with entertainment on fall Friday nights. Amid the depressing atmosphere of the mill town, where men missing fingers or arms or legs wander the streets, juvenile delinquency is virtually unknown. Equally astounding is the way football builds school spirit and keeps boys from dropping out. In a school of 456 male students, Martins Ferry had only four dropouts this year. "Our people are hard-working and hard-living mill hands and miners," says School Superintendent Harold Meyer. "The very nature of the animal has left its imprint on our kids. But football has been able to keep it within bounds. Lord, are we grateful for that."

Thus no one wonders that Martins Ferry, the birthplace of William Dean Howells of American literature, is more renowned as the birthplace of Lou Groza, the kicking star of the Cleveland Browns. Mrs. Groza still runs the tavern where her son, "The Toe," was born —though with less *elan* since she was held up a year ago by two masked citizens who thereby demonstrated another of the chief occupational hazards for Valley merchants. ("They'd still be at it," says Ma Groza, "if they hadn't shot that young man up at the A&P.")

The biggest football hazard by far confronts the coach. This hazard is known, in all innocence, as the team Booster Club. Composed of well-meaning downtown merchants, it sells tickets and programs, raises money for football equipment, arranges for a team's transportation and otherwise helps with scores of items that cannot be fitted into a school's skimpy budget. In return these downtown quarterbacks expect to have some say about how the team is run. In Valley mill towns this say-so can get pretty salty.

In one town, after the coach had lost three games in a row, he woke up one morning to find a large FOR SALE sign on his front lawn. At the barbershop and around town he saw small signs which read, "So long, Ed" and "It's been nice knowing you, Ed."

One booster group presented its coach with a new automobile after an undefeated season. The following fall, after the team lost two games, it took up a collection to buy the coach fifteen gallons of gas and a road map. The message was loud and clear.

A coach is often protected from these unsubtle tactics by his team. Players have been known to leave home because their parents spoke out against their leader. When a fan started riding Bob Wion during a losing game some seasons ago with cries "When does your train leave, Coach?" one of Wion's players leaped into the stands and closed the fan's mouth and left eye.

Wion, touched by such votes of confidence, was moved once to return it in kind by assaulting a former deputy sheriff who was abusing one of his boys. This impulsive act cost Wion $500 and his victim 18 stitches in his forehead.

Gambling, one of the Valley's most controversial if *sub rosa* industries, contributes to football. Though the bigtime dice operators never make book on a high school game, they will use their gambling table muscle to help raise money for flu shots for the high school team. In this region it is the highest form of patriotism.

Mercifully, the dice men are a Valley minority. Though they could be a demoralizing influence on the impressionable youngsters, the kids out for football are too occupied looking up to the Valley's heroes. What boy in Bellaire, for example, would not work and fight for a chance to be as famous as former lineman Jim Harris, who is revered around town not only as a successful coach at Holy Cross but also as the man who was the last substitute Knute Rockne ever made. To match that— wouldn't that be something?

Season after season much of the best and toughest high school football
in the country is played in towns scattered along a short stretch
of the Ohio River Valley near Steubenville, Ohio, and Wheeling, West
Virginia. For these sons of miners and millworkers, football is
more than recreation: it offers an opportunity to leave the Valley
and go on to college. In photographs on these pages MARK KAUFFMAN
reveals the determined mood with which football is played in the Valley.

Game day at Bellaire, Ohio

Into the mud . . .

. . . after a pre-game prayer

Strategy around a locker-room stove

Part of the grind is getting to practice.

197

This was Kyle Rote's day—December 4, 1949—as recorded in the sports pages of the Des Moines Register-Tribune.

ALMOST BY ROTE

Bert McGrane

Kyle Rote, a trim, 190-pound package of poise and daring, patrolled the end of the Notre Dame road here Saturday and almost wrecked the fabulous Irish with his sensational versatility.

Notre Dame won, 27–20, but it was Southern Methodist's indomitable array that dashed away, chins high, at the finish, with most of the 75,457 customers who jammed the Cotton Bowl still roaring a Mustang tribute that began with the kickoff and hasn't ended yet.

This was a hair-lifting, breathtaking uprising by an underdog team that positively could not have made a greater effort.

The effort was not quite effective enough, however, so Notre Dame finished its fourth straight undefeated season, climaxed its national championship drive with victory No. 10 and stretched to 38 its string of games without defeat.

The Irish scored the winning touchdown late in the final quarter, Bill Barrett going over from the S.M.U. six.

And what inspired opposition the Irish survived in pulling out the triumph after Southern Methodist had tied the score at 20–20 in as brilliant and deadly a last-half assault as you'll ever see!

There was Rote, always concocting some-thing fiendishly effective to explode in the faces of the Irish. Because of him the indomitable Notre Dame poise faded out.

Those Irish almost never had an easy moment. Mostly they were constantly confronted by possible disaster.

They saw the Mustangs start with a wide spread formation featuring a double flanker, take to the air on the very first play and use that air threat all the way.

With Rote's cunning deception they used the pass threat to pile up substantial yardage on the ground. The Irish secondary just didn't dare move up for a tackle when Rote had that ball.

There wasn't a more brilliant player on the field than Rote. He ran for a net total of 115 yards in 24 tries and completed 10 passes for 146 more.

But it was the direction, the dazzling leadership he provided that threw the scare into the Irish.

The guy was great. Southern Methodist played without its famed Doak Walker but, in the face of the remarkable demonstration by Rote against the team that has earned the No. 1 spot in the nation, this observer respectfully inquires:

Who's Walker? If he's better than Rote was

198

this bleak and hazy afternoon he's something more than human.

Rote started by firing an 11-yard pass to Zohn Milam on the first play. He hit Dick McKissack with a shorter shot next, then fired for 10 to Rusty Russell. Three plays, three throws, three completions.

That's how it started. There's reason to believe that the dazzling tactics of the Mustangs had not been entirely anticipated by the Irish. Their defense indicated that much.

They seemed jittery as they met Rote's versatile operations with a 5-3-2-1 or a 5-4-2 defense.

And spearheading that Irish defense was a man who stood out with the daring Mustang leader, but in a far different role.

He was Jerry Groom of Des Moines, the one-time Dowling star who intercepted two Mustang passes in telling spots, blocked the conversion kick that would have put Southern Methodist ahead in the fourth quarter, and felled runners or wrecked pass attempts throughout the afternoon.

It was Groom's first-quarter interception that stopped the Mustangs after they had connected on three straight throws.

His theft gave the Irish a scoring chance from Southern Methodist's 31 but they couldn't do anything about it. A clipping penalty and a loss in yardage resulted, instead.

They fought a give-and-take game through most of the first quarter but near its end one of Fred Benner's passes was captured by John Petibon of Notre Dame. Benner alternated with Rote in passing for S.M.U.

Notre Dame swung into gear and it looked like Irish superiority immediately would assert itself. The Irish marched 73 yards in seven plays for a touchdown.

Bobby Williams arched a long pass downfield from the S.M.U. 42 while Bill Wightkin raced under it. He caught it behind Rote on the 7 and plowed on into the end zone. Steve Oracko's kick gave Notre Dame a 7–0 lead.

The first quarter faded out and Southern Methodist lifted the scalps of the bystanders with its sensational retaliation.

From his 17 following a Notre Dame punt, Rote swung wide to his right. Far out, he slipped the ball to John Champion on a handoff. Meanwhile, Milam had streaked downfield, a football mile beyond the Notre Dame secondary.

Milam took the lengthy pass from Champion and streaked on for a 78-yard gain. And it was only master maneuvering by Mike Swistowicz

in evading blockers that Milam was stopped at all.

Swistowicz finally bounced him over the sideline on the Notre Dame 6.

There were the Mustangs, just 6 yards from the tying touchdown. Three desperate plays put the ball just a foot short of the Irish goal.

But when they untangled after fourth down, Rote's power attempt ended 6 inches short of the goal and Notre Dame took the ball.

Then followed another spine-tingler. Williams, attempting a sneak for the Irish, barely got out to the 1-foot line. Two plays later, with the ball on his 1, he faded into the end zone, was hit down, and the ball bounded away from him.

They racked up a safety on the scoreboard but, after long discussion by the officials, the play was ruled an incomplete pass and the two points were not charged against Notre Dame.

The Irish got out of that hole and in short order they were marching again. They took the ball on the Mustang 34 when Bill Gay intercepted a pass. They rolled to the 20 in four plays.

From that spot Williams passed into the end zone and the pass couldn't have been better covered. Zohn Milam, Bob Folsom and Bill Richards all were there to take care of Ernie Zalejski, the intended receiver.

But the ball bounced off the anxious hands of one of the Mustang defenders and it dropped into Zalejski's arms as he ran across the end zone.

So touchdown No. 2 for the Irish included a big break with a Notre Dame tinge to it. Oracko missed the kick and Notre Dame held its 13–0 margin through the half.

In the face of Southern Methodist's inspired play the Irish had not been exactly dominant in the first half. And things went badly for them in the third quarter.

They had driven ahead on a kickoff march to the Mustang 16 early in the third period. Then Zalejski bolted through tackle for 8 yards and dropped the ball, S.M.U. recovering.

The Mustangs punted out and the Irish were starting back again when, from his own 44, Zalejski raced away for 18 yards—and fumbled again. Once more the Mustangs recovered.

This time they drove through Notre Dame with fury. Rote, using his threat of a pass to the very utmost, ran for 15 and followed with 23 more.

Then he sent Champion through Notre Dame's right tackle as a reverse for another 18 yards, this time to the 3.

This time Rote bolted through a gap at Notre Dame's right tackle and scored standing up. Bill Sullivan kicked the point.

Southern Methodist was tougher than ever now. But Notre Dame wasn't exactly quitting. It was football for men out there, with the tackles and blocks bordering on the savage.

The Irish, storming downfield, reached the Mustang 35 when Williams fired a jump pass to Wightkin. Bill caught it, then fumbled on the S.M.U. 17 and Notre Dame lost the ball again.

But that was offset in a moment. Rote launched a hurried pass which was hit by an Irish arm. Jim Mutscheller captured it on the Mustang 22.

A pass to Hart and a lateral to Frank Spaniel put it on the 12 and Bill Barrett and John Landry bucked it through to the 7.

Hart, hitting from fullback, went 3 before Barrett raced wide around the Mustang right end for the third Notre Dame score. Oracko's kick made it 20–7.

Two plays after the ensuing kickoff the Mustangs were almost responsible for mass heart failure. Rote spun a pass upfield to Champion, who raced down the sideline, saw his path cleared by Milam with a mighty block, and stormed on for 68 yards.

Another desperation tackle by Swistowicz, this one from behind, brought Champion down on the 1-foot line. And Rote stormed over the pile on the next play to score. Sullivan kicked the point and it was 20–14.

Southern Methodist was on fire now, and the structure of the Cotton Bowl must have tottered under the din.

The Mustangs kicked off to Notre Dame. It was fourth quarter now. Spaniel ran the kick-off out to his 22 but Notre Dame was charged with clipping on the play and penalized back to its 1.

The tumult was deafening.

On the first Irish play the wild Mustang charge threw Barrett for a 2-foot loss—dumped him on his 1-foot line.

Williams punted—a fine kick to midfield but Champion came flying up to take it and sprinted clear down to Notre Dame's 14 before he was tackled.

The Mustangs were literally scorching the Irish with their flame.

Rote, using his pass threat again, stormed outside Notre Dame's right end for 11 yards to put the ball on the 3. And don't think those Irish defenders weren't tumbling head over heels before the S.M.U. blockers.

Groom stopped Rote on the next play but on the following effort Rote found a gap at Notre Dame's right tackle and scored. It was 20–20.

Billy Sullivan, a lad with an Irish name in a Mustang uniform, made careful preparations for the kick.

As he kicked Groom of Notre Dame shot through like a bullet to block the point that would have put S.M.U. ahead.

A dozen minutes remained. Notre Dame bounded back, receiving the kickoff and running it back to its 44, then moving 56 yards in ten plays to regain the lead. It was Barrett and Sitko now, with Hart powering from fullback once and Bill Gay hurtling through for a gain.

With the ball on the 5, Barrett bolted around the Mustang right end for the final touchdown. Oracko's kick gave the Irish their ultimate 27–20 lead.

Something over six minutes remained after Notre Dame regained the lead and in the first three of them Rote froze the hearts of Notre Dame followers with another thrilling advance. He passed and he ran. He covered ground in no time at all.

And it looked like curtains for Notre Dame, when, on fourth down on his 28 with 11 yards to go, Rote jogged off and Fred Benner came in as drillmaster for S.M.U.

Benner's fourth-down pass to Rusty Russell covered 23 yards and put the ball on Notre Dame's 5.

Groom took charge for the Irish. He stacked up Russell for a yard loss on the next play and two plays farther along snatched Rote's jump pass on his 2 and killed the Mustang threat by running the ball out to the Notre Dame 7.

After that, the Irish controlled the ball until the end.

It must have been the toughest game Notre Dame had experienced in all of its four-year string.

And when it was over Coach Frank Leahy called the Irish, who were so sorely pressed all the way, the greatest team he has coached.

This short game account belongs because it was the result of a famous columnist's trip to the Rockies to witness, first hand, the exploits of one Byron (Whizzer) White. The Denver Post *ran McLemore's story, November 7, 1937, under the headline, "White Amazes Noted Writer With Spectacular Scoring Runs"—all of which would be an embarrassment to the U.S. Supreme Court Justice today.*

THE WHIZZER VS. UTAH

Henry McLemore

Byron (Whizzer) White, Colorado University's sensational quarterback, picked up the white man's burden again Saturday and single-handed carried his team to a 17–7 victory over a big and strong Utah eleven.

White, one of the nation's top scorers, lifted his season's total to 79 points, and kept Colorado in the select undefeated and untied class by tallying 17 points. He started his great day's work with a 15-yard placement kick, and followed with amazing touchdown runs of 95 and 57 yards.

Utah, the underdog in the betting, was leading 7–3 when the fourth period opened, and the partisan crowd of more than 18,000 had high hopes for Utah's first victory over Colorado in three years. But on the first play of this period White took a high punt on his own 12-yard line and never stopped until the last stripe was crossed. As he caught the ball six Utah men surrounded him and drove him back to his own 5-yard line, and apparently pinned him in a corner. But they couldn't put their hands on him. Twisting, squirming, ducking and dodging, he eluded them and set out down the sidelines. Once in the clear he put on full speed ahead and simply outran his pursuers.

A few seconds later he kicked the extra point, putting Colorado out in front, 10–7.

In the middle of the period Whizzer, on a straight off tackle slant, once more broke into the open and headed for home. With Utah tacklers all about him, he cut to the sidelines and, coolly picking up blockers as he went, swept 57 yards for the score that definitely ended Utah's hopes. Again he booted the extra point.

White started the Colorado scoring in the third period with a perfect place-kick. He put the ball in position for the kick with a brace of long end runs, and a long pass to Halfback Antonio. This lead did not last long because Utah, after being balked on the 1-yard line early in the quarter scored on a brilliant 75-yard return of a punt by Halfback Gene Cooper. This little fellow, who was a menace to the enemy all afternoon, took one of White's long boots on his own 25-yard stripe, and, behind deadly blocking, scampered through the entire Colorado eleven.

White drove through two blockers on the 5-yard line to collar Cooper but the little fellow carried him across. Page added the extra point. Utah, supposedly a team with little or no offense, tested Colorado's line to the limit in the

201

first half. In the second period the Redskins drove to the 1-yard stripe before being hurled back, and twice moved so close that attempted field goals missed by inches.

The leaders in these drives were Cooper and Karl Schleckman, a really fine tackle who tore the opposing line to ribbons with his charges. The game between the old mountain rivals was savagely fought, with nearly 100 yards being meted out for rough play. On White's final touchdown dash, Dewey Gunn, Utah tackle, suffered a compound fracture of the left leg.

"That was only the end of the first quarter...!"

CARTOON BY GALLAGHER

In 1950, the late New Yorker *writer John McNulty, so long identified with the City, the people and places on Third Avenue, and the racetracks just beyond the city limits, visited Columbus, Ohio, for Homecoming Week. It was, in a way, homecoming for McNulty, too. Although he was an easterner, born in Lawrence, Massachusetts, he had spent a dozen years, beginning in the early 1920's, as a newspaper reporter in Columbus. One of his friends on the rival paper in town was James Thurber. McNulty went back to Columbus to observe the week-long buildup of civic hysteria for the Ohio State-Michigan game. The '50 game, played in a raging blizzard, turned into one of the most bizarre homecomings ever at O.S.U. Good newspaperman that he always was, McNulty stuck it out with the 50,000-odd people who refused to stay away from the stadium.*

RETURN TO COLUMBUS

John McNulty

One night a few weeks ago, while I was having a smoke on a sidewalk on West Forty-eighth Street between the acts of a play, I met Warren Park, a man I used to know in Columbus, Ohio.

"You ought to come out to Columbus and see the old place," he said after we had exchanged a few pleasantries about the play. "They've gone entirely nuts this year on football."

"They always do in Columbus. Craziest football town in the world," I said. I used to live out there many years ago.

"But they're worse than ever this year," Warren said. "On account of Ohio State being just about the best team in the country."

"That's what I see in the papers," I said.

"Come on out for Homecoming Week, why don't you?" he suggested.

"O.K., maybe I shall," I answered. And I did go out there, leaving New York the Tuesday before the Saturday of the game with Michigan. The last game of the season is always the one with Michigan, and it is always, on the alternate years it is played at Columbus, the Homecoming Game.

It didn't take long, wandering around Columbus after I arrived there on Wednesday, the day before Thanksgiving, to discover that Homecoming Week is observed just as fervently as it ever was. Everywhere I went, preparations were being made for the returning alumni. One reason Ohio grads return for Homecoming Week is that they hate the State of Michigan so much—in a nice way, of course. This is odd reasoning, but that's how it is. There was some gloom in the town, because on the Saturday before, after my brief talk with Warren Park, Ohio State had been defeated, 14–7, by Illinois. That marred the record somewhat, but by the time I reached the city, the 374,770 residents of Columbus (1950 census) were madly intent upon the game with Michigan, for by defeating Michigan, Ohio State would cinch the championship of the Western Conference—the Big Ten. So universal is football daffiness in the region that during the recent political campaign, one canard circulated about a candidate had it that his entire foreign policy could be summed up in two words: "Beat Michigan!"

The rivalry between the states of Michigan and Ohio is apparently part real, part synthetic. It has been going on for a hundred and fifteen years, since 1835, at which time Ohio and Michigan were at war with each other. At least, there was an armed shindy between the two, perhaps the most hot-tempered incident of the sort in our history, not counting the Civil War, of course.

Hugh Huntington, a Columbus attorney with a liking for history, once dug into the past and came up with the information for football fans that the war between Ohio and Michigan started when the Northwest Territory was being broken up into five states. It was originally provided that the line separating Michigan from Ohio and Indiana should run east and west through the southern tip of Lake Michigan, extending eastward to the territorial line in Lake Erie. That brought the boundary south of the city of Toledo and put Toledo in Michigan. "However, when Ohio was made a state," Mr. Huntington told some friends, "its constitution provided that the boundary should be on a line from the southern tip of Lake Michigan to the north cape of Maumee Bay, in Lake Erie. That was eight miles farther north and put Toledo in Ohio. The matter came up in Congress, and the then Representative John Quincy Adams made a recommendation in favor of Michigan and against Ohio. The Ohio legislature immediately passed an act providing that Ohio law and Ohio officials would govern the disputed territory. Michigan did exactly the same thing, favoring Michigan, naturally, and two sets of officials were elected—one set of Ohioans, one set of Michiganders—in the April, 1835, voting."

The sheriff of Monroe County, Michigan, organized a posse and carted some Ohio partisans off to jail, and all hell broke loose. An Ohio prosecutor then obtained an indictment against Governor Mason, of Michigan, and double-dared him to come to Ohio and be arrested. Mason refused. "Governor Lucas, of Ohio, levied troops and moved into the eight-mile zone north of Toledo," Huntington said. "Governor Mason, on his side, levied troops, who marched around the Ohio military and seized Toledo from the south. The Michigan rowdies, as one account put it, 'overran the watermelon patches and robbed all the hen roosts.' The Michiganders had to live off the country because the Ohio army had cut off their supplies."

The war was ended when President Andrew Jackson sent two commissioners from Washington to study the situation. On the basis of their findings, Congress gave the eight-mile strip to Ohio but placated Michigan by giving her the large and now valuable Northern Peninsula, taking it away from Wisconsin. "There were

few inhabitants in Wisconsin and they neither knew nor cared what became of the Peninsula," Mr. Huntington said. "Michigan and Ohio have had a hundred and fifteen years of honorable fighting history. There have been no deaths and few casualties, but both sides have had an immense amount of fun in those hundred and fifteen years. In recent years the fighting has been especially inspiring."

I began to realize just how synthetic much of the rivalry between the universities is these days when I came across William G. Wilcox, public relations director of Ohio State University, and he said to me, "We are endeavoring to start a new tradition at the Michigan game this Saturday." The notion of a new tradition's being laboriously and cold-bloodedly established struck me as peculiar, and I asked him what he meant. He explained that Dick Sims, president of Sphinx, a senior men's honorary society at Ohio State, was to present the Toledo Cannon, which may or may not be a relic of the ancient war, to the Ohio State, or Buckeye, student body between the halves of the game, as a symbol of the Ohio-Michigan rivalry. "The secret about it is," said Mr. Wilcox, further clarifying the process of starting a new tradition, "that sometime next week Michigan is going to steal the cannon, and won't give it back until the next time Ohio State beats Michigan. That's the secret part, the stealing. I believe it will be a good tradition, don't you?" I agreed that, as traditions go, it seemed good enough.

I was rather surprised to find that, as one Columbusite after another buttonholed me, it was not Vic Janowicz, the star Ohio State player —or the football team at all, for that matter— that I was told about. Instead, it was the band, and the wonders the band would perform before the game and between the halves. The whole city, it appeared, had been terribly hurt when LIFE, not long before, had called Michigan's band the best in the land. That was more than Columbus, and a large part of the rest of Ohio, could take.

"Would you have felt so bad if LIFE had said Michigan had the best football team?" I asked one man.

"No, I don't think so. No, we wouldn't," he replied. "There's room for argument about that, perhaps. But there can't be any argument about the band. Everybody knows we've got the best marching band in the whole history of music in the world."

There were even remarks about treason in connection with the bands. I was frequently told that Michigan's band wouldn't amount to a row of pins if Michigan, in its snide way, had not managed to lure a graduate of Ohio State to Ann Arbor to direct its band. "After all," wrote Roger Nelson in the *Ohio State Journal* column called "Broad and High" (that's the principal corner in Columbus), "the Michigan band copies the Ohio State formations, lock, stock, and barrel. A Buckeye grad is at the helm of Wolverine formations and he's taught them what he learned on the Ohio State campus."

Only one old grad among the dozens I talked to before the game was at all irreverent about the band situation. "Personally, I think Ohio State will win Saturday's game by twelve trombones," he said.

In my wanderings about the town, I happened to come across an advance copy of the official program, and therein I studied a synopsis of the marvels that were planned by the band for Saturday. It read:

Entering from the north end of stadium in ten files, the Band steps onto the field to the tune of the "Ohio Bugle March." As the front man in each file reaches the 20-yard line, they suddenly turn and the spectator is confronted with three lines stretching across the field. To the tune of the "Buckeye Battle Cry" three lines surge towards the south goal posts. As they reach the middle of the field, they pivot and turn and pivot again in a flashing drill. To the tune of "Michigan Victors" the steady rise and fall of white spats takes the Band into a large "M."

A fancy about-face heads the group for the west sidelines and the outline of a camel takes form as the music changes to "In a Persian Garden." The loudspeaker informs the spectators that this is a saga of the buckeye and that originally the buckeye came from Persia bringing with it Persian mystery, glamour, and magic. During this announcement the Band forms the outline of a dancing girl who dances to the accompanying music. "The Last Time I Saw Paris" takes the Band into the outline of the Eiffel Tower as the loudspeaker points out the fact that in France the starch of the buckeye is used in laundering clothes. During this announcement, the formation changes to an old-fashioned washing machine and Bandsmen go through the wringer to show the effect of the starch that is in the buckeye.

Next, a tepee takes form upon the field and Indian dancers point up the fact that the Indians were the only folk capable of overcoming the bitterness of the buckeye in using it as food.

Suddenly the music of Oley Speaks' "Trees" bursts forth and the Band marches into the outline of the buckeye leaf. The Band halts and a solitary trumpet plays the music which accompanies the lines, "Poems are made by fools like me." The Band crescendos to a large forte with the music to the lines, "But only God can make a tree." As the final chord is reached, banners unfurl on each side of the leaf formation showing the new Band patch donated to the Band by Milt Caniff [the cartoonist is a Buckeye graduate] and the new University flag authorized by the Board of Trustees. With the beautiful new emblem outlined on the field, the strains of "Carmen Ohio" now echo through the stadium and loyal Buckeyes all over the world are urged to join in the singing of the Alma Mater.

Some of the intricate maneuvers thus described appeared to me to be only remotely pertinent to the game of football. Still, as an old softy with a weakness for the tingling effect on the spine of massive bands swinging into college songs, I looked forward to the game and its attendant music with zest.

"The band is one of the biggest things in university life here," I was told by Ed Penisten, as loyal an old grad and sports authority as Ohio State has. "There's a waiting list to get on the band that's probably longer than the list of those trying to get on the football team." Shortly after my chat with Mr. Penisten, I saw in the *Dispatch* an ad that read:

A skilled and flashy baton twirler, boy or girl of any age, is bound to be held in high esteem in Columbus. Time and time again that week, I heard at football luncheons and dinner parties (in Columbus, most luncheons and dinner parties for several days before the big game are football affairs) glowing praise of two Ohio State immortals. One was Chic Harley, believed in Ohio to be the greatest football player who ever lived. He was All-America in 1916, 1917, and 1919. The other immortal, about whom I heard as much as I did about the peerless Harley, was Tubby Essington, reputed to be the most spectacular drum major and strutter who ever twirled a baton. Tubby flourished some thirty years ago, shortly after the Harley era.

This year's Ohio State-Michigan game was sold out last August. Enough, and more, applications for tickets were received by return mail after the announcement that they had gone on sale to dispose of every seat available, and the assumption was that the attendance would be the maximum 82,300. The normal seating capacity of the stadium, stretched tryingly for the game with Michigan, is 78,413. Laid out like a horseshoe, with walls ninety-eight feet high, the stadium covers ten acres. It cost $1,341,000 to build it, in 1922, and because the admission fees paid by the crowds that Chic Harley had attracted went a long way toward providing that sum, the stadium is frequently referred to around Broad and High Streets as "the house that Harley built."

Hotel reservations for the weekend of the Michigan game start coming in to Columbus and towns nearby six or seven months ahead. "We've been booked up for this weekend for several months," Tom Sabrey, of the 655-room Neil House, told me. "Some applications were made as early as last April, and all we have accepted have been paid for in advance." Nevertheless, a late cancellation enabled Mr. Sabrey to give me a front room in in his establishment, facing South High Street. Looking out my window, I could see, in the yard of the State House, a statue of President William McKinley. The statue was put up as a sentimental tribute to McKinley, who, when he was Governor of Ohio, lived at the old Neil House (torn down years ago to make way for the present hotel). McKinley's wife was an invalid, and she used to sit in a wheelchair at a window of their suite, and each morning her husband would turn and wave to her as he walked through the State House yard on his way to the Governor's office. The statue stands just about at the spot where he used to turn and wave. Columbus is like that.

From my window, I could also see the northeast corner of the State House yard, the corner where, I remembered, a truckload of penitentiary trusties used to arrive each workday morning when I was living in the town. They'd jump off the truck and saunter up through the State House yard on their way to such chores as cleaning and sweeping the State House offices, mowing lawns, and raking leaves. At noon, they'd assemble on the same corner to be taken back to the prison for lunch, and then they'd return to the State House for the afternoon, and go back to dinner and their cells at night. In summer, some of them would be dressed in sporty-looking trousers made from remnants of the blue-and-white-striped ticking the convicts used in making mattresses for public institutions—one of the prison industries. The trousers, worn with a white shirt and sneakers, created a gay ensemble that was in sharp contrast to the grim walls the men had left behind them. The vogue for this ticking as a sports fabric, I have noticed, has since spread to folk who are innocent of penitentiary offenses.

It began snowing on the evening of Thanksgiving Day. The snow continued, intermittently, all day Friday. That day, the thousands arriving in town for the game looked like extraordinarily well-to-do refugees from a war-torn region, so laden were they with parkas, blankets, boots, sweaters, Daniel Boone caps, stocking caps, heating devices, binoculars, umbrellas, bags, and suitcases. Bellboys were all but immobilized by the travellers' impedimenta. The lobby of the Deshler-Wallick Hotel (about a thousand rooms) had been stripped of furniture as a precaution against the antics of its share of the throng. Restaurants were jammed at every meal, of course, and toward evening the rapidly heightening storm, with its numbing effect on traffic, warned of a tough Homecoming. As things turned out, it didn't warn half enough.

By Saturday morning, more than nine inches of snow had fallen, and it was still snowing. Hopefully, the Weather Bureau predicted a tolerable fifteen degrees above zero for the game, but at midmorning the temperature was down to seven and a stiff wind was blowing. The roads to the stadium were clogged. The temperature continued to drop, the wind rose, and the snow fell more thickly. By noon, the snow was no longer falling, really, but was being driven horizontally by the bitter wind.

Suddenly, tickets, which had been impossible to procure for nearly four months, became readily available. In the restaurants, they were being offered at their original prices to the lines of customers waiting for tables. Here and there, a frightened scalper offered a pair at less than box-office prices—and found no takers.

Every Saturday on which Ohio State plays a home game, a luncheon for about four hundred of the elite among the faculty members, officials, distinguished alumni, and prominent Columbusites is given at the stadium itself, in a section of a dormitory built under the stands. This time, only about two hundred guests managed to fight their way through the blizzard to attend. Dr. Howard L. Bevis, president of the University, loyally made it, and stood in the receiving line as snow-covered guests staggered in with the latest bulletins on the storm. "It's nearly zero now and the wind is getting tougher," one announced. Word went around that the band would not play. It would be impossible in that cold to put lip to mouthpiece, people said. "The plan is to go through with the maneuvers and use canned music for it," a courier reported.

The Michigan team, making the trip aboard a special train from Ann Arbor, had spent the night in Toledo. By Saturday noon, railroad travel was coming to a halt all over Ohio, but the train got through, and, together with two or three special trains loaded with fans from Detroit, pulled up on a spur a quarter of a mile from the stadium entrance. The Michigan players climbed out and fought their way to the stadium. Tarpaulins that had been spread over the playing field were covered with snow and frozen to the ground. Several hundred undergraduates, groundkeepers, and Boy Scouts were hard at work struggling to peel the coverings off. For a while, there was doubt that the game could, or would, be played. Coach Wesley E. Fesler, of Ohio State, did not want it to go on. But no Western Conference game had ever been postponed.

Up in the stadium, crowds, unbelievably, could be seen clambering toward their snow-covered seats. Now, as they battled the storm and plodded beneath their burdens of blankets and other paraphernalia, they looked like a trek of despondent refugees crossing some arctic tundra. Many of the people had had to park their cars more than a mile from the stadium gates. Richard C. Larkins, the athletic director of Ohio State, and H. O. (Fritz) Crisler, the athletic director of Michigan, were fearful of disappointing such determined, dogged souls. Nobody mentioned so crass a factor, but there would be a refund due of around two hundred thousand dollars if the game were called off. At about one-thirty, though the snowfall showed no signs of abating, the word came: "The game is on!"

It took until two o'clock to bare the field, with some of the huskier of the newly arrived spectators lending a hand, and when the tarpaulins were finally removed, it was only a matter of minutes before the yard lines were obliterated by the snow. The reports about the band's not playing proved to have been wrong. The tarpaulins had hardly been hauled away when a brave blare of brass sent the "Buckeye Battle Cry" riding on the wind, which, a moment or two later, was officially announced as blowing at twenty-eight miles an hour. A hundred and twenty strong, the bandsmen—a hundred and ten of them brass and the rest percussion—manfully swung into the maneuvers for which they are famed. The temperature then was an official ten above, but one scientific-minded spectator, complete with thermometer, informed me that it was really only three above. Bandsmen said later that their lips peeled when they put them to the mouthpieces of their instruments. Each of the band's hundred and twenty

men had been counting on using the yard lines as guides in forming the intricately diagrammed figures on the field. But now, of course, there were no yard lines, or at least no yard lines to be seen.

Yet the bandsmen went on, and cheers from the astonishingly large crowd greeted their performance. It was not what it would have been on a sunny day, but it was good, and it seemed incredibly stout-hearted of them to be out there at all.

The game itself was no doubt as grotesque as any on record. The players all wore gloves, including the ball-handlers. Every few minutes the ball became covered with a thin coat of ice, like frigid cellophane. A kerosene heater was set up on the sidelines, and after every two or three plays a warm ball was put into the game and the old one thawed out and heated. For the most part, neither team wanted to have the ball unless it could have it on the other fellows' ten- or twenty-yard line. It was plain that the strategy on both sides was to kick the ball to the opponent, then pray that he'd fumble it in his own territory. Both teams treated the ball as if it were a bouquet of poison ivy.

"The official attendance," said the loudspeaker at about three o'clock, "is 50,503." A little figuring with a pencil in numbed fingers showed that this meant 31,797 persons had stayed away. Presumably the 31,797 were hearing some radio versions of the game. (Televising football games is forbidden by Western Conference rules.) Several thousand spectators left at the half, but most of those departing stayed long enough to see the bandsmen go through with the rest of their performance. "We just carried out two women with frost-bitten feet," a cop told me as we had coffee at a counter beneath the stands between the halves. "One was a young woman, and, by God, the other must have been fifty! They were both heavy as hell, let me tell you."

In the last half, the snow was so dense, and the wind that carried it so strong, that the play frequently could not be followed from the stands. Yet thousands remained until the final whistle, nearly two and a half hours after the start of the game.

As for the game itself, for a time Ohio State was ahead, first 3–0, following a field goal, then 3–2, after a safety was scored against it. Then Michigan went into the lead, 9–3, when a kick by Ohio's Vic Janowicz, on a third down, was blocked and Tony Momsen, of Michigan, fell on the ball behind the Ohio goal line. This crucial kick occurred only forty-seven seconds before the end of the second quarter. No one scored from there on in, so the game ended Michigan 9, Ohio State 3. I'm sure that blocked kick will be discussed at Broad and High twenty years from now. It was the first time in the memory of man that a team won a football game without once making a first down.

Many of the autos to which the spectators perilously made their way from the stadium after the game were buried under snowdrifts. Skidding cars and stumbling, half-frozen men and women jammed the narrow roads that led back to the railroad spur and to the gates of the University.

A friend of mine and I were riding toward the gates in his car when he saw two people more sorely beset than the rest in the lines of trudging fans. One was a man, the other a woman. Both were bent to the wind. The woman was trying to help the man, who seemed about to fall at every step. My friend stopped the car beside them and asked them in. The man must have been past seventy. Beyond all doubt, he was at the end of his rope. He could hardly get into the car, even with the assistance of the woman, whom I took to be his daughter. Exhausted, his eyeglasses covered with ice, his face purple with exertion and cold, he slumped into the seat. It was fully two minutes before he could speak.

"I haven't missed a Michigan-Ohio State game in twenty-five years," he finally managed to say.

"I'm going to see that you miss the next one," said the woman. "We'll never go through this again."

We left them at a train on the spur—a train bound for Detroit, their home.

It was not until the following Wednesday or Thursday that the last of the visiting fans got out of Columbus. Roads had been closed by the blizzard, trains were running ten and fifteen hours late, all planes were grounded. Just before I left the city, the Homecoming over, I met Danny Cronin, a Columbus racing man and an old friend of mine. Danny's a great hand at figures, as many racing men are.

"Best I can say about that whole thing on Saturday is this," he told me. "They sold 82,300 tickets and 50,503 people were out there. On my figures, that proves that exactly 50,503-82,300ths of the population of Ohio and Michigan are off their rockers, out of their heads, and crazy."

"Were you there, Danny?" I asked.

"Oh, sure," he said. "Do you think I'd miss a Michigan game?"

*"...and this term we don't want any trouble with the
Bureau of Internal Revenue—get your economics professor
to help you fill out your income-tax returns correctly!"*

CARTOON BY IRWIN CAPLAN

© Fawcett Publications, Inc.

"Whaddaya mean...unnecessary roughness? That was <u>necessary!</u>"

CARTOON BY JACK TIPPIT

Reproduced by permission, *Sport* Magazine, © Macfadden-Bartell Corp.

This quiet piece, written in 1954, is about an average Big Ten football player ("a good operational man") with more ideals than press clippings.

NO. 44

Gilbert Millstein

In the peculiarly martial argot of bigtime American college football, the University of Michigan's starting left halfback, No. 44, is, to sum up the opinion of his coaches, "a good operational man." Considerably more about No. 44 is implied here than may be read or, for that matter, than might have been found in a report made on him by the scouting staff of the University of Indiana a week or so before Indiana unexpectedly beat Michigan 13–9 at Ann Arbor. "Has had more playing time than any other back," said the estimate of No. 44. "Good safety man. Uses his speed to flow well versus passes. Good speed on offense, but not a power runner." All of this is useful, of course, but incomplete. The fact is that aside from the minimum physical equipment any football player must have, what makes No. 44 a good operational man is that, like many of his contemporaries, he is an idealist, a conformist, a realist, an authentic amateur in a world of subsidized football and a reproach to cynics.

No. 44 is a senior, a premedical student of regular if somewhat undifferentiated features and pleasingly malleable ways, who will be 22 years old next month. He is five feet, ten inches tall and generally weighs about 168 pounds. (He has lost as many as ten pounds in a game.)

His name is John Daniel Cline and he comes from Brockport, N.Y. where his father, who was once an outstanding college football player and track man, is the eastern supervisor of management training for the General Motors Institute, and before that coached football and track and was director of athletics at the high school in Midland, Michigan. "I was brought up to love competition," No. 44 said one night not long ago in his slow, deliberate fashion. He rarely attempts to verbalize his *mystique*. Most often when he does, it comes out in the form of stereotypes and popular rationalizations.

"Dad would have been disappointed if I hadn't played football," No. 44 went on, "but he never pushed me or Earl." (No. 44's younger brother, Earl, is a halfback at Hamilton College and went there because he felt he was too light to play at a big university.) He remembered that when he was three his father bought him a complete football uniform and remembered that one day, when his father opened the door of the house, No. 44 had tackled him, hit his head against his father's knee and fractured his skull. "Dad played halfback at Central Michigan," No. 44 continued, "and he was an All-America in track, a high-jumper and decathlon man. He qualified for the high jump in the

Olympics in 1928, but he popped a muscle in his leg and they told him he'd never jump again. On the day the Olympics were held in Amsterdam he was jumping at the Cadillac Athletic Club in Michigan. He jumped 6 feet 4⅜ inches, and that's just what Bob King jumped at Amsterdam. Dad taped a piece of broomstick to his leg to hold the muscle in place."

The extent of No. 44's dedication may be gauged at two points in time, three years apart. In the spring of 1951, on his application blank for entrance into Michigan, he wrote in a required autobiographical note: "I have heard nothing but good things about the U. of M. and have been a rabid football fan for many years. If I attend the U. of M. it will be a prophecy fulfilled, for when Tom Harmon was 'All American' halfback at Michigan he autographed a picture for me which said, 'To Danny, Class of '51, U. of M. Squad. Sincerely, Tom Harmon.'" (Cline has never met Harmon but his aunt, a plump, pleasant woman who teaches high school in Gary, Indiana, once had Harmon as a student and got him to autograph the photograph for her nephew.)

On the basis of past performance, No. 44's play in the Indiana game was slightly substandard. He carried the ball thirteen times for a net gain of 33 yards. He passed eight times for a net gain of 10 yards. Two of his passes were completed, and two were intercepted. None materially affected the outcome of the game. He also caught two passes for a total gain of 22 yards. He played fifty minutes and forty seconds, which is about average for him. A week later, against Illinois, he gained 70 yards on the ground and threw a 21-yard touchdown pass that won the game. In last Saturday's game with Michigan State, he did another good afternoon's work—not startlingly spectacular but generally competent. He played all but about seven minutes of the game, and was taken out only when the game was in the bag and he wasn't needed any longer. He carried the ball a few times, and averaged 4.3 yards a carry. As safety man, he returned some kicks. He defended his zone adequately. He tried six passes. Only two were completed—sometimes his fault, sometimes the fault of the receiver—but one of them, a bullet pass to Lou Baldacci near the 5-yard line which Baldacci ran for a touchdown, was the real turning point of the game. Now comes Ohio State, which has turned out to be the most menacing rival of Michigan's season. No. 44, like his colleagues, will be "up" for the game. There's work to be done, and he'll be in there doing it.

A couple of hours after the Indiana debacle, in which his lips had been bloodied and his face scratched, the bridge of his nose battered and several ribs in his left side bruised, No. 44 was dressing for the evening, painfully and awkwardly, in the disorderly yet somehow monastic two-room suite he shares in the Sigma Chi fraternity house, with a big, fourth-string center named Bowman. He picked up his varsity jacket and then decided against it. "I don't think I'll wear it," he said to Bowman. "There's no use being seen around campus in *that* tonight." Bowman, who has never played in a game and who has been used simply to scrimmage against the varsity ever since he was a sophomore, gulped manfully, turned away and said, in a low voice, "That's the way it goes, Danny."

The University of Michigan is a representative member of the Big Ten Conference and, in the minds of its 150,000 alumni, as much consecrated to football as to scholarships. It has a stadium that seats 97,239 people, cost well over a million dollars to put up (when it was built in 1927 to seat 79,000 people, the original cost was $950,000; currently, the press box alone is being remodeled at a cost of $30,000), and is the largest college-owned structure of its kind in the world. It is used no more than half a dozen times a year, and then only for football. (No. 44 once remarked, in a casual conversation, that he found the stadium more awesome—even a little frightening—empty than he did when it was full of customers.)

Although he is not familiar with the exact figures, and doesn't know, for example, that it costs $124.95 to equip him and up to $11,000 to feed the squad for a month-long preschool training period, No. 44 is neither unaware that he is part of a large-scale enterprise nor resentful of the fact, and in this is typical of his kind. He has been called among other things, a "player's player," a "good, solid guy on the right side of things," a "man who gives 150% of himself," and an "everyday player—in every way—not just a Saturday player." His opinions are respected, as one football player put it, not so much because of what he says as the affirmative way in which he says it. Thus, he has won the Fielding H. Yost Honor Award, established in the name of the coach who probably did most to make Michigan a bigtime football institution, which is given on the basis of moral character and good citizenship, physical ability, scholastic achievement and the capacity for leadership and success. This year, he was also elected to Michigamua, a senior honor society which taps only 25 men a year.

"You realize the importance of football to a school like this," No. 44 said in his characteristically candid, persuasive way. "It pays for every other sport. You can see the—I'm searching for a word—that it seems reasonable that a football player should get some financial aid for the money that football does make for the university. But at Michigan you couldn't possibly consider yourself an employe like you could at some other schools where they go in for football in a big way. Here you get money to enable you to go to school; you don't get money for going to school. I figure it's a privilege to go to Michigan and also to play football for Michigan." He added, a trifle self-consciously, "After four years of college, you've got the rest of your life to live. You can always be respected for having gone to Michigan."

At present No. 44 is living on a $900 Elmer J. Gedeon Memorial Scholarship, the terms of which roughly parallel those of the Yost award (which pays him nothing). He saved $350 last summer out in South Dakota where he worked in a playground and also played baseball in an amateur league made up mostly of college players like himself.

He is the 1955 captain of Michigan's baseball team and has been scouted by a number of major league organizations. There is a Michigan alumnus who is "interested" in No. 44 and who recently invested some money in stocks for him, which brought No. 44 $240. His parents send him money now and then, but there was a time—in his freshman year—when he waited on table for his meals.

"Michigan certainly doesn't overpay," he observed matter-of-factly. "Financially speaking, it was the worst offer. I could have been *making* money going to other schools." There never was any question in his mind that he would play football in college and that football would pay for his education—there were a brother and sister his parents intended to send to college, too, and that entailed a financial burden No. 44 fully appreciated. At the end of his junior year at Brockport High School (where he was a letter man in four sports, to say nothing of being a sectional champion in skiing), No. 44 deliberately transferred to Aquinas Institute in nearby Rochester which, in the football business, has the reputation of being a sort of Eastern farm for the the big colleges and maintains a stadium seating 25,000 people, for a showcase.

He played football there for a semester, re-turning in the spring to Brockport to get his diploma. He was approached by, among others, Indiana, Cornell, Rochester, Villanova, Yale and Brown, No. 44 said. "One place," he said, "offered me room, board, tuition, books, three trips home by plane every year and spending money. They came after me even after I'd entered Michigan." He also received a Congressional appointment to the Naval Academy, but turned it down because there was no certainty that he could pursue a medical education there. At Brockport, he was graduated third, scholastically, in his class. At Michigan he has maintained an average that fluctuates between a high C and a B. His instructors—this year he is taking 15 hours of philosophy, speech, zoology, anthropology and geography—regard him as alert and intelligent. "I couldn't make it any stronger than that," his philosophy instructor said not long ago. "He's not just a lunk—he follows what's going on. At crucial times— when I've asked questions—he's had an answer. I'll put it this way: he's no Einstein, but neither am I."

Apart from football practice, which takes place every afternoon until about 6 o'clock, No. 44's academic week varies little from that of any other student enrolled in the university. He attracts no unusual attention in the classroom. He must do his studying at night, and generally goes to the library to do it. Recently, when he has returned late to his fraternity house, he has taken to rousing the sleeping brothers by reading items off a bulletin board at the top of his voice. The brothers are tolerant of this behavior: they don't think he's crazy— just blowing off steam, releasing the tension that builds up between games. He neither smokes nor drinks (Ann Arbor is dry) and he seldom has dates during the week, though he may take in an occasional movie.

So it is football that dominates No. 44's life and it is even, quite literally, the stuff his dreams are made of. On the Wednesday night before the Indiana game he composed himself for sleep before 10:30, as usual, and as usual at that time of week, began to dream about football. This time he dreamed that Michigan had kicked off. The ball described a low arc, hit an Indiana man and dropped dead. No. 44 picked up the ball. He remembers lateraling it to a tackle named Art Walker, and then the dream trailed off into something else he is unable to recall. His sleeping fantasies are of a type psychiatrists call "examination dreams," that is uncomplicated dreams of passing some forthcoming test. They are never, as No. 44

put it, "dreams of glory," but rather defensive ones, "dreams of trying to stop the other team, of capitalizing on their mistakes." If he is carrying the ball it is always in short line bucks, if he is passing it is usually for short gains over center. "I guess it's because the coaches try to impress us with the rock and sock of power football," he has explained. "Single wing is power football. It's the fundamentals and rules we've learned that come out in the mind, like tackling hard, being sharp, knowing the rules, charging for that extra yard like they want us to."

Consciously, No. 44 sees in football a good many analogies to his daily life. "You get a sort of enjoyment in doing your part," he said, "in accomplishing an objective as part of a team. It seems like there are more obstacles to overcome than in any other game. You can't do it all on your own and you've got to come to realize that. You take it and you dish it out. Other games, you get mad, but you can't do anything about it. You can't make that contact, you can't get your shoulder in there. This releases—well, I guess you'd call it inner tensions."

At the time No. 44 said all this he was getting ready to call on his girl, a pretty blonde named Jan Garrett, who is a sophomore and waits on table and has even served No. 44 at training table. Her picture stands on a shelf in his bedroom, and the sight of it apparently stirred some other thoughts in his mind. "You know," he said, "I felt awful lost as a freshman. This way, you're not just another student. People meet you on campus and you've got something to talk about with them. When you go to a school like this, when you walk down a street or into a store, a lot of people know you. You get a kick out of that and you want to do well for that reason. Another thing: I won't forget the first touchdown I made. It was last year's Ohio State game. It was an off-tackle play and I went over standing up. I got kind of a glow and warm all over, like when you hear the band play 'Hail to the Victors.' It's never the same after that. After that, it's like practice."

The Four Horsemen, labeled by Grantland Rice in 1924 (see page 250),
were a going company at Notre Dame as early as 1922. From left:
Don Miller, Elmer Layden, Jim Crowley, Harry Stuhldreher. In 1924
the Horsemen and their helpers were undefeated and won
the Rose Bowl game, too.

LEGENDARY BACKS AND BATTERY MATES

When the Green Bay Packers were the best pro team in the West in the
late 1930s, a good many of their touchdowns resulted from the graceful
collaboration of passer Cecil Isbell (17) and end Don Hutson.
An all-time All-Pro, Hutson still has a long list of National Football
League pass receiving records. Among them: 101 touchdown passes
caught in eleven seasons.

At six feet, four inches and approximately 250 pounds, Ron Mix is a most unlikely-looking young author. Yet these excerpts from his diary prove he has a sensitive touch at the typewriter. Mix, a graduate of the University of Southern California and an all-pro tackle with the San Diego Chargers, has been called the best—and smartest—offensive lineman in the American Football League.

PRO LINEMAN'S DIARY

Ron Mix

I placed the essentials in my 1958 blue Chevrolet, accepted a goodby-my-son kiss from my mother and began the drive to Rough Acres. East on Highway 80 for 66 miles. The sun was glaring white. The surrounding area was rocky hills, mountains and flatland that defied the growth of normal vegetation. Even the stinkweeds looked sickly. Here and there a fairly clear section of land supported a ranch or a town. Places with appropriate names like Tierra Del Sol and Wild Acres. A couple of miles past a sign that announced the population of Boulevard to be 50, I turned down the serpentining dirt road that led to Rough Acres Ranch.

Rough Acres looks like the dude ranch it is meant to be in the future. Down from the main lodge are diamond-shaped stone duplexes, forming a long horseshoe. There are a few trees. To the left of the living area, as one looks down from the lodge, is the football field. And as far as one can see is the barren, rock-covered land. The practices will be miserable in this setting. This I know. It might be nice for vacationers to sip a drink in the sun, but to practice football in this heat! . . . I decided to ask Coach Sid Gillman for $1,000 more than I had intended to ask for.

The coach answered my knock on his office

door wearing a pair of workout shorts, no shirt. Clearly the advantage was mine. I did not believe a man in shorts could discuss business, especially with his stomach hanging over the shorts.

"Tell you what I'll do," he said. "You sign this contract, and if we win the division title and if you make All-AFL, I'll give you an extra $500."

I laughed at all those ifs.

Finally we reached a point where we were $1,000 apart. "Ron," he said, "I have too much respect for you to quibble over $1,000."

"Coach," I said, "I have too much respect for $1,000 not to quibble."

He laughed, we met halfway, and I sold my body for another year.

I checked the room list and found I would be rooming with Jacque MacKinnon. Jacque and I are good friends and get along well together. He had come into camp with the rookies to get into condition. He bounded into the room late, announcing, "The kid with the blond hair and the blue eyes and the big heart is here." He always calls himself that.

I asked him about the camp.

"Sid has really stuck it to us this time," he said. "I'm not fond of practice anyway, and

this heat doesn't help, but I expect tough practice. But when they're over I want to relax, and
you can't do it around here."

"What about after lunch?" I asked. "Don't
you have time to relax then?"

"Time!" he said, throwing his hands up.
"Sure we got time, but it's too hot. Look, if
you're lucky enough to fall asleep in the afternoon, you wake up in a pool of sweat. And at
night it's no better. It's still hot, and the insects
come out to play and—well, hell, you've seen
how it was today. Wait until you're tired from
practice, too, then you'll see what I mean."

I can hardly wait.

JULY 18

Everything is set for the beginning of practice
tomorrow. Uniforms have been issued, physical
and dental examinations have been taken, and
Sid held a squad meeting.

"Gentlemen," he said, "a camp is not a
country club. We are going to have fun, but
when we work, we work. We must get in top
physical condition for the 19 games. In addition
to our normal workouts, we are going to begin
a concentrated program of weight training and
isometrics. One of the outstanding men in the
field, Alvin Roy, will be in camp in a couple of
days to begin instruction.

"If you have an appointment, keep it. It'll
cost you one dollar a minute if you are late.
And if we have reason to believe that you were
late intentionally, the fine goes up to $10 a
minute. Any excuses better be good ones. Now,
if you really want to test us be late for curfew.
Curfew is at 10:30. We put in a hard day and
feel we need the rest. The fines for being late
will be doubled for each repeated infraction.
And last among our moneymaking procedures is
the notebooks. These notebooks contain everything in our system. They are our lifeblood.
It'll cost you $200 if you lose a notebook.

"One thing I must caution you on is gambling.
There are very few of us who can gamble for
high stakes. When we lose a lot it affects the
team morale. Penny ante is all right. And when
I say pennies, I mean pennies."

The meeting ended.

"Well," said Paul Lowe as we walked down
the hill toward our rooms, "here we are again.
How about some poker? Penny ante, of course."

In a few minutes seven of us were in Paul's
room, sitting in chairs around the bed, betting
pennies just as Sid said we must. Paul, Don
Norton, Dave Kocourek, Ernie Ladd, Charlie
McNeil, Ernie Wright and myself placed our
dollar bills in the pot. Someone said: "I bet 100

pennies." Someone else: "I call, and jack you
200 pennies."

In two hours I had lost 4,700 pennies.

JULY 19

The first day of practice. Had I ever left this
dressing room with its long rows of lockers? I
wondered, as I pulled on my pads along with
the other big bodies that were sandwiched in
the limited space. Soon there would be more
room. Empty lockers would begin to appear
each day as a reminder of the insecurity in a
professional training camp.

Each day players will be looking for some
clue to find out how they are doing. Checking
the publicity-shot list for your name is a
favorite indicator. Offensive linemen have a
more tangible indicator—Coach Joe Madro.
When he stops yelling, swearing and making
suggestions to a player, then you know that the
player's time in camp is limited.

Joe is a chunky, craggy-faced perfectionist
with a startling command of the language. Joe's
method of expressing himself is a mishmash of
Don Rickles, Aldous Huxley and Henry Miller.

He was in rare form for opening day.

"All right, gentlemen—and though I address
you as such, I hope that none of you turn out
to be gentlemen on the football field.

"We are going to start at the beginning this
year in the hopes that this will stunt any growth
of lambsie pies.

"Lambsie pies! The Houston Oilers said we
had some lambsie pies in our offensive line after
they beat us in the championship game two
years ago. Well, I guaran-damn-tee you they
won't say that this year. First we are going to
hit the sled from a six-point stance, then from
a four-point, and then from your regular three-
point. I hope that this will teach you to fire out.
Fundamentals! That's what we are going to
work on."

After that it was all business:

"On the go! On the color! Get set! Blue, go!

"That's fine—good uncoil, arched body, head
up!

"Bring the elbow high, form a wedge in
there.

"Don't wind up, Shea! If you wind up, you
transmit power on a curved line. We want
power on a *what*, Pat? On a straight line!"

Poor rookies, I thought throughout the practice. Joe's probably got them scared to death.
They'll learn soon that Joe doesn't really hate
anybody.

When practice ended, a lot of the veterans got
together to work on their particular phases of

the game. Henry Schmidt and Ron Nery were working with Sam Gruneisen and Ernie Wright on pass rush and pass protection; Dave Kocourek and Don Norton were running pass patterns for Tobin Rote; Dick Harris and Bud Whitehead were working against Dave and Don; Sherman Plunkett was doing wind sprints in an attempt to trim down from his reporting weight of 324 pounds. The field was as busy as it had been during the regular practice session.

JULY 20

Practice started out on a pleasant note today. On my way to the field Bob Burdick, our publicity man, told me that he would need Earl Faison and myself for some pictures. We spent the next five minutes posing with Miss San Diego Charger of 1963. I casually let her know that I was single, and she bluntly let me know that she had only recently graduated from high school.

Earl and I jogged back to practice. We reached the group just in time for the one blocking and tackling drill that players check the workout schedule for every day—hoping it isn't there. One-on-one it is called by the coaches; the players call it the pit drill, and this is a more fitting name. A defensive man and an offensive man line up opposite each other within the confines of two blocking bags that are spaced about two yards apart. Behind them is a back who must carry the ball within the same confines. Surrounding all of them is the rest of the team, rooting for its respective group.

It is tough enough blocking those big defensive mooses when they don't know whether to expect a run, pass or draw, but in the pit drill they know it is going to be a run and they know what count it is coming on.

Knowing these disadvantages did not make me less humiliated when I was defeated on my two trips to the pit. Had nobody been there to witness the defeats, I would still have felt bad. With the whole team and coaching staff watching, it just killed me.

JULY 24

The first scrimmage of the year is going to be held tomorrow afternoon. It couldn't be more important to me if it were a league game.

In this morning's practice I was too slow in pulling out of the line on a sweep play, and Paul Lowe ran up my back and kicked me in the calf. A bruised calf—that should be really great in the scrimmage tomorrow! Getting in and out of my stance a couple hundred times a day is beginning to take its toll also; the small

of my back is so sore that it is difficult to straighten up.

Twelve minutes in the whirlpool will help, but rest is the only sure cure for these ailments. Since I had to be fit by tomorrow, I decided to sort of worm my way through the afternoon's practice. Just do the bare minimum. Not volunteer for anything. If they called for a man to jump in at a position, I would move toward the empty spot—but not fast enough to actually reach it before some eager-beaver rookie who was certain to move toward the spot also. I didn't even bother to warm up during the 15-minute period allotted for this. I was hoping that practice would start off on a slow pitch and I could gradually warm up on the coaches' time.

It was my lucky day. Joe became long-winded as he explained a new play we were taking on; then there were a couple of time-consuming questions, and the first period was over. After working on individual pass protection with the defensive line (a 15-minute period in which each man gets only a couple of turns), the line and the backs got together for team practice. After practice, I told our trainer, Kearney Reeb, that my back hurt. He prescribed some exercises to strengthen it and told me to climb into the whirlpool tub.

JULY 25

Had an unknowing observer walked into the dressing room today, he would have sworn that the Chargers were getting ready for a regular-season football game rather than a scrimmage. The usual prepractice jabber was absent. Some men were silently putting on uniforms that were still damp from the morning practice. Others were taping pads on their hands and arms, or having them taped on by the trainers. A few of the rookies were making a last desperate attempt to master the assignments from the play books. Everybody had their game faces on: somber faces, tightly set jaws and lips that took deep, loud, nervous breaths.

In the early part of training camp, players make the team by knocking their friends around. This is one reason why scrimmages are not popular. The other reason is that a player feels if he gets injured in a scrimmage it is a pointless, unnecessary injury. If one must get injured, make it during a game, not on the practice field.

Earl Faison was already resting a sore knee and was being withheld from the scrimmage. Bob Mitinger started in his place at left defensive end. George Gross, the strong, bulky, 275-

pound rookie from Auburn, started at left defensive tackle. Tobin Rote took advantage of the relative inexperience of these two (this is Bob's second year) and called a draw on the first play of the scrimmage. The job of the right guard and myself is to set up as if we were going to pass-protect, the guard enticing the defensive tackle to rush to the inside, I enticing the end to rush from the outside, and as soon as they take the bait, we pop into them with a shoulder and wheel them away from the play. Bob Mitinger is so quick that I decided to throw my body at him instead of just a shoulder. It worked, and our fullback, Gerry McDougall, bulled through for 15 yards before being smothered by defensive backs and linebackers. It was going to be a good day, I thought as I jogged to the huddle.

On the next play I had to block down on the defensive tackle. Gross must have read the play perfectly, because as I came down on him he was braced and waiting, exposing only a low shoulder and knee to hit. He moved into me, dipping his shoulder and shrugging my block off, and got into the tackle. Maybe it wasn't going to be such a good day after all, I thought to myself as I walked back to the huddle, mad at myself for missing the block, looking at Paul Lowe brushing himself off after being thrown to the ground at the line of scrimmage.

JULY 27

It happened today—Joe almost cracked up. I noticed it in the meeting tonight as the squad was reviewing the films of the scrimmage. You would have thought we had lost a league game the way Joe carried on. True, the offense didn't exactly blast the defense off the field, but that is normal for a first scrimmage. The defense doesn't have as much to learn, and so they are usually ahead of the offense in their development. We catch up to them as soon as we receive and polish our entire system.

As we watched the films, Joe ran each play back many times, stopping the projector before the play was completed, making assorted caustic comments and then running it over again. He soon had all of us dizzy and nervous from watching ourselves never complete a play. The screen would show us run to the line of scrimmage, get into our stances, begin to make a block, and then Joe would throw the film into reverse. So the screen would then show us coming off our blocks, back into our stances, raising up from our stances and running backward to the huddle, and finally disbanding the huddle. It was slapstick comedy at its best.

Ernie Wright started counting the number of times that Joe was rerunning each play. When the total on one reached 17, Ernie leaned over and informed me that Joe had just broken a four-year record. Joe heard him.

"So you're getting tired, huh, Ernie," said Joe. "Well that is exactly how you looked on that play—tired! Maybe if you would lose some weight you wouldn't feel that way. Tell me, how can a young fellow like yourself stand to have a barrel gut?"

No comment from Ernie. It would not have been heard anyway, because the rest of the linemen were laughing loudly over Joe's remark. It was not that funny—but Ernie is one of the two linemen supposedly safe from any nasty remarks from the coaches. I am the other one.

Joe ran off another play, making comments.

"Plunkett, don't raise up so soon when you are trying to get downfield," he said. "You must fire out hard in order to get past those defensive men. Look what happened to you. You never got past the line of scrimmage. You'd make a helluva good statue. If we could just freeze you, we'd stick you in a park and make the pigeons with poor aim happy."

Joe kept up a continuous monologue throughout the hour-and-a-half meeting. Nothing escaped his sarcasm.

In fairness to Joe, he actually has good reason to be overly excited about the first exhibition game. We are going to play the league champions, Kansas City (formerly the Dallas Texans), and our performance should indicate if we are going to be as improved as we think we will be.

JULY 29

Fred Gillett was cut from the squad yesterday. It was an inevitable occurrence, but we hated to see it happen. He was a pleasant fellow, and a pretty talented fullback, too. However, in the pros a position on the team is hard to earn. The fullback combination of Gerry McDougall and Bobby Jackson was too strong to crack.

"I must have been crazy to come out here anyway," said Fred as he was packing his suitcase. "It has been a great experience for me, though, and I'll never forget it. I really feel good now—you know, all the pressure is over and I can relax. But I love the game. I would have loved to have made the team, but . . . ."

"What are you going to do now?" I asked.

"Well, if I could have stuck around for the year, I would have had enough money to finish building my race car. That's what I would like to do some day, be a competition driver. Now

I'm not sure what I'll do. I hope I can catch on with some other club. There can't be two good fullbacks on every club in the league. Maybe I shouldn't have come out here anyway; I have a beautiful wife at home, and I come out here and fool around with a football. Here, have you seen her picture?" And he showed me his wife's picture for the last of many times.

AUGUST 2

The long-awaited day arrives tomorrow—the first game of the season. We play Kansas City, but who we play is not what lends importance to the day. With the first game come the better things in life to a football player: money, rest and free time. The money we earn for each exhibition game is just a symbol showing that we are professionals. Sixty dollars is the paycheck.

What we really welcome is the free time and rest that accompany the start of weekly games. Workouts are cut to one a day. A meeting takes the place of the morning workout. We have taken on most of our offensive plays now, so, unless the coaches decide to have meetings for the sake of having meetings, we should have a couple of free evenings each week.

The rookies have been getting a mental and physical working over. They are getting a shock course in professional football. Special meetings are held for them so that they may learn the system before the first game. The veteran defensive men have been rough on the offensive rookies whenever they have had the chance. But the rookies have held up well under the abuse.

Earl Faison and Ron Nery have treated them the nastiest. When one of the rookies would line up against a veteran for a blocking drill, Ron, feigning grave concern, would warn the veteran to be careful, that this was a vaunted rookie he was facing. Ron loves to humiliate new men with his patented defensive end moves. He has his moves numbered. The other members of the defensive unit always join in the fun by yelling out the number of the move they want to see him dump the new man with.

And Earl did more dumping than Ron. Earl normally is a pretty nice fellow on the practice field, and usually does as little as possible, saving everything for the game. This week he was different. As Joe put it, "Staying at Rough Acres has given him a nasty disposition." Ernest Park. Walt Sweeney and Tyrone Robertson were all on the receiving end of Earl's testimonial on his ability. They spent part of the time on the ground, but they learned a great deal about offensive tackle play from one of the best defensive ends in football.

We had a brief workout this afternoon, just enough to break a sweat. Afterward, at the evening meal, the linemen got together to discuss how we could best do our jobs. Pat Shea had never played against Paul Rochester, so he sought some advice from me, since I had played guard last year and faced Rochester then.

"You've got to use a lot of techniques on him on pass protection," I said. "He's the type of guy I like to cut on occasion, because he charges hard. Of course, he uses his hands well, too, so you have to be careful not to try cutting too often. You know, just use it to keep him honest.

"Also you can try firing out on him, and then dropping back. I like to do that, but sometimes it gets me into trouble if the defense has a stunt going. If the man is slow in his stunting movements, then it doesn't matter; but if he is fast, then I'm liable to miss him and open the gates on the quarterback."

"Rochester looked pretty quick in the movies we saw of last year's game," said Pat. "And Dallas fools around with stunts. I think I'll wait until there have been a few fire-out pass protections called, and then decide if the fire-out would work on normal drop-back protection."

"That's a good idea," I said. "Start off using the usual pop-and-fight method, and throw in the other stuff when you think it will work."

"Why don't you junk everything and just grab ahold of him every play and not let go?" said Sam Gruneisen.

"Yeah, that's great," said Pat, "if you don't get caught. I'll play it straight, unless things get desperate."

I did not know who would be playing over me, so I quickly uttered the offensive linemen's prayer: that this unknown fellow would be skinny, slow, weak, stupid and love football but hate body contact.

AUGUST 3

Game day, or rather, game night. The difference between a day game and a night game is that instead of getting sick at one meal, you get sick at three. Coach Gillman, in an effort to stop the pregame sickness that stems from a nervous stomach, told us yesterday that a liquid protein supplement would be substituted in place of the usual meal of steak and potatoes. He advised all players who usually throw up before a game to drink their meal, because, theoretically, it would be digested by game time, whereas the solid food might still be lying in your stomach.

"That's right," Paul Maguire had chimed in, "if you drink this stuff, you will be able to throw up a lot easier—no big chunks of meat to get caught in your throats."

Paul had drawn more vocalized boos from his comment that the subvocal boos that Sid drew from his announcement, so I guess most of the players feel he has a good idea. A few hate to lose their steak. Personally, I would prefer the steak before an evening game and the liquid before a day game. On day games I wake up nervous, but for evening games I know I have the whole day to sleep and rest, and the result is I am more relaxed for the pregame meal.

Today my rest came in between phone calls, all of them for Jacque. He had worked as maître d' at Joe Hunt's restaurant in La Jolla during the off season, and it seemed that every bar buddy he had made was dunning him for tickets to the game.

Apparently the rest I missed was not important, however, because I felt full of energy the entire game. Part of the reason for the added energy came from the incentive of having been chosen, along with Emil Karas, to act as co-captain for the opening game. During the exhibition season a different set of co-captains is chosen each week, but that does not dim the honor. It is a great thrill to be the official spokesman for a group of fellows whom you admire, respect and like.

On the field I knew how to fulfill the responsibilities of captain; in the dressing room, however, I felt inadequate. I felt, as captain, I was expected to say something to the squad before the game. What to say is the problem. Each player is a mature, dedicated athlete who knows what he has to do without being reminded that we must play hard, we must win. And yet there we were, minutes before game time, some sitting, some standing, all sweating from the heavy uniforms, the pregame workout, the nervousness. It seemed like something had to be said. Coach Gillman had told us to relax and have a good time out there, and if we made any mistakes to forget them and keep playing good football. Then he had left us so that we could have a few moments to ourselves before the game. When he left, the room became quiet.

Now, what I put down here as having been said to the squad will not be a verbatim report, because what I said was spontaneous and total recall is impossible. It was something like this:

"Fellows," I began, not sure what would follow, or what could follow, a beginning like that, "what Coach Gillman said is true; if we go out there with the idea that we are going to have a good time, everything will fall in place and we'll do well."

Oh, what to say, I thought, knowing I was groping, embarrassed for having reiterated the coach's words. And then I knew what had to be said, the only thing that was right to say to these men.

"We all know the importance of winning, and know what must be done to do so. We have a responsibility to the club and to our teammates to do that, but we must remember that our first responsibility is to our families and to ourselves; we must make the ball club. This is our job, our livelihood, and it is during the exhibition season that the squad is chosen—just a few weeks to show that you deserve a position on this team. And that's why we must go out there and play as hard as we can for the whole game.

"And for those who are mainly running on the special teams tonight, remember they're important also. There are players each year who are kept on the squad because they show the coaches they are tough on the kickoff team, the punt team and the rest. Pat Shea is a good example of this. Last year he was a special-team player during the games, but during the week he developed his line play until he became a fine football player. So let's go hard on everything. We can have a good time, but remember it's our job."

The speech will never win any awards for articulateness, and it certainly did not break open a ray of enlightenment upon the men, but sometimes it is good to try.

The game ended 26–14, Chargers. Then it was time to drag ourselves to the dressing room, slowly pull off the sweaty, dirty uniforms and take a long, cool shower, head back, eyes closed, letting the water wash away the dirt and ease the aches. It is a time to replay the game in your mind, and try to remember what you did well and what you did poorly. And hope you did well enough to keep your starting position or, if you are a rookie, hope that you showed enough promise to justify the coaches keeping you around another week, because you'd show them then.

The good times and money are only a short distance away. Training camp will be over, and league play will begin. The pressure will keep growing, the nervousness will not stop, but nobody minds walking to the bank with a nervous stomach.

I am certain also that when the training camp

does end I will feel an accompanying sadness that will belie all the complaining I did during the camp's duration. I will not delude myself, or anyone else, by saying that the sadness comes because I miss the hard work and the nervous anxiety. The day that I gain some enjoyment from being hit in the throat with an elbow, or from seeing a friend heartsick because of having been cut from the squad, I will know it is time to quit football.

Yet these things, too, are a part of the something that is missed when camp is over. It is the feeling of having experienced pain and weariness and mental anguish and having met each in a way that made you feel good afterward. Perhaps you did not meet and answer every challenge in a way that would be considered noble the first time it was encountered. There always came a second chance. And you were better prepared the second time because you had done a little soul-searching and decided what is important.

There may have been a time when you became so tired during a game that you loafed until you no longer felt the ache in your chest and sides. Then you were disgusted with yourself for having done so. The challenges must be met with honor if you intend to go on respecting yourself. Existing on a steady diet of challenges, such as a training camp provides, makes a person nervous and tense. I sometimes long for the day when I can relax completely. But when? After my football career is over, then there will be the challenges that must be met in everyday life.

I believe that someday I will be thankful for the lessons of self-discipline that were learned while playing football. And sometimes I wish that every boy in America were given the opportunity to spend a few weeks in a training camp. Not because I think it is important to be an athlete, but because it would serve as invaluable preparation for the day when they set out to make a niche for themselves in this competitive world. They would learn early that it takes hard work to become a success. They would learn that when there are setbacks, and when you are knocked down, you must get up. If they saw only the value of this—getting back up again—then it is certain that their chances for accomplishment in any vocation would be enhanced.

And in the space of just a few weeks, they would discover the greatest value of all: having close, trustworthy friends. Friends you can confide in, joke with, share success and failure with. This is what I shall miss when training camp ends: the close companionship and the continual laughs that occur when 50 guys are together. I will miss the daily card games with Lowe, Wright, Kocourek, Harris, Ladd, Faison, Hadl and McNeil. I will miss the "world problem solving" sessions with DeLuca and Coan; the arguments that Lincoln and Ladd go into each noon as they played off for the World Ping-pong Championship; the singing and guitar-playing sessions with Norton; the sound of bare feet outside after bed check, which meant that somebody was sneaking out for a late date. When I think of all these things, camp seems to have been one big laugh. However, this will not slow me up in gathering my clothes, books and other belongings and making the trip home. And if any of the players should pass me and say:

"Isn't this great? Leaving this place—boy, I thought it would never end. Isn't this great?"

"It sure is," I will agree. If I say anything else, he will think that I have run under one kickoff too many.

"*Now then, as <u>I</u> was saying.*"

The excerpt from poet Howard Nemerov's bitter-humorous novel, The Homecoming Game, *offers a few elevated thoughts on why so many people gather at football stadiums on Saturday and Sunday afternoons. To appreciate these ideas the reader does not necessarily have to know that Charles Osman, in the story, had good reason to wonder about the honesty of the game at hand.*

From *THE HOMECOMING GAME*

Howard Nemerov

Of thousands of people sitting around the stadium on this brilliant November afternoon, Charles Osman was certainly the only one who believed himself to have personally guaranteed, so far as any man could, the honesty of the game. This belief, of which he was, to be sure, only intermittently conscious, had raised to a new power the nervous intensity of his feelings about football generally, so that, just as in his undergraduate days, he was unable to eat his lunch or, indeed, pay attention to much of anything else. He had walked past the stadium a number of times, telling himself it was ridiculous to be so before-handed, and suddenly, three-quarters of an hour before game time, as early as the gates were opened, in fact, he had gone in, bought an inordinately expensive and glossy souvenir program—something he generally did not do—and taken his place in the mediocre seat to which as a faculty member he was entitled: about halfway up on the home team's side, between the 25- and the 30-yard lines.

His purpose in buying the program had been to assure himself that Raymond Blent was in-

deed in the starting lineup; and so he was, bearing the number 7, standing 6 feet and 1 inch, weighing 183 pounds. Of course Charles realized at once that the sort of assurance the program gave, since it must have been printed a fortnight before, was purely formal, official, and so to say historical; yet such was his nervousness that he would not readily have done without this paper. Also, by coming early, he was enabled to watch the practice sessions of both teams and there, since the players appeared without helmets, identify Raymond Blent for himself and make sure (as though suspecting up to the last minute some trick) that he was wearing the number 7 as certified in the program. It remained to see that he would play, but of this Charles now felt reasonably certain, since there would otherwise be no point whatever in the boy's appearing at all.

The sky was a pure blue; the sun already halfway down the sky, concentrated its royal golden light in the circle of the stadium whose intervals were marked in white. The field itself had a kind of totemic or sacrificial appearance, a ground to be kept inviolate on all profane occasions, then to be torn up by one fury only; even the players seemed aware of this quality, when they came out walking delicately as Agag; they sniffed the cold, bright air, tested the spring of the ground with a toe, danced a few tentative, mincing steps before first digging their cleats into the new green space which belonged to them and finally throwing themselves down, rolling around, turning somersaults —actions which no doubt had a rational purpose of warming-up and reducing tension but which reflected also some new, delightedly innocent relation with the earth itself. Their uniforms, the red and white on one side, black and white on the other, made the same effect of brilliant purity, of cleanliness carefully preserved for the one ceremonial destruction.

For his part, Charles, accustomed to taking long views, felt already something of the melancholy which was the inevitable outcome of all this excitement; that this game, which seemed to stand brilliant and secure in the very path of time, an occasion, an event, a something of magnificent solidity devised by the wit of man to make the sun and the moon stand still, was doomed to be itself merely a part of time; that for its two hours' impression of timeless vigor, immortal and anonymous youthfulness, time exacted its usual price; which only the historian, perhaps, was condemned to be gloomy about in advance.

He had not slept well the night before, and still suffered from a little, wandering headache, scarcely so much a physical pain as a feeling of mental remoteness, a tendency of the eyes to blur out of focus as though simply refusing their attention to mere spectacle and showing an undefined wish to see something else. Charles now and then was confusedly reminded of having dreamt very numerous and very fatiguing dreams during his broken sleep, and felt (though he could remember little or nothing of all that) as though he had come here from a long, futile, miserable life spent elsewhere.

Well before game time the stadium was nearly full. The players retired to their dressing rooms; the band, in red jackets and white trousers and caps, paraded up and down the field, going sturdily from tonic to dominant and back with a fine resonance of thumps and blares and booms and a fine reflection of the light from their golden horns; six drum majorettes, high stepping with naked knees and black boots, went before, twirling, twisting, tossing and catching their batons. It seemed as though everyone began to roar, and yet as though no individual had any part in the sound produced.

Charles made no noise, the people around him seemed not to be making any particular noise, yet the sound continued to roll out in waves; one felt that *something,* not necessarily human, had begun to roar. The band formed itself up before the visiting team's side and played *their* "Alma Mater"; then came back to the home side and played *their* "Alma Mater": two solemn, mournful airs which, harmonically at any rate, were hardly to be distinguished one from the other; yet when so addressed the graduates and undergraduates of each institution stood solemnly up, held felt hats against their chests, and sorrowfully sang. Many an eye was wet.

What in the world could it all be for? Charles glanced impatiently at the clock on the scoreboard, which told him nothing since it was designed to measure the game alone, and therefore had not begun to move. What a heroic view of time! That clock would move, during the afternoon, only during the instants of (allowing for a nicety of legal definition) actual play; when either side felt that things were going wrong, or had gone far enough for the moment, the clock would be stopped: *time* would be *out.* That clock, in fact, since it measured at no time any space of time greater than fifteen minutes, did not need (and did not have) a hand to tell the hour; that hour of which one might paradoxically say, considering it from a certain point of view, that it was eternal while it lasted. It was hard to say, about football as about games in general, which was more impressive, the violence or the rationality; whether the most important element was the keen demonstration of hostility and aggressiveness (with consequent arguments, developed by Plato and Aristotle, as to whether such demonstrations intensified or harmlessly liberated those passions) or, quite the contrary, the demonstration of control, of order, plan, and human meaning in the universe. Orderly violence! Did that oxymoron define civilization? Surely, to begin with, order and violence had been, or been considered to be, opposites, and order was imposed as a means of doing away with violence, on the famed model, in the individual, of reason quelling the passions. But was there in nature any violence so violent, so furious-cruel, as the violence of reason? Was any creature not gifted with reason capable of producing such orderly explosions of force as, say, the symphonies of Mozart or the advance of human armies to the assault? The avowed ideals of society were measure and reason; measure and reason had made society in the image of an armed camp, until the model of its life, the city with its squared and numbered streets, betrayed itself as based however inefficiently (for history and tradition had moved blindly in this matter at many times) upon logistical considerations, to the end that an absolute force might be instantaneously (and in an orderly manner) mobilized.

It was this, then, that thousands of apparently good-natured citizens were here in the stadium to celebrate, the ideal maximum of violence short of death or (it was hoped) serious injury, combined with the ideal maximum of the most pharisaical rationality and control. It would not do to say that people came to be entertained, for one had to ask at that point what it was that entertained people, and why of all things they were entertained by, particularly, this. Perhaps war itself, in its beginning, had been no more than such a ceremony as a football game, and scarcely more heroic or more dangerous than that village game of football anciently played in England, on Shrovetide Tuesday, where the unmarried women were always, by law, defeated by the married women. It might be—again the odd joke of history!—that the earliest form of war was predetermined as to its outcome, having a magical purpose and a ceremonial arrangement which, entering history as garbled traditions, were misinterpreted as both real and necessary: a nasty joke, if true. But civilization at present, and historically, depended on one decision and one decision alone: that it was better to sacrifice, at need, thousands and millions of men by accident—that is, in reality—than to sacrifice one man by pre-election—that is, ceremonially. Better? No, it was absolute, there was no choice allowed. And this same civilization paradoxically preserved at its very root a supreme instance of the other sort: better that one man should die for the people. . . .

The reappearance of the teams on the playing field caused Charles to break off at this place the thread of these somewhat elevated considerations. The captains advanced from either side to the center and there conferred with the referee. After this, both sides lined up for the kickoff and stood to attention, along with the entire audience, while the national anthem was played by the band and metallically sung by a tenor voice.

The game should have begun forthwith but there was a further delay. A devout voice, on the same public address system, began to intone some species of prayer mixed with explanations, from all of which Charles obscurely was able to gather that someone, a student, had somehow managed to fall into that bonfire last night at one stage or another of the proceedings, that this person had been terribly burned and taken to hospital that he—or she, Charles did not catch the name—was on the critical list and might not live. The voice ended by suggesting a minute of silent prayer, and since no one in the stadium controverted the suggestion, that minute then followed, while the football players stood uneasily with bowed heads and held their helmets like extra heads in their hands. At the end of one minute exactly, the voice coughed and said "Amen." The Homecoming Game then began.

When it was over, when in the cold shadows of the coming dark small mobs of people tore down the goal posts, while others seemed to stray aimlessly over the torn battleground as though seeking something they had lost, when the great crowd migrated slowly through many gates and dispersed, moving with the sheepish, bewildered resignation of men and women wakened from a dream in which some sad and terrible truth has been revealed, which they are unable to interpret although they will soon reduce it to the practical commonplaces of their daily lives, Charles remained for a long time where he was. . . .

It, whatever it was, at any rate was over. Charles stopped outside the gate and looked at the black implacable bulk of the wall, at the stars, at the remaining band of pure, red-gold light in the west, outlining the hills. Autumn, football, the pale, clear, fictitious glory. Adolescent glory. But what would you put in its place? Football is unreal, if you care to say so; but as you grow older many things become unreal, and football stands out somehow as an image. And there under the shadow of the stone, empty stadium after the captain and the kings depart, after all the others too depart, in that last lonely and cold air, you may, if you care for games, experience something of what is meant by vanished glory. Symbolical—perhaps. But it is commonly allowed that you may more easily call the things of this world symbolical than say what they are symbolical of.

In three successive games in the mid-1930's, two of college football's biggest powers, Pittsburgh and Fordham, battled to a scoreless tie. Here are the details of an historic stretch of frustration.

0 TO 0

Jack Newcombe

Football games of the 1930's, like the wars of that age, were fierce struggles of youthful courage and strength waged over small pieces of ground. Force drove headlong against force. Gains came in feet and often just in inches. Players were trained to block on offense, tackle on defense and to give and take it all the time. It was a game that hurt, a game of pads slapped against unguarded faces, of two men charging point-blank into an opponent and driving him to the ground, and of thumping blocks as a wave of interference rolled a man out of the play. Deception—the fancy feints and decoys—was only a small part of the design. The idea was simple enough: sock it to them until they reeled back across their own goal line.

Compared with the present game of intricate pass plays and quick, concealed ground strikes it was dull, unimaginative sport. But it was a more perfect expression of football's hard-core elements, blocking and tackling; it was a tougher game played by a hardier breed of players. Stripped down to the raw business of eleven men throwing all of their speed and might into a maneuver of great precision, the game had a basic appeal that the complex modern version lacks. It was easier to understand the game and easier to see that it took guts to play it well.

This hard-leather-helmet brand of football came to a resounding climax in a series of games played by the University of Pittsburgh and Fordham University in the mid-1930's. Three times, in 1935, 1936 and 1937, these powerful teams met and fought to scoreless ties. Whether or not the results are destined to represent the most frustrating 180 minutes in football history, the games stand as three of the fiercest and most intense ever played by two college teams. They also marked the end of an era in football. Soon after, the T-formation came into vogue, quarterbacks began tossing the ball around like vaudeville jugglers, guards and tackles stood up and played Doe-See-Doe across the line, and the solid whack of shoulder pads was never again so loud on the campus.

The Pitt-Fordham series matched what was probably the strongest running attack ever put together by a college team (Pitt) and the best defensive line of that day (Fordham). Pittsburgh shunned the pass as if it were a jerry-built weapon that might explode in its hands. Instead the Panthers ran the ball against defenses that massed on the line of scrimmage, ramming ahead with onslaughts mounted as precisely as an army division on the move. There was nothing crude or lumbering about Pitt on the attack. The quick slam off tackle or the unwinding deep reverse were as beautifully conceived and executed as any play in football. Such was the speed, coordination and viciousness of the blocking that no team—except Fordham—could contain Pitt for long. And Fordham, as will be seen, held on only by relentless fortitude and with the help of a weird set of Pittsburgh misadventures.

Fordham, which ran its plays from the Notre Dame box formation, could not match Pitt's striking power. But it had an amazingly mobile and instinctive defense that hit back with more force than it took. The Fordham line could carry out its offensive assignments in routine fashion but it played with the pride and fury of United States Marines on defense. The goal-line stands led to the famous nickname the "Seven Blocks of Granite." It wasn't just that they were hard to move. They were deadly at heading off a play and merciless at finishing off the ball carrier. In 1937 the Blocks did not allow a touchdown, although eight rivals managed to score 16 points against Fordham by more devious methods than running with the ball.

Both Fordham and Pitt were striking reflections of the personalities of the men who coached them. Dr. John Bain Sutherland's Pitt teams were hard, conservative, sure. They abstained from anything flashy or daredevil. On the attack Pitt was as precise and methodical as an English butler serving tea. Sutherland was a dour, unmarried Scotsman from Coupar Angus in the Strathmore Valley. He coached Pitt for fifteen years, during which he became the recognized master of the single wing. He permitted no frills and few mistakes. He gave no pep talks. "He was always extremely considerate, kind and traditionally silent to me before a game," says Marshall Goldberg, one of Jock's greatest players. A supreme Sutherland compliment in the locker room following a good performance was: "That's what wins football games." He never bawled out his players in public. But he drilled and worked them until the games on Saturday began to seem like weekend gambols by comparison.

Dick Harlow said that Sutherland "had the greatest ground attack against the strongest teams. He ran Notre Dame right off the Pitt schedule (Pitt beat ND five out of six years after 1932). Pitt could pick off, check and destroy a shifting defense better than any team I ever saw."

What made it so frustrating and frightening to face a Sutherland team was knowing what was coming and not being able to do much about it. The cyclone formed in the huddle and twisted toward the target in a predictable path. There was no sure defense. Pitt appeared to mock opponents by hitting their stiffest areas. Sutherland knew the balance of power was in his hands. He once explained: "We get the odds in our favor by having two linemen on the side away from the play pull out and run interference. That gives us three men and the ball carrier. When the nearest two secondary defensive men come into the picture, four to two means we're going to gain ground."

Football was more than just a game of drill steps and thundering blocks and tackles to Dr. Sutherland. He was not a man of excesses or visible emotion but he cared deeply about the sport and wanted it played well. Occasionally his feelings toward his players poked through his dour appearance. After Pittsburgh whipped Washington in the 1937 Rose Bowl game he cashed all the travelers' checks his Scotch conscience had allowed him to take to California and gave each of his players $8 to spend on the town.

Fordham and its coach, Sleepy Jim Crowley, pulled on their uniform pants one leg at a time, just as Pittsburgh and Sutherland did, but that is about all they had in common. Fordham believed that the best offense was a versatile one. The team was tough, unpredictable, unawed by better opponents. Although Crowley played more Poles and Italians than Irish his teams had an unmistakable Celtic flair. When technique failed, spirit took over and often saved the day. On occasion, Fordham would flounder hopelessly on offense and then rise up nobly on defense. Pitt never really understood what made Fordham tick.

Compared with the stoical Sutherland, Crowley was an outlandish buffoon. He was an expert at needling, coaxing and inspiring individual players. He could be tough and he could be funny. He had gained a reputation as a wit during his undergraduate days at Notre Dame where he was one of Knute Rockne's famous Four Horsemen. He still gets credit for a famous squelch of Rockne. Crowley and the other Horsemen were catching hell from Rockne in the locker room after a shoddy practice session one day. "Crowley," Rockne yelled, "is there anything in the world dumber than a dumb Irishman?"

"No, sir," Crowley said, "unless it's a dumb Swede."

Once Jim was caught by a priest in an off-limits hangout about three miles from the Notre Dame campus. The priest said, "Mister Crowley, I'll give you exactly three minutes to get back on the campus."

Crowley looked out the window and shook his head. "I don't think I can make it, Father. Not against this wind."

Crowley, who became a popular teller of Rockne tales on the banquet circuit, occasionally tried the old Rockne technique of getting a good cry or an angry rise from his players in the locker room. Before one of the Pitt games at the Polo Grounds he broke the locker-room hush with the announcement that his aged Irish mother had come some distance to see Fordham play for the first time. He dragged the story out to its dramatic conclusion: "I want her to go home knowing one thing," he said. "I want her to know that her fighting son has a fighting team."

Crowley had come to Fordham in 1933 from Michigan State College where his teams had won twenty-two and lost eight in four years. He brought with him an all-Notre Dame staff that included Frank Leahy, Glen Carberry, Earl Walsh and Hugh Devore. Leahy got a lot of credit for developing the Seven Blocks of Granite. He was barely out of college but already a tough, uncompromising teacher. Crowley gives Leahy his due for polishing the linemen but points out that no one invented the Blocks. "All the coaches had a hand in that line," he says. "Leahy worked mostly with the centers and guards. Those boys were great players to begin with. They didn't take much building."

In 1935 most of the Fordham and Pitt players who became responsible for the three historic games were freshmen and sophomores. Fordham drew heavily from the New York-New Jersey-Connecticut area, raking in high school talent that Notre Dame overlooked or did not want. The boys were mostly from lower middle-class Catholic homes. They were all getting a "ride" of some sort—room and board, tuition, money or a small job to cover the incidental costs. Because they were poor boys in poor times they were more appreciative of their opportunities than the modern, free-riding football player. "I remember them as a serious bunch," a former Fordham student said. "They were serious about football and about college, too. They never seemed to have time for horsing around." There was little of the old rackety-rax about Fordham football. It was sophisticated big-city football. The "campus stadium" was the Polo Grounds. Fordham seldom played an away game.

The center Block and best player on the Fordham teams from 1935 to 1937 was a light-haired Polish boy whose name became famous before he did. Alexander Wojciechowicz was the son of an immigrant tailor in South River, New Jersey. Wojie, as he was and is still called, could defy any ball carrier to run by him and anybody to spell his name and win on each count nine out of ten times. He was twice an All-America center. After that he was one of the best pro linemen in the National League for ten years. He took fierce pride in the way he played football, in his name and in his nationality.

Wojie's most prominent linemate was a stocky, effervescent Italian from Jersey City named Edmund Franco. Crowley called Franco the best college lineman he had ever seen. Franco was relentless on the field and an energetic man-about-the-campus. He was elected president of the freshman class in 1934 by his 450 classmates. The Pittsburgh players who faced Fordham in the three deadlocked games most often mention Wojie and Franco as the toughest opponents. An exception is Fabian Hoffman, Pitt's right end, who said: "Franco played such lousy ball against me I always wondered where he got that All-America rating."

Because they spanned a couple of seasons the Seven Blocks were really at least ten in number. In 1936 they included, besides Wojie and Franco, guard Vince Lombardi, the present coach of the Green Bay Packers; guard Nat Pierce; end John Druze, who has coached at Marquette and Notre Dame; end Leo Paquin and tackle Al Babartsky. In 1937, when no one was able to score on the Blocks, Paul Berezney was one of the tackles, Mike Kochel was one of the guards and Harry Jacunski, present assistant coach at Yale, was the starting left end. All of these have clear credentials to membership in the Seven Blocks.

Except for Wojciechowicz there was nothing distinctive or unpronounceable about the names of the Seven Blocks, contrary to the legend that has grown up around them. They lacked the clean nationality cleavage of the famous 1930 Fordham line that numbered "three Poles, three Micks and Tony Siano in the middle." On one side of Siano were Elecewicz, Miskinis and Wisniewski. On the other side were Conroy, Foley and Tracey.

The 1935 team had one back who, when the

spirit moved him, could run with anyone in the game. He was Joe Maniaci, a senior from Hasbrouck Heights, New Jersey. "Manucci," as he was called, had the thick legs and chest of a fullback and the swift, unpredictable gait of a halfback. As a sophomore he had run wild, and Fordham was sure it had come up with a one-man equivalent to the Four Horsemen. But Joe proved to be human—and a lackadaisical one, too. In his senior year he turned in a couple of drab games and the rumor got around that Captain Joe wasn't starting because he no longer was trying hard enough. The day before the next game Crowley told the team that one of his players had been accused of dogging it. Crowley said that to prove to everyone he had no slackers he was going to start the boy in question. Maniaci started and ran back the opening kickoff for a touchdown. After he left Fordham Maniaci was a good pro back with the Dodgers and Bears.

Right halfback Frank Mautte and left halfback Al Gurske were hard-hitting runners for Fordham but, unfortunately, the slick payoff runner did not come along until the Blocks had graduated. He was Len Eshmont, a sophomore in 1938.

Pitt, on the other hand, had a set of great backs and a couple of platoons of hard-nosed linemen who did the dirty work for them. When Pitt appeared in New York in 1935, fullback Frank Patrick was the leading scorer in the East, although he shared the job with Bill Stapulis, also a sophomore. The pair, who could have played on any team, were interchangeable for the next three years. At right halfback—the climax man in Pitt's deadly deep reverse—was Bobby LaRue, probably the neatest, most elusive runner Dr. Sutherland ever had. John Michelosen, the present Pitt coach, did the heavy blocking at quarterback. The next season he split the job with a hot sophomore, John Chickerneo. Marshall Goldberg and Harold (Curly) Stebbins, who were to turn Pitt's ground game into the best in football, joined the team in 1936.

The Sutherland organization was as thorough in recruiting as it was in the midweek practice work. In the the mid-thirties the staff rounded up the finest assortment of manpower to be found anywhere. It resulted in Pitt's—and Sutherland's—super team, the 1937 outfit that had uniform quality through the first 22 men. Such was the team's numerical strength that Ben Kish, who was a star for the Philadelphia Eagles for eight years afterwards, was a third-stringer on it.

End Bill Daddio, who made many All-Americas, shared the job with Frank Souchak. Tony Matisi, Pitt's other All-America lineman, was considered one of the more erratic players on the squad. When Tony was good he was very good—but he had his off days. Tony became the goat in the most famous and critical play of the Fordham-Pitt series.

Most of the Pitt players, like Fordham's, were from depression-ridden backgrounds. They came from mining towns in Pennsylvania and West Virginia and the industrial cities of Ohio. About a third of them lived in fraternities, the rest in the dreary rooming houses scattered around the residential streets below Pitt's giant hilltop stadium. Pitt's football stature, its big-time intersectional schedule and the professional attitude that Sutherland required, all contributed to the team's feeling of superiority over Fordham. This over-confidence cost them their first embarrassing draw at the Polo Grounds on November 2, 1935.

Pitt went to New York a 9–5 favorite and there were few loyal Rams among the 38,000 at the ball park brave enough to bet on Fordham even at those odds. Pitt had more and better players, more speed, more bigtime experience—more of everything.

Pitt's well-being was badly shaken early in the game by Joe Maniaci. The young Rams appeared helpless to move the ball from their offensive formations, but then Maniaci would catch a punt—Pitt kicked nine times—boom up the field, and put Fordham within striking distance of the Pitt goal line. "He looked easy to catch," Don Hensley, Pitt's sophomore center of that year, remembers. "He ran laterally and we were sure we could rack him up on the sidelines. Once George Delich and I thought we had him cornered. But just as George was about to cream him, Maniaci seemed to relax. George relaxed, too. The next thing we knew Maniaci had belted him in the stomach and was driving for another 5 or 6 yards." Twice Maniaci broke into the open and ran head-on into Bobby LaRue, knocking wind and half his consciousness out of him.

The game became a grueling, cold-hearted tug-of-war. Pitt hammered away with its massive off-tackle slants—plays 28 and 29 that were called over and over in the huddle. When Stapulis, who stood only 5–7 and weighed 180, came through on the fullback bread-and-butter play, No. 26, he was viciously handled by Franco or Wojie or Amerino Sarno. Fordham's bucks and reverses broke up in the arms of linebacker Nick Kliskey or the big tackles Bill Glassford and Dante Dalle-Tezze. There were moments when the frustration and the force of the body collisions nearly loosened angry passion on both sides. It was the roughest of the three games.

Late in the day Fordham started a drive that set the Polo Grounds reverberating with excitement. On its own 38 Fordham lined up in right formation and Maniaci followed Franco through a hole for 12 yards. Fordham shifted left and Warren Mulrey hit for 6 more. Maniaci slammed 9 yards off tackle. Mulrey struggled for 1. Maniaci carried twice and Fordham had fourth down and two on Pitt's 33. Crowley called on quarterback Andy Palau to try a field goal. Palau, an indomitable little man of only 160 pounds, had been battling against giants all afternoon. Once when he and guard Nat Pierce were supposed to run interference on a reverse, he discovered that Nat had forgotten to pull out and he alone was approaching the awesome Tony Matisi, who was standing his ground at tackle. Matisi picked up Palau in his hands and hurled him to the ground, then looked around for the ball carrier. Andy's fighting spirit proved truer than his foot. He missed the long-distance kick and Fordham's last chance dribbled away with the ball.

Pitt suffered frustration and error all afternoon. Hub Randour zigzagged 80 yards with a punt only to learn he had zigged out of bounds at midfield. Pitt's second-string quarterback pulled a play that backfired and bounced him out of the game. Pitt had a fourth down on Fordham's 35. In the huddle Arnold Greene stunned his teammates by calling for a pass from punt formation, A lineman asked for a check on the play and Greene said, yes, he intended to throw the ball over the goal line. Under the rules in force then, a last-down pass that fell in the end zone was ruled a touchback and the ball was brought out to the 20-yard line. Greene, who was proud of his throwing arm, had once passed 75 yards in practice. From deep behind the line Arnold wound up and let fly. The ball dropped on the 10 and Fordham took over on the 35. Sutherland rushed John Michelosen into the game.

The nearest miss of Pitt's bungled game belonged to George Delich. Pitt's All-America Ave Daniell blocked a punt that rolled free on the Fordham 15. Delich raced in and fell on the ball. The error of his choice still needles his memory. "I could have waltzed over with the ball," he says. "But two weeks before that I had missed a fumble in the Notre Dame game. Shakespeare landed on it and they scored on the next play. For ten days I practiced falling on fumbles. But if I'd picked it up and scored with the loose ball there would have been no scoreless tie, no famous series with Fordham."

A year later Pitt returned to New York with essentially the same team, older and wiser and better steeped in the Sutherland system. The most important change was at left halfback where sophomore Marshall Goldberg took over as soon as he drew his uniform. Goldberg was a standout as a personality and a player. He was a dark, soft-spoken Jewish boy from West Virginia. He was considered something of an intellectual because he enjoyed writing poetry for campus magazines. His father, Sol Goldberg, operated a movie house in Elkins which he called the Roosevelt out of an avid loyalty to the New Deal. Sol gave up the movies each fall and traipsed around the country watching Pitt and his son play. He showed his enthusiasm for the game he did not understand very well by giving parties to celebrate Pitt victories. He was a popular addition to the Pitt football entourage.

Goldberg's football ability, which brought him All-America clippings for two years and led to a fine career as a pro with the Chicago Cardinals, was not easy to assess. He was quick and sure-handed. He was an excellent basketball player but Sutherland would not let him waste time on the sport. He had great straightaway power and he hit the line with splintering force. Wojciechowicz whose friendship with Goldberg started in the Polo Grounds and developed on pro fields, thinks Marshall's starting speed made the difference. He was heavy-legged but it took him only a step or two to break into top speed. He had another strong quality—a great pride in doing things well. He worked until he had mastered each move of the game. He was quick to learn, as the poker-playing members of the team found out in 1936. On the way to the Nebraska game the card sharks took him for $30, a lot of money for a college boy then. A few weeks later, when Pitt was on the road again, Goldberg nearly cleaned the squad. He had taken a little time to study the game.

Fordham had run up four victories before the 1936 Pitt meeting—two easy ones over Franklin & Marshall and Waynesburg, and close wins over Southern Methodist and St. Mary's. The Blocks had become firmer and tougher. But Maniaci was gone and without him the attack lacked its old explosiveness.

Pitt had beaten Ohio Wesleyan, West Virginia, Ohio State and Notre Dame (26–0) but had been upset by its city rival, Duquesne. Sutherland's addiction to the ground game, no matter how invitingly the situation called for a pass, was never more apparent than against Ohio State. Facing a nine- and sometimes ten-man line, Pitt did not pass once. Later, in the Fordham game, Chickerneo called a spot pass over center against a nine-man line with backers wide and completed it. He called it again and completed it. Sutherland pulled him out. The coach was sure the next one would backfire. Pitt stuck to its one-arm offense and by season's end was ranked No. 1 in the country.

In the locker room before the Fordham game Sutherland gave what was an impassioned oration for him. He said he wanted the team "to look good in the big city." He reminded the players, "If you want to make All-America you can do it against this team."

The game was played before a jammed crowd of 57,000 at the Polo Grounds three days before the Roosevelt-Landon presidential election. President Roosevelt was in the city to make a fighting New Deal speech at Madison Square Garden that night. He would have been proud of underdog Fordham. Pitt hammered away at the short-handed Rams, who substituted only nine times.

Wojie still remembers the sight of the white-jersied hordes bearing down on him. "We played a loose six-two-two-one," he said. "I was the outside linebacker. On those end runs and deep reverses they had five men coming at you. I always knew where the play was going. I just followed the quarterback. But I wondered how long we could hold them back."

The Pitt backfield that had shredded Notre Dame the week before—Goldberg, Patrick and LaRue—began to roll against the Seven Blocks. In making four first downs, Pitt drove 52 yards. Fordham right tackle Al Babartsky was reeling from punishment but he refused to leave the game. Pitt moved to the Fordham 12 and the Polo Grounds fell silent as Referee W. T. Halloran waved a first down. In three shots against the furious Fordham line Goldberg and LaRue gained 9 yards. The crowd stood, dreading the inevitable and roaring encouragement to the defiant Rams standing at their own goal line. When Pitt ran out of the huddle everyone in the ball park knew what was coming. LaRue stood deep in left formation. He took the pass from center and knifed into the wedge at tackle. Wojie was there. LaRue hit him, bounced and was nailed to the ground at the line of scrimmage. That was as close as Pitt was to come for another year.

Pitt threatened once more when Goldberg took off on Pitt's pet reverse, No. 112, and would have gone 70 yards to score if he had not cut the wrong way behind his center, Don Hensley. Instead he ran 35 yards. Marshall still regrets the mess he made of the Hensley block. Fordham was handicapped by an injury early in the game to Captain Frank Mautte. The Rams made one strong drive, from their 19 to the Pitt 27. But fullback Dulkie slipped and fell on fourth down with a yard to go.

Once more Pitt walked out of the Polo Grounds frustrated and aggravated by scoring failures. And Fordham once again had achieved more with less.

The Rams went through the rest of the 1936 season with hope that they would be invited to the Rose Bowl. They probably would have been, too, if N.Y.U. had not upset them in their final game. Pitt went to Pasadena instead and convinced the Far West of the superiority of Sutherland-style football by whipping Washington, 21–0.

The Rose Bowl trip was followed by an unfortunate sequel a year later. Pitt's 1937 team was the national champion and belonged in the Bowl again. When the bid came to the University, the players were asked to vote yes or no in a secret ballot. The athletic office considered it a mere formality. But 15 voted in favor and 16 against. Most of the 16 dissenters had been to the Coast twice the year before, to play U.S.C. and Washington. They weren't eager to give over the month of December to hard work again. Some of them may have resented the fact that each Washington player had received $200 expense money after the '37 Rose Bowl game. Their only extra money had come out of Dr. Sutherland's pocket. As soon as the balloting results were heard, the rumor, and then a newspaper story, spread that the Pitt players had refused to go to the Bowl because they weren't getting paid. Those who had voted no realized they had made a mistake; whatever their true reasons were, their decision was bound to sound crassly commercial. Some of the players walked up to the football office on the hill to talk with Coach Sutherland about it.

Jock clearly was stunned. "What bowl bid?" he said.

The athletic office had never told him his team had been invited back to the Rose Bowl. "Jock was not an emotional man," said one of the players who was in the room. "But after we told him about it he turned his chair toward the window and I thought sure he was going to cry. We were so mad we didn't know what to do." It was too late to do anything. Dr. Sutherland spent only one more year at Pitt. The gulf between his dedication to the game and the school administration's attitude toward it had grown too wide.

When the Pitt squad rode from New York City to the Westchester Country Club on Friday, October 16, 1937, there was not a doubt in the busload that they would score— and win—against Fordham the next day. The futility and mistakes of the previous two games were buried under their brimming confidence. They were Rose Bowl champions. They now knew what to expect of Fordham. Their new backfield, later called the Dream Backfield, was the best that Pitt had put together. John Chickerneo, a darkhaired Romanian boy from Warren, Ohio, was the No. 1 quarterback. Goldberg was still the heavy runner at left halfback. At right half was a curly-haired, lazy-looking boy from Williamsport, Pennsylvania, named Harold Stebbins. He had a good singing voice and liked to croon with jazz bands. On the field he was as high-strung and skittish as a race-horse—and almost as fast. Dick Cassiano, son of an Albany, New York, chef, was beginning to work in as a halfback. By season's end he had gained 620 yards, even though he was only a second-stringer. For the third year Patrick and Stapulis shared the fullback job. The Pitt linemen—Bill Daddio, Tony Matisi, Don Hensley, Steve Petro, George Delich and Frank Souchak—were old hands at Sutherland's football ABC's.

On the Fordham campus that Friday night Crowley sent his players back to their halls with the belief that they could knock off Pitt and go on to the Rose Bowl after all. (Fordham did stay unbeaten that year—and also uninvited.) As part of his careful defensive preparation he had switched Ed Franco to right guard in the hopes of stalling Pitt's inside reverses. Paul Berezney was assigned to start at Franco's left tackle position. The other Blocks—Jacunski, Kochel, Wojie, Babartsky and Druze—were ready to stand in the trenches again.

Jock Sutherland wanted badly to win this game in "the big city," as he always called New York. He asked Goldberg not to dress or practice with the team on Friday, an extreme precaution for Sutherland and the first time it had ever happened to Goldberg. Actually Curly Stebbins probably deserved more special care. Earlier in the week he had jammed his hand in scrimmage when a sub smelled out a play and threw him for a loss. As he ran signals on Friday center Don Hensley noticed that Steb-

bins was still handling the ball gingerly. But the hand swelling was gone and Stebbins insisted he was all right.

Just before Fordham took the field for its pre-game squad prayer, Jack Dempsey, the old heavyweight champion, walked up to wish them luck. Dempsey told them to glory in the role of the underdog. He said that with a helluva fight they could catch Pitt this time. The sight of the champ and his pep talk gave Fordham an extra emotional charge, which came in handy right after the kickoff.

Pitt started out by pouring it on Crowley's new left tackle. Before Franco could be rushed back to the position and Bernard sent in at guard, Goldberg-Stebbins-Patrick had covered 37 yards. But there the old wall formed up and held. Early in the second period Fordham had one of its few big surges. Quarterback Angelo Fortunato faked a pass and cut for 13 yards. A classy sophomore, Don Principe, burst for 20 yards but it was lost by a penalty. Pitt took over and fumbled, the first of six times, and Fordham tried a field goal from the 23. Johnny Druze missed it.

Late in the second period the swift Stebbins of Pitt returned a Woitkoski punt 35 yards and the Panthers were under way again. A completed pass that nearly brought Sutherland to his feet and Patrick's three darting runs put the ball on the Fordham five. Here Pitt went for the touchdown on a play specially rigged for this game. In the huddle it was called 318. It was a halfback-to-halfback reverse instead of Pitt's conventional fullback-to-halfback handoff. Stebbins took the pass from center and slipped the ball to Goldberg, running left to right. The new reverse caught the Seven Blocks off balance and Goldberg easily cut over the goal line for a score. The tension that had been drawn taut through two and a half bitter football games snapped with a roar from 50,000 voices. But the noise suddenly changed tempo and now it was the Fordham crowd that was on its feet whooping it up for the referee. Pitt had been caught holding. There was no touchdown. The score didn't count. Goldberg's and Pitt's brief glory was covered by a referee's handkerchief near the one-yard line. The violation was charged against Tony Matisi on Fordham halfback Al Gurske. It turned out to be one of the most flagrant and useless holds in football.

Matisi was game captain that afternoon and had given the squad a little pep talk before the game about socking it to them. In the huddle before the crucial play he had followed Chickerneo's call with the warning: "Anybody holds on this play, he'll answer to me." Tony wanted to win and to avoid holding as much as anyone, but his arm and his eagerness to see Goldberg score undid him. Actually Goldberg did not need the block—or the hold. Gurske, who had an injured leg, said he never could have caught the runner anyway. After the game Matisi told Sutherland he was sure he wasn't holding. Sutherland accepted his explanation. But that night when the team returned to the Hotel McAlpin the players began thumbing the New York *Sunday News*. In the sports section a vivid action picture of the game showed Matisi with a tight armlock on Gurske's leg.

Through Pitt errors Fordham got close enough for a couple of field goal attempts in the second half. But the incredibly close misses were all Pitt's. Once Stebbins picked off a Fordham flat pass with his bad hand. He had a clear field but he dropped the ball. Twice in the fourth period Wojie and Stebbins met head-on and Stebbins lost the ball. After the game a New York sportswriter asked Sutherland why he didn't take Stebbins out after his fourth fumble.

"I didn't know he was going to fumble five times," Sutherland replied.

Pitt could not second-guess its ball-handling but the team later suffered anguishing second thoughts about a decision made in the huddle. It is still being second-guessed by Pitt players 23 years later. Pitt moved into a field goal situation and Chickerneo turned to Bill Daddio, who along with Souchak did the placement kicking, and said: "Want to try one, Bill?" Daddio had a heavily taped leg and his affirmative reply left some of his teammates unconvinced. Hensley called for a time out and suggested they discuss the matter. He asked Souchak if *he* wanted to kick. Frank said it wasn't up to him, that if Daddio wanted a shot at it he should have it. Chickerneo said *he* was calling the plays. They returned to the huddle and Daddio was called to place kick. He swung his bad leg —and missed by less than a foot.

A year later, before 75,867 fans at Pitt Stadium, Daddio broke the most grueling, frustrating and most famous drought in football history by scoring against Fordham with a field goal and Pitt went on to win 24–13. But few football fans remember that Pitt-Fordham game.

No pro has endured as did former Texas Christian star Sammy Baugh—16 seasons with the Washington Redskins. High among his passing marks is his lifetime total of 1,709 completions.

Big wheel for the machinelike Cleveland Browns in the early 1950s, Otto Graham led all pro passers at efficiency; he made good on over 55 percent of his passes.

Small but oh, my— Davey O'Brien, worthy successor to Sammy Baugh at T.C.U., was a workhorse passer, runner for the Philadelphia Eagles. He completed 33 passes in one game in 1940.

UPI

UPI

INTERNATIONAL NEWS

The following report in the New York Times *may fail to explain exactly what Jim Thorpe did against Army on November 9, 1912, but it leaves no doubt that he was a marvel. Army's right halfback, Dwight Eisenhower, like most of the other Cadets, does not get a call.*

THORPE AND HIS REDOUBTABLE BAND

The New York Times

Jim Thorpe and his redoubtable band of Carlisle Indian gridiron stars invaded the plains this afternoon to match their prowess against the moleskin gladiators of Uncle Sam's Military Academy, and when the two teams crossed the parade ground in the semidarkness of late afternoon the Cadets had been shown up as no other West Point team has been in many years. They were buried under the overwhelming score of 27–6, figures that no other team has been able to reach against the Cadets since West Point loomed up among the big football teams, and to make the defeat all the more humiliating, every Cadet knew deep in his heart that this big score still did not show the relative strength of the two teams, based on today's performances.

It was a game such as the old reservation has seldom, if ever, staged. In a way, it carried a distinct shock to the 3,000 spectators who had firmly believed that the big Army team had passed the stage where such a thing might happen. But the unexpected did happen, with an exhibition of football by the wards of the Nation that distinctly places the Carlisle team among the great elevens of the year. The Indians simply outclassed the Cadets as they might be expected to outclass a prep school. They played football that won by its steadiness rather than novel formations. Speed and accuracy marked every move of the redskins, and they showed that football can still be spectacular while the so-called old-style methods are employed most of the time.

Standing out resplendent in a galaxy of Indian stars was Jim Thorpe, recently crowned the athletic marvel of the age. The big Indian captain added more luster to his already brilliant record, and at times the game itself was almost forgotten while the spectators gazed on Thorpe, the individual, to wonder at his prowess. To recount his notable performances in the complete overthrow of the Cadet would leave little space for other notable points of the conflict. He simply ran wild, while the Cadets tried in vain to stop his progress. It was like trying to clutch a shadow. He did not make any of the four touchdowns credited to his team, simply because the brilliant Arcasa, Thorpe's backfield mate, was chosen to carry the ball on three of the four occasions when a plunge meant a score, and Bergie the other time.

Thorpe went through the West Point line as if it were an open door; his defensive play was on a par with his attack and his every move was that of a past master. In the second half the game was delayed for three minutes because of an injury to Thorpe's left shoulder—the recurrence of an injury which had come back twice in previous games—and for a time it seemed that the great Indian must leave the game. For a full minute he lay prone on the field; then he was helped to his feet and first aid was applied. When Thorpe walked back to his position behind the line the West Point crowd gave him an ovation that was remarkable in view of the fact that he was the one big obstacle between Army and victory.

Thorpe tore off runs of ten yards or more so often that they became common. His zigzagging and ability to hurl himself free of tacklers made his running highly spectacular. In the third period he made a run which, while it failed to bring anything in points, because of a penalty, will go down in the Army gridiron annals as one of the greatest ever seen on the plains.

The Indians had been held for downs on West Point's 3-yard line, and Keyes dropped back behind his own goal line and punted out. The ball went directly to Thorpe on Army's 45-yard line. It was a high kick, and the Cadets were already gathering around the big Indian when he clutched the falling pigskin in his arms. His catch and his start were but one motion. In and out, zigzagging first to one side and then to the other, while a flying Cadet went hurtling through space, Thorpe wormed his way through the entire Army team. Every Cadet in the game had his chance, and every one of them failed. It was not the usual spectacle of the man with the ball outdistancing his opponents by circling them. It was a dodging game in which Thorpe matched himself against an entire team and proved the master. Lines drawn parallel and fifteen feet apart would include all the ground that Thorpe covered on his triumphant dash through an entire team.

West Point's much talked of defense, which had held Yale to four first downs in a full hour of play, was like tissue paper before the Indians. To a corresponding degree the Carlisle defense,

which had been considered so much inferior to the attack, was a wonder. The Cadets got one first down in the first period; and in the second, when they showed their only bit of rushing ability, they got four, three of these coming just before the touchdown was made. In the second half West Point did not make a first down. In fact, barring the second period, the Cadets spent all their time on the defense. They got the ball occasionally, but only to make futile advances and then punt.

From a Carlisle standpoint the game was simply one first down after another. In midfield the redskins ran wild, but the Army had the habit of tightening up when the goal line was threatened, and four times the Indians lost the ball after traveling to within the 5-yard line. Twice the loss came on downs and twice forward passes were tried on the final down. The Indians got away four passes that were very cleverly executed, and these gained considerable ground. The Cadets tried the forward pass a few times and it failed every time.

Roughness marred the game to such an extent that two of the best players were relegated to the side lines. In the first period Powell, the Indian fullback, was sent off the field for a mix-up with Herrick, and in the second half captain Devore of the Cadets drew a similar penalty.

Arcasa and Guyon ranked next to Thorpe in the honors of the afternoon. Arcasa starred as a ground gainer, and he teamed with Thorpe on the old-time crisscross, which seldom failed to fool the Cadets.

The Indians lost 75 yards in penalties, and the Cadets lost 45.

THE LINEUP:

Carlisle 27		*West Point* 6
Large	le	Hoge
Guyon	lt	Rowley
Garlow	lg	Jones
Bergie	c	Purnell
Busch	rg	Herrick
Calac	rt	Devore
Vedernack	re	Markoe
Welch	qb	Prichard
Thorpe	lh	Hobbs
Arcasa	rh	Eisenhower
Powell	fb	Keyes

Although the names and numbers have changed since this was written in 1960, the mental process of preparing the New York Giants' defense remains much the same. This article by Life *staff writer Paul O'Neil, is an excellent definition of what it takes to put a strong pro defense together.*

THE DEFENSE: A TRIUMPH OF MIND

Paul O'Neil

When the New York football Giants move into Yankee Stadium each fall, the gladiators' helmets—dark-blue plastic shells with one red equatorial stripe and skeletal iron snouts—are placed, one by one, on the topmost shelves of their owners' dressing-room cubicles. Six days a week henceforth, since they are worn only in actual combat, they ring the big, green-carpeted room, grinning like gaudy skulls. By inspecting them, as an anthropologist might inspect Neanderthal remains, it is not only possible to discover which of them belong to the huge forwards of the defensive platoon, but to say exactly how many games each man has played. Week by week the helmets of the first-line defenders pick up streaks of foreign color—the red of San Francisco, the bright yellow of Pittsburgh—as their owners bang heads, literally, with their foes of the National Football League.

Defense as played by the hardened professionals of the N.F.L. should never be confused with defense as played by college teams or even, for that matter, by the newly hatched pros of the rival American Football League. It is so advanced in both concept and practice

as to give football a new dimension, and it has been heavily instrumental in generating the enormous excitement now attendant on the professional game. The Giants have been the leaders in this flowering of violence and exactitude. For three years, win, lose or draw, New York's defensive players have been the toughest opponents in football—almost certainly the toughest in football history. They have also replaced the traditional heroes of the offensive backfield as the darlings of the New York crowd. The big audiences before whom the Giants play at home are salted with some of the world's most hideously discontented spectators. But no matter how dark the moment, they roar as gleefully as the Roman mob sighting lions when New York gives up the ball and the defensive team trots ominously forth to take over.

One need look no further than the Giants' last (and sixth straight) victory over the resurgent Cleveland Browns to understand the basis of this startling sentimentality. Cleveland's awesome fullback, Jimmy Brown, and his lightning-fast partner, Bobby Mitchell, are

238

widely heralded as the most irresistible running combination in the game, but New York limited Cleveland to a total of 6 yards by rushing, forced them to pass a slippery ball against their will and upset them 17–13.

The secret of the Giants' animal efficiency in proceedings like these might horrify their most vociferous admirers. Their ascendancy, in a league where brawn, speed and experience are commonplace, is essentially a triumph of the mind. The very violence of their performance springs not so much from sheer brute strength as from concepts of defense more complex and daring than any ever before attempted in football, and from a stringent and demanding intellectual discipline. The heaviest burden any defense must bear is the inevitable burden of ignorance: the fact that the offensive team knows exactly what it is going to do in the moments after the ball is snapped and that the defense is forced to guess. It is the Giants' ability to calculate and memorize the probabilities ahead of time, to reduce both guesswork and error and to eliminate time-lag in execution on the field, which has led them to their present eminence.

For all their best-laid plans, the Giant defenders cannot be perfect. It is axiomatic in the N.F.L. that any team will score on any other team and that all will be beaten some time during a season. The Giants, whose offensive team has not been consistently high scoring, are no exception. But no other defensive team except Baltimore has kept opponents' points to such low levels. None has risen to such heights as New York achieved against Cleveland, none has so hamstrung that ferociously competent old passer, Pittsburgh's fiery Bobby Layne, who publicly calls them "the greatest defense I have ever seen."

Each member of the 16-man New York defensive squad is handed a big, leather-bound, loose-leaf notebook when he reports to training camp in July. During the next six months it is not only his most important single item of equipment but the focal point of his professional life. In it, week by week, he takes the lecture notes and keeps the charts, diagrams and predictions upon which his reactions will be based in the game ahead. If he is a rookie, he will spend the better part of two years mastering the system which all this bookkeeping has been conceived to serve. Even if he comes to the Giants as a knowledgeable professional, he will spend a full season learning to think anew. And, even when mastered, the notebook is a demanding instrument. The Giants report to Yankee Stadium's dressing room at nine-thirty in the morning five days a week, toil over intelligence reports until eleven, hustle out to the field for a two-hour workout, hustle back for a shower and a quick box lunch, and sit in lectures and conferences until five. They are expected to take the notebook home for an hour or two of additional study at night.

Both the defensive Giants and their bruising intricacy of method are essentially the creatures of Tom Landry, one of football's original thinkers, who is now head coach of the N.F.L.'s newly organized team in Dallas. Landry, a soft-voiced, sharp-featured Texan, was a defensive halfback with New York in the early 1950's and became defensive coach in 1954. The magnificent athletes of his platoon—most of whom still play for New York—became the laboratory instruments with which he evolved a new philosophy of defense. The Giants are passionately convinced that they can dominate, rather than simply contain, an opposing team. They expect, rather than hope, to make yardage through fumbles, interceptions and tackles behind the line. They are confident they can set up scores, force enemy quarterbacks into untenable situations and shape the pattern of a game.

Professional football's defenses have been through a long process of evolution—from the 7-1-2-1 or "seven diamond" formation used when the game was played basically on the ground, through patterns with ever shortening forward lines (the 6-2-2-1, the 5-3-2-1) which were prompted by the increasing success of of the forward pass and the resultant defensive need to cover more territory. As the game changed and their duties changed, the sizes and shapes of the defensive players changed too, until both their arrangement and their physical conformation was finally dictated by the 4-3-4, the formation on which most N.F.L. defense is predicated today.

The 4-3-4 anchors four huge men (240-290 pounds) on the line of scrimmage, and puts three burly, cat-quick linebackers (215-230 pounds) a step behind them, two on the flanks and one in the middle. The linebackers provide the defense with enormous elasticity: they can step into the line, charge through it into the enemy backfield, slide laterally against plays to the outside, or fall back against short passes. Four fleet and vicious backs (185-200 pounds) hold station behind them against deep runs or passes. Even so, the team with the ball—by possession of the split seconds it takes the defenders to react—generally holds an advantage in time and with it most of the initiative.

The Giants, by their ability to anticipate a play rather than respond to it, have seized these split seconds for themselves.

Most defensive teams still feel impelled to augment the 4-3-4 with other formations, to push linebackers up into the line for the advantage of an extra step or, like Baltimore, to go to a three-men line in passing situations. New York never varies the 4-3-4 before the ball is snapped, thus showing the offensive team the same inscrutable if menacing face before every play. But, with the advantage of their blink of time, they are able to dissolve out of it into any of twenty predetermined patterns of counteroffensive as plays begin. It is a system not only calculated to harry opposing teams on the field, but also—since twenty defenses are obviously harder to anticipate than two or three—to harry opposition backfield coaches in the week before a game as they attempt to diagnose Giant weaknesses. The Giants, on the other hand, confidently refuse to waste a second of forethought on plays an opponent has not used with success. It is their firm conviction that any opposing quarterback must revert, under sufficient pressure, to basic, well-proved methods of attack, that they can force him to fall back on them, and that these are the real key to his jugular.

By the time Tom Landry left New York for Dallas last winter the Giants were so advanced in theory that it would have been all but impossible to replace him from the outside. Head Coach Jim Lee Howell, as a result, adopted a system long considered heretical in U.S. football: this year's defensive team, like the rugby and rowing clubs of Oxford and Cambridge, is self-directed. Right Linebacker Harland ("Swede") Svare has over-all command of its activities and bears the burden of preparing its intricate weekly intelligence data. He is assisted by big, dark-eyed, dark-haired All-Pro End Andy Robustelli in coaching the line, and by All-Pro Safety Man Jim Patton, a hard and handsome Mississippian, in coaching the backs. The Swede, a barrel-chested, deceptively placid fellow from Poulsbo (pop. 1,503), Washington, is a complex man. At 29, after eight years in professional football, he is one of the most vicious tacklers in the N.F.L. He also plays the works of Franz Joseph Haydn on the Spanish guitar, and is part owner of a California drive-in restaurant chain which is expected to gross a million dollars this year.

On Monday morning, more often than not, a professional football player is so bruised and beaten that he may have real difficulty in getting out of bed. But each Monday morning by N.F.L. procedure the Giants receive eight reels of 16-mm film—movies of their next opponent playing two previous games. The battered Svare rises early, puts on a pair of horn-rimmed spectacles, tunes his hotel room radio to a station which plays classical music and sits down with a movie projector and the reels devoted to offense. By running them endlessly forward and back in slow motion, he checks the moves of every man on every play, and transcribes them on sheets of special diagram paper. It is a task which usually takes him until two or three o'clock the next morning. He snatches a few hours of sleep, drags himself up again and meets Robustelli and Patton at the stadium to begin matching offensive plays with the defensive maneuvers best calculated to ruin them. By the time the rest of the team has arrived and dressed in workout gear (sweat suits, football shoes and baseball caps) the first of the week's plans are ready for discussion and rehearsal on the field.

This, however, is only the beginning of mental preparation. There are, in the Giants' view, only four basic offensive formations in professional football: the double wing and three variations of the T. Every player must not only know the list of plays which can be best produced from each of these formations, but must be able to pick the one play an enemy quarterback is most likely to use every time the offensive team comes out of its huddle. To prepare them ahead of time for this instant analytical thought, Svare & Co. draw up complex weekly charts which predict an opponent's most probable response to any given situation and which reveal his habits and patterns of thought. Most football teams, for instance, are basically right-handed; that is, they almost invariably run more plays to the right than to the left. But almost all teams will turn left-handed on specific occasion. The charts also show how often a foe has passed, where he passed, to whom he has passed and his percentage of completions. They record behavior patterns based on prosperity and adversity—the list of plays an opponent has called on second down with only 3 yards to go, for instance, as opposed to plays called on third down with 7 to go.

The long weekday meetings at which the Giants digest and discuss these massive doses of intelligence are conducted amidst an atmosphere oddly reminiscent of an aircraft carrier's ready room. Though they may look like padded, steaming monsters from outer space when seen from the stands on Sunday, the Giants are, like most professional football players, well-spoken and well-mannered if enormously muscular college graduates. They have come to the sport to cash in for two or three years and have remained out of a hypnotic preoccupation with its tactical problems and the danger, applause, camaraderie, and savage satisfactions it affords them. The jargon with which they communicate has a curiously sardonic ring. Charging linebackers "shoot, blitz, storm, or blow." Pass receivers "fly out, square in, and run double circles." A man being directed to hurl himself, in human sacrifice, at a wall of charging blockers is simply told to "strip the play." The men lounge comfortably, cigarets smoldering, during their endless conferences. But conversation is terse and precise, and the players react to the repetitive slow-motion movies which end each day with an almost visceral attentiveness.

The Giants must not only be ready to make dozens of informed decisions every Sunday, but ready to make them instantly and unerringly while exhausted, stunned, deafened by the clamor of 60,000 people and in the full knowledge, as Coach Howell puts it, "that eleven other large men can do them bodily harm." The damage they risk can be serious: the season ended for Left End Jim Katcavage when he broke a collarbone stemming a rush by the Philadelphia Eagles. But the Giants, it must be stated, are not unprepared to do physical violence themselves. Tackles Roosevelt Grier and Dick Modzelewski weigh 285 and 260 respectively. Famed Middle Linebacker Sam Huff is capable of fielding plunging fullbacks as lesser men catch medicine balls. Halfbacks Lindon Crow and Dick Lynch and Safety Man Dick Nolan are not only fleet pass-defenders but men who genuinely enjoy collisions with other men's rib cages. "You've got to have experience," says Andy Robustelli. "We've played together, drunk together, traveled together, beefed together. We're close. We're proud of each other. We know each other so well we can almost feel each other think."

Even so, the mechanical complexities of executing the Giants' defenses demand ceaseless, burning concentration from every muscular man. Although the defensive team must operate as one responsive whole, it is, in actuality, four little federated teams, each of which adjusts itself to "unit calls." These are cries of "Mambo! Samba! Omaha! Denver! Banjo!" that are shouted as offensive plays begin. Each flanking linebacker redirects himself and his associated end, the middle linebacker calls changes to the two tackles, and the backs and safety men react as a group to unit calls of their own. As plays develop, furthermore, each man must remember that any call made behind him takes precedence over any call he has made himself.

Professional football is a game in which morality is firmly based on practical considerations. Almost any offensive lineman who can safely delay a defensive man for a precious moment by illegal holding will do so unless illegally discouraged (favorite tricks: hooking an ankle, holding with the arm away from the nearest official, grabbing a jersey at the moment of legally executed impact). The Giants must devote some thought to simply staying alive. Defensive halfbacks are expected to cry "Crackback! Crackback!" if an enemy split end turns back to "blindside" a defensive linebacker, and every player must remind himself to run briskly past any completed tackle. "Stop too soon," says Halfback Lynch, "and one of these big blockers will just accidentally break you in two."

The Giants make a rite of bringing their small sons to Yankee Stadium on the Saturdays before home games. The small fry play noisy touch football near the empty, echoing stands while their fathers limber up for a half hour on the field, and then troop proudly back through the dugout with the team. As the children scuffle and drink pop from the dressing-room vending machines, the defensive squad gathers for a final quiz: "Third and eight, Sam. Balanced left, split right. Who do you cover?" Attendants begin laying out equipment for the morrow's combat, the big room slowly empties and the tensions of what Svare calls "the long, long wait" begin in the mind of every man. A few weeks ago Left Linebacker Cliff Livingston, 30—ex-U.C.L.A. end, sports-car driver, sailor, off-season man-about-town—stayed on in the silence to wrestle with his personal devils. He sat down at the movie projector, loaded film, cut the lights and stared for a long time at two ghostly football teams moving forward and back, forward and back across the dressing-room wall. He watched but one play—a sequence he had already studied at least a dozen times during the week. "That halfback," he finally muttered into the darkness. "I think he sets just an inch or so higher when he knows he's going to screen."

RACKETY RACKET

Tom O'Reilly

This is a tale that has needed telling for many years if only because it belongs to the great sporting lore of America. It concerns the truth as to why football was abolished at one of the most respected institutions in this land—Sing Sing. There has been no football at Sing Sing since 1934.

At that time, it was announced that Warden Lewis E. Lawes banned the game because he felt that the attending crowds were too disturbing an influence on the Sing Sing routine and attracted entirely too much attention to his charges. There was also something about one of the players who didn't quit running in the end zone.

That is true as far as it goes but it is not complete. Football lost face at Sing Sing because of an attempt at one of the most outrageous betting coups in gridiron history—an affair that rocked the old institution from front gate to solitary cells, causing fights, minor riots and near murder.

As you know, when football was introduced at Sing Sing, in 1930, the players had little talent. Coached by Notre Dame's perfectly named prison preceptor, John Law, Sing Sing's eleven was shellacked by such semipro outfits as the Danbury Trojans, the New Rochelle Bull-dogs and, saddest of all, the Port Jervis Police. While lacking in talent, however, the players were earnest and the police reporters, wittily calling them Caged Tigers, Black Sheep, Zebras, etc., said they had plenty of time to learn, with quotes around the word time.

This was true. Practicing faithfully the year round, Sing Sing's team soon became a power in its district. In fact, by 1934, it was so good that it outclassed all its opposition. This proved to be a curse in disguise. Since Sing Sing is filled with gentlemen devoted to taking chances, it was only natural that football provided them with plenty of sport.

Every week during the season it became customary to bet money, tobacco, shoes and even food on the games. By 1934, however, the team's excellence made it impossible to bet on mere victory or defeat. Any man wishing to back Sing Sing had to give away 21 points. In other words, if Sing Sing won by only 20 points supporters of the team lost their money, tobacco, etc.

Sing Sing was hot that season, beating everybody by scores ranging from 27–0 to 40–0, until the big game with the Port Jervis Police. Then an unforeseen thing occurred. Coach John Law, happy in the knowledge of his team's superiority, announced that he would not be on hand for the game with the Cops.

In addition to master-minding the Sing Sing games on Sundays, he was acting also as a Fordham scout, for his old Notre Dame pal, Jim Crowley, on Saturdays. On the Saturday before the Sing Sing-Police game he had to scout N.Y.U., in Georgia. Naturally he would be unable to return to Sing Sing in time for the game next day. He told his men, confidently, "You know what to do. Go ahead and do it." They did.

The members of the starting eleven quickly got together and selected secret agents to go through the prison quietly betting against Sing Sing's chances of winning by 21 points. They were so delighted at the idea that they gave nice odds and didn't even inform the members of the second team, who were among the biggest bettors.

Well, when the great day arrived and the game started it became apparent, quickly, that the Cops were no match for the home team. Within 2 minutes of the start, a large and loose-hipped lifer galloped 40 yards for a touchdown. Following a kickoff and punt he did it again. On both occasions, Sing Sing's kicker easily scored the points after touchdown. In the second period, Sing Sing scored on straight line plunges.

Then, with the score at 20–0, the usually consistent place-kicker booted one far wide of the mark. Other strange things followed. No matter how hard Sing Sing tried, it didn't seem able to hold the ball near the goal line. It would march 50 yards to the goal and then fumble. Invariably the Cops recovered. This happened twice and nobody thought anything about it. When it occurred for the fifth time, however, substitutes began to trot out on the field. But the regulars waved them back and refused to leave the game.

In the meantime, Coach Law got a break in Georgia. Ed Huntsinger, who was with him, met an old Army pal who was flying a transport plane and obligingly offered to give them a lift back to New York. As it turned out, Law arrived at Sing Sing between the halves.

There was an argument of gigantic proportions going on in the dressing room when he entered. On his appearance it stopped abruptly and he swears that one of his Negro stars nearly turned white. When told of the situation Law said nothing. He sent his first team back into the game for the second half. He watched them fumble once and then sent in the second team. The substitutes played like madmen and walloped the Cops, 50–0. The double-crossers were double-crossed. The repercussions that followed caused trouble for months and finally football was queered forever.

THE GRAND OLD MAN

Edwin Pope

To me, the coaching profession is one of the noblest and most far-reaching in building manhood. No man is too good to be the athletic coach for youth. Not to drink, not to gamble, not to smoke, not to swear . . . to be fair-minded . . . to deal justly . . . to be honest in thinking and square in dealing . . . not to bear personal malice or to harbor hatred against rivals . . . not to be swell-headed in victory or overalibi in defeat . . . to be the sportsman and gentleman at all times . . . these should be the ideals of the coach.

—AMOS ALONZO STAGG

When Lonnie Stagg was a child, just after the Civil War, he asked his father for the bladders of the two hogs the family butchered each November and March. He then blew up the bladders with a quill and used them for crude footballs.

Two world wars and seventy years later—ten years after the University of Chicago, which Stagg helped build, had made him professor emeritus—he was named football coach of the year 1943.

On mileage alone Stagg rates as the number-one coach of all time. But there is a great deal more to Stagg's story than longevity. No other football figure even approached the Grand Old Man of the Midway for inventiveness; he

was the game's Benjamin Franklin, Alexander Graham Bell, and Thomas Edison rolled into one. His brain children include:

The ends-back formation (1890)
Reverse play (1890)
First indoor game (1891, Madison Square Garden)
7–2–2 defense (1891)
First book on football with diagrams, with Minnesota's Dr. Henry Williams (1893)
First intersectional game (1894, Chicago-Stanford)
Huddle (1896)
Direct pass from center (1896)
Wind sprints (1896)
Line shifts (1897)
Lateral pass (1898)
Man in motion (1899)
Unbalanced offensive line (1900)
Lights on practice field (1901)
Backfield shift (1904)
Awarding letters (1906)
Numbering players (1913)
Cross-blocking (1918)
Knit pants (1927)
6–2–1–2 defense (1932)
5–2–1–2–1 defense (1943)
Double flanker with twin backs and blocking back (1947)

Stagg even invented the indoor batting cage in baseball and pioneered the head-first slide.

He conducted the first tour of Japan by American baseball players. A track trail blazer, too, he served on the Olympic committee from 1906 through 1932, and coached James Lightbody to an Olympic "triple" in 1904. Clyde Blair, first man to run the hundred meters in less than ten seconds, was a Stagg protégé. For good measure, Stagg invented troughs for overflow in swimming pools.

Think of versatility and you think of Stagg. He nearly starved, studied for the ministry, made All-America end on Walter Camp's first football selection in 1889, and struck out twenty men in one baseball game for Yale before he ever started coaching. He once presided over a folk-dance society and twice was honored by the Boy Scouts for distinguished service to youth.

When Chicago tried to pension him in 1933, Stagg said, "I could not and would not accept a job without work. I am fit, able, and willing. I refuse to be idle and a nuisance."

No man, added seventy-year-old Stagg, has the right to retire as long as his work benefits his fellow man.

Above all, Amos Alonzo Stagg kept football in its place. He never viewed the game as an end in itself. A tackle complained to Stagg in his senior year that he just had not caught on to the game; the youth believed his college education had been wasted. "You're dead wrong, boy," Stagg said. "You've learned to dress right, speak right, how to act around good people. And if you never passed a college course you still would know a thousand things that not one out of ten other men know. Don't ever tell me again that your college term has been wasted."

Stagg's devotion to clean play is fact and no part of the mythological sportsmanship attributed to many coaches by overenthusiastic publicists. In 1922, Chicago was embroiled in a bloody game with Princeton. Fritz Crisler, then Stagg's assistant, suggested that the Old Man send in Alonzo, Jr., at quarterback to call an end run. Stagg flatly refused. Chicago lost, 21–18. Later Crisler asked Stagg why he had not directed the most effective strategy. "The rules committee," Stagg said levelly, "deprecates the use of a substitute to convey information."

In 1909 Stagg asked officials to call back a Chicago touchdown because, he said, his team had broken a rule.

He often had opponents' signals sent to him by well-wishers. He never even read them, just tore them up and threw them away.

The physical world was revolutionized during Stagg's lifetime. He was thirty when the first gas buggy was visited upon America, over eighty at the coming of the atom age. But Stagg never changed. He campaigned relentlessly for plainer diets and cleaner living. He scrimmaged with his players until he was forty, jogged a mile daily at seventy, took walk-and-run hikes at eighty. "The greatest pleasure one has," he said repeatedly, "is keeping and feeling fit. Live in a way that makes you feel good, and get your fun out of feeling good."

Paradoxically, Stagg believed that kids raised in the city are better equipped for both sports and life than country kids: "They're more alert."

Stagg was fifty before he had to wear glasses. Forever trying to prove that sports were beneficial, he conducted a survey of old University of Chicago athletes and noted that the percentage of baldness was tiny. He said this showed that sports were advantageous to health.

Hairy-headed or not, all old C men quickly stamp out their cigarettes in Stagg's presence.

He is a stickler for the simple diet. "Keep the hot dogs in the stands where they belong," he preaches. "I never ate one in my life."

He allowed his players a sufficient sum for each meal on a football trip, and if they charged more to the team bill, he collected the difference. "I am a stoic," he said, "not an epicure." On his eighty-ninth birthday in 1951 he dined on pea soup, two ears of corn, peaches, and milk.

The stocky little man (he weighs 166 pounds today, some 70 years after he played as a 150-pound end and halfback) never smoked or used profanity, but numbered at least two dozen pupils in his famed Double Jackass Club. "Just calling a man a jackass," he would say, "is too good for some of them. They make the Double Jackass Club."

Illinois's Bob Zuppke agreed that Stagg never swore at his men, "because he doesn't have any men. He calls this man, then that man, then another, a jackass. By the end of the workout there are no men playing—just jackasses grazing."

One of Stagg's Chicagoans, Norman Barker, asked Mrs. Stagg why the Old Man was so critical of him. "Why, Norman," said Alonzo's beloved Stella, "whom the Lord loveth, he chasteneth."

That about fit. Stagg wasted no time with the washouts or the unwilling. One self-styled hotshot came to practice at Chicago in a bright new uniform. Stagg moved the scrimmage to a muddy sector and told the quarterback to give the ball to the great man. After five dunkings, the V.I.P. quit.

Before a big Chicago game with Illinois, Stagg walked about the dressing room peering under benches, chairs, towels, and out the window. The player nearest him asked him what he was looking for. "A right end," Stagg snapped.

"I'm a right end," said the boy.

"Well, we're going to play you at right end," Stagg said, "but we won't be fooling Illinois a bit, because they know you're not a right end."

Stagg beamed his pep talks toward team pride: he specifically refrained from building resentment against the opposing team. "In athletics, or in business," he maintained, "you won't get far by teaching your men to hate your competitor."

Amos Alonzo Stagg won 254 games, lost 104, and tied 28 in forty-one years as Chicago coach. When he took over there in 1892, Gentleman Jim Corbett had just beaten John L. Sullivan for the heavyweight championship and Knute Rockne was a child of four in Norway.

Stagg's fourteen-year record at College of the Pacific was 59 victories, 77 losses, and 7 ties—achieved with inferior material and schedules that played hob with his record but netted C.O.P. $230,000 and helped pay off the mortgage.

When C.O.P. tried to make him a "consultant" in 1947, Stagg observed that he believed in consistency and felt the same way about a job with no coaching contacts with youth as he had at Chicago. He joined son Alonzo at little Susquehanna College in Pennsylvania and for six seasons went on the field daily for vigorous coaching of offense. Susquehanna had a perfect record in 1951.

In 1953 he went back to Stockton College as an aide.

Today, nearing 100, he remains a firebrand.

When Quarterback George Ratterman, formerly with the Cleveland Browns, retired from pro football he left few marks in the record books to remember him by. But he did leave some scattered examples around the league, in the form of jokes and anecdotes, of his lively wit. Ratterman was one of those rare football players who could play the game seriously and well and yet never lose sight of its lighter side. His friend, writer Bob Deindorfer, has gathered the best of the Ratterman tales—plus a few others—in a book they call Confessions of a Gypsy Quarterback.

CARE AND FEEDING OF QUARTERBACKS

George Ratterman with Robert G. Deindorfer

A funny thing happened to me on my way to the showers my first year in the National Football League. Pausing in the Los Angeles Rams' locker room after a game to say hello to Bill Smyth, an old teammate from Notre Dame, an intriguing scrap of conversation rolled up from behind a row of lockers.

"What will we do with the Ratterman money?" an anonymous voice asked.

At first I suspected someone over behind the lockers had seen me slip in and was trying to pull my leg. As Bill explained it to me in lurid detail, however, my leg might possibly have had something to do with the remark, only nobody had pulled it quite hard enough earlier in the afternoon, during one of my infrequent games as the starting quarterback.

Stripping down for his shower, Bill Smyth proceeded to give me the facts of life, at least as they applied to the Los Angeles Rams in 1950. Before every game the team played, each player on the squad threw a dollar bill into a kitty. Afterwards, the $32 jackpot was awarded to whoever shook up the rival quarterback to

the point where he had to be removed from the game.

The problem that particular day was that I had stood up under the punishment and finished the game in one piece. Consequently End Elroy Hirsch, the informal squad treasurer, had asked his fellow shareowners how the Ratterman money should be disbursed. As I recall now, the boys decided to give $25 to a lineman who had suffered a $25 fine during the afternoon, possibly trying for me and that $32, and to sweeten the jackpot the following week with the remaining $7.

The point here isn't so much that it was Ratterman those barbarians were shooting at all afternoon, although that water on the knee didn't come from the whirlpool bath. The important point involves a rather larger issue. As the starting quarterback I happened to be the heart of the New York Yank offense and automatically the primary target for everyone wearing different-colored playsuits.

In the roughneck realm of pro football the quarterback generally amounts to nothing less

247

than Public Enemy No. 1. He's looked on by rivals not as a friend, a neighbor, a former teammate, a lodge brother in the Players Guild or even as a fellow human being—not during a game anyway. Equipped with the arm, the brains and the flimflam to beat the opposition, he is always regarded as the Enemy.

The logic of all this is beyond dispute. In an age of high-scoring T-formation football, it's the quarterback who gives the offense its kick. Along with everybody else, Coach Jimmy Phelan of the Dallas Texans (and elsewhere) recognized the value of his top banana without any prompting. In the last quarter of a game his Texans were losing by a bleak 27–0 score. Phelan decided he might just as well rest his starting quarterback and send in a substitute who wasn't nearly as good. As the reserve whipped a few practice passes along the sidelines, the Texans dramatically recovered a fumble deep in enemy territory.

"Sit down, my boy," said Phelan to the substitute, "we're not giving up yet."

Of all the men who strapped on shoulder pads, a kind and articulate Illinoisan named Otto Graham is the best quarterback I ever saw. Graham could do everything, and do it incredibly well. For years to come other passers will be shooting at some of the records he ran up while he carried the Browns to nine division championships.

If Graham is the greatest quarterback who ever played, and I'm only one of many players convinced of it, it's conceivable that I might be the second best. After all, it was Graham who kept me glued to the bench four years in Cleveland. Since I never had an opportunity to prove myself over an extended period, nobody will ever know for certain, although I do have my own suspicions.

With all the nosegays heaped on them by fans, sportswriters, and coaches, the quarterbacks themselves can't help but be aware of their dazzling contributions to the game. Down in the locker room jealous teammates have spread the slander that an outsider can identify the quarterback because he's the one wearing a size-8 ego.

Probably the most glaring example of this candor came years ago when the quarterback for the old Canton Bulldogs appeared in court as a character witness for a friend. Under questioning by an attorney he was direct and right to the point.

"What do you do for a living?"

"I play football."

"What position do you play?"

"Quarterback."

"Are you a good quarterback?"

"I'm the best quarterback in the business."

Since the quarterback had always seemed modest enough, his coach was surprised by his extravagance in the courtroom. He pulled him aside and asked why in the world he ever told the lawyer he was the best quarterback in the business.

"I had to tell him, Coach," he said. "They had me under oath."

During my own rococo career I took the view that while quarterbacks might not be able to solve Blaberski's Equation they—or, more accurately, we—happened to be inordinately bright and gifted and our value to the team was beyond any calculation. Nobody disputed this except centers, guards, tackles, ends, halfbacks and fullbacks.

No matter what unappreciative tackles, guards, centers, etc. might say to the contrary the quarterback is blessed with more than an arm and a leg. He possesses a lively, reflective mind and during a game he uses it to choose all or at least a great majority of his team's offensive plays—unless he lives in Cleveland, where Coach Paul Brown calls signals from the sidelines himself. In training camp Brown frankly offers his prospective quarterbacks a choice: Either they run the plays he sends in with courier guards or else they can pack up and catch the next bus home.

The only known instance of mutiny against the robot system was really no more than a slight misunderstanding. In a game during my first year with Cleveland the team rolled up a score so monstrous that Brown thought it would be safe to give me a brief spin at quarterback. Standing in the huddle a few plays later, I listened while rookie Guard Joe Skibinski recited the magic formula he had breathlessly carried in from the coach.

"I don't like the play," I said jokingly. "Go ask Brown for another one."

Skibinski dutifully turned around and started running toward the bench with my message. Fortunately, several of us managed to catch him and bring him back before it was too late. Otherwise the next signal Brown sent me might have been a 6:02 bus ticket for Fort Thomas, Kentucky.

MARVIN RICHMOND

UNHAPPY TURN FOR THE CRUSADERS

As the quick kick rolled toward the Georgetown goal line, two Holy Cross
linemen, Tom Kelleher (68) and Bill Stetter (17) tensely
followed it like a pair of plungers watching the slowing spin of a
roulette wheel. When the ball finally tumbled over the goal,
costing Holy Cross a chance to put Georgetown deep in a hole,
Kelleher and Stetter showed all the anguish of two who had been
suddenly stabbed by fate.

249

Army-Notre Dame, 1924, and Grantland Rice unrolled a legend with the lead of his game story in the New York Herald Tribune.

BIRTH OF THE FOUR HORSEMEN

Grantland Rice

Outlined against a blue-gray October sky, the Four Horsemen rode again. In dramatic lore they are known as Famine, Pestilence, Destruction and Death. These are only aliases. Their real names are Stuhldreher, Miller, Crowley and Layden. They formed the crest of the South Bend cyclone before which another fighting Army football team was swept over the precipice at the Polo Grounds yesterday afternoon as 55,000 spectators peered down on the bewildering panorama spread on the green plain below.

A cyclone can't be snared. It may be surrounded, but somewhere it breaks through to keep on going. When the cyclone starts from South Bend, where the candle lights still gleam through the Indiana sycamores, those in the way must take to storm cellars at top speed. Yesterday the cyclone struck again as Notre Dame beat the Army, 13–7, with a set of backfield stars that ripped and crashed through a strong Army defense with more speed and power than the warring Cadets could meet.

Notre Dame won its ninth game in twelve

Army starts through the driving power of one of the greatest backfields that ever churned up the turf of any gridiron in any football age. Brilliant backfields may come and go, but in Stuhldreher, Miller, Crowley and Layden, covered by a fast and charging line, Notre Dame can take its place in front of the field.

Coach McEwan sent one of his finest teams into action, an aggressive organization that fought to the last play around the first rim of darkness, but when Rockne rushed his Four Horsemen to the track they rode down everything in sight. It was in vain that 1,400 gray-clad cadets pleaded for the Army line to hold. The Army line was giving all it had, but when a tank tears in with the speed of a motorcycle, what chance has flesh and blood to hold? The Army had its share of stars in action, such stars as Garbisch, Farwick, Wilson, Wood, Ellinger and many others, but they were up against four whirlwind backs who picked up at top speed from the first step as they swept through scant openings to slip on by the secondary defense. The Army had great backs in Wilson and Wood, but the Army had no such quartet, who seemed to carry the mixed blood of the tiger and the antelope.

Rockne's light and tottering line was just about as tottering as the Rock of Gibraltar. It was something more than a match for the Army's great set of forwards, who had earned their fame before. Yet it was not until the second period that the first big thrill of the afternoon set the great crowd into a cheering whirl and brought about the wild flutter of flags that are thrown to the wind in exciting moments. At the game's start Rockne sent in almost entirely a second-string cast. The Army got the jump and began to play most of the football. It was the Army attack that made three first downs before Notre Dame had caught its stride. The South Bend cyclone opened like a zephyr.

And then, in the wake of a sudden cheer, out rushed Stuhldreher, Miller, Crowley and Layden, the four star backs who helped to beat Army a year ago. Things were to be a trifle different now. After a short opening flurry in the second period, Wood, of the Army, kicked out of bounds on Notre Dame's 20-yard line. There was no sign of a tornado starting. But it happened to be at just this spot that Stuhldreher decided to put on his attack and begin the long and dusty hike.

On the first play the fleet Crowley peeled off 15 yards and the cloud from the West was now beginning to show signs of lightning and thunder. The fleet, powerful Layden got 6 yards more and then Don Miller added 10. A forward pass from Stuhldreher to Crowley added 12 yards, and a moment later Don Miller ran 20 yards around Army's right wing. He was on his way to glory when Wilson, hurtling across the right of way, nailed him on the 10-yard line and threw him out of bounds. Crowley, Miller and Layden—Miller, Layden and Crowley—one or another, ripping and crashing through, as the Army defense threw everything it had in the way to stop this wild charge that had now come 70 yards. Crowley and Layden added 5 yards more and then, on a split play, Layden went 10 yards across the line as if he had just been fired from the black mouth of a howitzer.

In that second period Notre Dame made eight first downs to the Army's none, which shows the unwavering power of the Western attack that hammered relentlessly and remorselessly without easing up for a second's breath. The Western line was doing its full share, led by the crippled Walsh with a broken hand.

But there always was Miller or Crowley or Layden, directed through the right spot by the cool and crafty judgment of Stuhldreher, who picked his plays with the finest possible generalship. The South Bend cyclone had now roared 85 yards to a touchdown through one of the strongest defensive teams in the game. The cyclone had struck with too much speed and power to be stopped. It was the preponderance of Western speed that swept the Army back.

The next period was much like the second. The trouble began when the alert Layden intercepted an Army pass on the 48-yard line. Stuhldreher was ready for another march.

Once again the cheering Cadets began to call for a rallying stand. They are never overwhelmed by any shadow of defeat as long as there is a minute of fighting left. But silence fell over the Cadet sector for just a second as Crowley ran around the Army's right wing for 15 yards, where Wilson hauled him down on the 33-yard line. Walsh, the Western captain, was hurt in the play but soon resumed. Miller got 7 and Layden got 8 and then, with the ball on the Army's 20-yard line, the Cadet defense rallied and threw Miller in his tracks. But the halt was only for the moment. On the next play Crowley swung out and around the Army's left wing, cut in and then crashed over the line for Notre Dame's second touchdown.

On two other occasions the Notre Dame attack almost scored. Yeomans saved one touchdown by intercepting a pass on his 5-yard line as he ran back 35 yards before he was nailed by two tacklers. It was a great play in the nick of time. On the next drive Miller and Layden in two hurricane dashes took the ball 42 yards to the Army's 14-yard line, where the still game Army defense stopped four plunges on the 9-yard line and took the ball.

Up to this point the Army had been outplayed by a crushing margin. Notre Dame had put under way four long marches and two of these had yielded touchdowns. Even the stout and experienced Army line was meeting more than it could hold. Notre Dame's brilliant backs had been provided with the finest possible interference, usually led by Stuhldreher, who cut down tackler after tackler by diving at some rival's flying knees. Against this each Army attack had been smothered almost before it got under way. Even the great Wilson, the star from Penn State, one of the great backfield runners of his day and time, rarely had a chance to make any headway through a massed wall of tacklers who were blocking every open route.

The sudden change came late in the third quarter, when Wilson, raging like a wild man, suddenly shot through a tackle opening to run

34 yards before he was finally collared and thrown with a jolt. A few minutes later Wood, one of the best of all punters, kicked out of bounds on Notre Dame's 5-yard line. Here was the chance. Layden was forced to kick from behind his own goal. The punt soared up the field as Yeomans called for a free catch on the 35-yard line. As he caught the ball he was nailed and slipped by a Western tackler, and the penalty gave the Army 15 yards, with the ball on Notre Dame's 20-yard line.

At this point Harding was rushed to quarter in place of Yeomans, who had been one of the leading Army stars. On the first three plays the Army reached the 12-yard line, but it was no fourth down, with two yards to go. Harding's next play was the feature of the game.

As the ball was passed, he faked a play to Wood, diving through the line, held the oval for just a half breath, then, tucking the same under his arm, swung out around Notre Dame's right end. The brilliant fake worked to perfection. The entire Notre Dame defense had charged forward in a surging mass to check the line attack and Harding, with open territory, sailed on for a touchdown. He traveled those last 12 yards after the manner of food shot from guns. He was over the line before the Westerners knew what had taken place. It was a fine bit of strategy, brilliantly carried out by every member of the cast.

The Cadet sector had a chance to rip open the chilly atmosphere at last, and most of the 55,000 present joined in the tribute to football art. But that was Army's last chance to score. From that point on it was seesaw, up and down, back and forth, with the rivals fighting bitterly for every inch of ground. It was harder now to make a foot than it had been to make 10 yards. Even the all-star South Bend cast could not longer continue to romp for any set distances, as Army tacklers, inspired by the touchdown, charged harder and faster than they had charged before.

The Army brought a fine football team into action, but it was beaten by a faster and smoother team. Rockne's supposedly light, green line was about as heavy as Army's and every whit as aggressive. What is even more impor-

tant, it was faster on its feet, faster in getting around.

It was Western speed and perfect interference that once more brought about Army doom. The Army line couldn't get through fast enough to break up the attacking plays; and once started, the bewildering speed and power of the Western backs slashed along for 8, 10, and 15 yards on play after play. And always in front of these offensive drives could be found the whirling form of Stuhldreher, taking the first man out of the play as cleanly as though he had used a hand grenade at close range. This Notre Dame interference was a marvelous thing to look upon.

It formed quickly and came along in unbroken order, always at terrific speed, carried by backs who were as hard to drag down as African buffaloes. On receiving the kickoff, Notre Dame's interference formed something after the manner of the ancient flying wedge, and they drove back up the field with the runner covered from 25 and 30 yards at almost every chance. And when a back such as Harry Wilson finds few chances to get started, you can figure upon the defensive strength that is barricading the road. Wilson is one of the hardest backs in the game to suppress, but he found few chances yesterday to show his broken-field ability. You can't run through a broken field until you get there.

One strong feature of the Army play was its headlong battle against heavy odds. Even when Notre Dame had scored two touchdowns and was well on its way to a third, the Army fought on with fine spirit until the touchdown chance came at last. And when the chance came, Coach McEwan had the play ready for the final march across the line. The Army has a better team than it had last year. So has Notre Dame. We doubt that any team in the country could have beaten Rockne's array yesterday afternoon, East or West. It was a great football team brilliantly directed, a team of speed, power, and team play. The Army has no cause for gloom over its showing. It played first-class football against more speed than it could match.

Those who have tackled a cyclone can understand.

In 1939, just 50 years—or was it 40?—after Walter Camp started his custom of selecting
All-America teams, Collier's *had Grantland Rice pick an anniversary all-time All-America.*
Rice refers to Camp's first All-America, in 1889, but he doesn't note that the team
appeared in Collier's *ten years later (along with that magazine's first All-America)*
and he gives no credit to Casper Whitney, Camp's co-selector. No matter—Rice's 50th
(or 40th) anniversary All-America was an impressive roundup of the stars who
played before World War II.

ALL-AMERICA—THE FIRST 50 YEARS

Grantland Rice

Fifty years ago Walter Camp opened the road to All-America football glory in *Collier's*. He laid the cornerstone for fifty million arguments. Next week *Collier's* will celebrate the golden anniversary of the team Mr. Camp named in the faraway and the long ago of 1889.

For the thirty-five years following, the Father of Football picked his All-America teams with fine judgment, missing only the war year of 1917.

After Walter Camp's death in 1925 this writer took up the task and began sagging into the quicksands after the first kickoff. This led to *Collier's* All-America Board. For Mr. Camp, a great part of the time, had worked in a far smaller football world. His terrain was limited. His first twenty-two All-America nominations were all Harvard, Yale and Princeton. In 1891, Adams of Pennsylvania crashed the sacred portal. In 1892 Thayer of Pennsylvania broke into the circle of the Crimson, the Blue, and the Orange and Black. And that was a circle of steel—the unassailable fortress of tradition.

It was not until 1898, six years later, that Herschberger, Chicago's famous kicker, became the first Midwestern entry. It was not until 1918, twenty years later, that Day of Georgia Tech carried the colors of Dixie into the select group. It was not until 1921 that Brick Muller of California brought All-America fame to the West Coast.

Football started in the East and for the next thirty years, up to Michigan's famous point-a-minute team, the East was in the saddle. Later, football supremacy moved from the East to the Midwest, then to the Far West—later to the South and the Southwest—until it finally became an all-nation blend as the winning tides swung back and forth. Football, after thirty years, finally became All-America. It became a game that belonged and belongs to almost every county in every state.

In the last few years, Texas has been one of the strong frontiers of the game. And yet it was not until 1934, forty-five years after Walter Camp named his first team, that William Wallace of Rice carried the banner of the Lone Star State into the gathering of football's great.

By 1925 the spread of football skill, material, and coaching had covered the entire country. There was no longer any leading section. There were outstanding stars from Oregon to Florida, from Texas to Maine, from Minnesota to Louisiana.

It was shortly after this that *Collier's,* realizing no one man could possibly cover millions of square miles of active football territory, decided to enlarge its field of observers.

These were selected from well-known football writers from each section—football writers who not only knew their stuff but who, in addition, were close to the leading coaches and the leading officials who annually give out their confidential opinions of the year's best players.

Each coach is asked to name not only the best men on his squad, but also the best on each team he has played against. As there are hundreds of coaches, this check is as reliable as any that can be devised.

Football has changed amazingly in many ways since Walter Camp named his first All-America in 1889. The canvas jacket and the flowing locks have long since disappeared. The dominance of the Big Three—Yale, Harvard, and Princeton—has passed away. There is no dominance anywhere today.

There were only a few enthusiasts watching games fifty years ago; over 40,000,000 now march to the school, college, and professional games for the greatest attendance any sport has ever had. Bowls and stadia are packed to capacity from ocean to ocean. In the Tennessee-Alabama game, played in Knoxville, I saw 40,000 massed in the stands with close to 20,000 outside looking down from the slopes and hills, from the trees and the housetops.

Single crowds of 80,000 and 90,000 are no longer uncommon sights. Outside of the millions taken in for gate receipts, football has become a national industry for trains, planes, buses and hotels all over the land.

All this has happened since Walter Camp named that first All-America. The mass plays of the 90's—the V-rush, the flying wedge, guards back, and other push and power plays—have given way to a greater demand for speed and skill as part of the game left the ground and went to the air in 1906.

In 1889 Shep Homans of Princeton was Snake Ames's substitute. Shep, still a substantial citizen of Englewood, New Jersey, never got to play a moment. In 1890 and 1891 Homans was named on Camp's All-America, and through those two years his substitute never saw a second's play. That could never happen under the physical, mental, and nerve pressure of the modern game, where winning teams usually run two or three deep, where sixty-minute men are almost as extinct as the great auk or the dodo.

Power still plays its part but, above all, this is the day of speed and dexterity—quick thinking in such highly technical maneuvers as spinners, wing-backs, forward passing, mousetrapping, deep reverses, cutbacks, and the rest of it. All these things have also happened since Walter Camp made his 1889 nominations for gridiron fame.

In these last fifty years of *Collier's* All-America football teams, around five hundred football stars have had their names entered on *Collier's* scroll. They have ranged from Pudge Heffelfinger to Whizzer White and Dave O'Brien, from Snake Ames to Marshall Goldberg. Each year it has become harder to make the All-America team, each year the selections have called for closer observation and a wider check.

Suppose we swing back through the half century. This was Walter Camp's first team:

End—Cumnock, Harvard	Tackle—Gill, Yale
Tackle—Cowan, Princeton	End—Stagg, Yale
Guard—Cranston, Harvard	Quarter—E. A. Poe, Princeton
Center—George, Princeton	Halfback—Lee, Harvard
Guard—Heffelfinger, Yale	Halfback—Channing, Princeton
	Fullback—Ames, Princeton

That must have been an amazing team. For example, from that lineup, Alonzo Stagg is still a winning coach at the age of seventy-seven, as alert and as keen as ever, at the College of the Pacific. His team beat California in the opening game.

From that lineup Pudge Heffelfinger was still playing football at the age of sixty-six. At the age of forty-four he almost wrecked a Yale line, playing on the second team. There was plenty of fiber in that old platoon. Plenty of iron. I doubt that any other man ever picked on an All-America team equaled the unbelievable iron-man, nonrust, steel-shod fiber of Heffelfinger and Stagg.

From the list of some 500 stars, picked by Walter Camp and *Collier's* All-America Board, over a period of fifty years, who should make up the all-time list, based only upon college and university play?

In making up such a list one must remember that backs who starred before the arrival of the forward pass had no chance to prove what they could do in the modern game. Perhaps the fame of such performers as Heston and Eckersall, of Michigan and Chicago, would have been even greater, also of Hinkey and Shevlin of Yale at end. But that must remain a guess. Certainly under the old system they were among the standouts. But the game then was played along the ground—and never in the air.

You look back over the long list. There was Frank Hinkey, "The Disembodied Spirit," the greatest football player, pound for pound, that ever lived, a stick of dynamite that wrecked 180- and 190-pound backs. Hinkey was one of the few to make Camp's team four years in a row. Truxton Hare of Pennsylvania was another. When you have 500 All-America entries to pick from it is easy to understand how much of the highway must pass through the quicksands of time and change.

The All-Time All-America is a selection from all the stars who helped to make college football history from 1889 to 1939—stars in turn selected from over 500,000 players.

CENTER

There have been great centers through every year of American football. But the greatest center I ever saw was "Germany" Schulz of Michigan—6 feet 4 in height, 245 pounds in weight and one of the fastest men on any field. In one game against a strong Pennsylvania team Schulz alone held Pennsylvania at bay for forty-five minutes. When he was carried from the field Pennsylvania ran up over thirty points, all in the final fifteen minutes of the game. Schulz backed up the line and supported both ends. Stone of Vanderbilt wasn't far away.

GUARDS

Pudge Heffelfinger of Yale, a member of Camp's first team, was the tops of all guards. He was the first to act as a running guard. He held the interference. Over thirty years after playing at Yale he was still too fast for Bo McMillin, Centre's star, to escape. Heffelfinger was a great football player for over thirty years.

Just back of big Pudge we find Cannon of Notre Dame and Pennock of Harvard. Pennock was the steadier but Cannon was a ball of fire.

TACKLES

The greatest of all tackles, according to old-timers who still remember, was Fats Henry of Washington and Jefferson. He was a human rubber ball at 225 pounds. There is little to choose between Fincher of Georgia Tech and Weir of Nebraska. The margin here is extremely thin. West of Colgate was another great tackle on this long list. So were Ham Fish and Cutts of Harvard and Hogan of Yale.

ENDS

The competition grows even keener at the ends.

Brick Muller of California was certainly one of the greatest. Fesler of Ohio State was just as good. Hewitt of Michigan was probably the best all-around star of the lot, but Hewitt played too many roles. Oosterbaan of Michigan is around the top—a fine end and a great pass receiver. Tack Hardwick of Harvard was also one of the greatest ends.

QUARTERBACKS

Walter Eckersall of Chicago was the star quarterback under the old regime before the pass came along. Eckie never had his chance to show what he could do with the new game. Bennie Friedman of Michigan was a brilliant passer, a fine blocker and a smart field general. But Red Grange at quarter and at half was a three-year sensation before he turned toward the professional pay roll. Grange was a star ball carrier. He was a good passer. And he was more than merely smart. You can add Sammy Baugh to this list.

HALFBACKS

It is the halfback posts that leave the jitters in their wake. Look them over—Heston, Thorpe, Mahan, Strong, Harley, Thorne, Feathers, Dodd, Pinckert, Grayson, Berwanger (one of the best on a weak team), Wilson, Clint Frank of Yale—a truly great back whatever the duty assigned, on and on. But I'll have to travel with Jim Thorpe and Ken Strong. Thorpe could do everything exceptionally well. So could Ken Strong. After the Carnegie Tech game Judge Walter Steffen, the Tartan coach, told me that in his opinion Strong was by far the best back he ever saw—ball carrier, blocker, passer and kicker supreme.

It is difficult to leave off such stars as Eddie Mahan of Harvard and a great many others. But there isn't room for all.

FULLBACK

Pop Warner always rated Ernie Nevers on a par with Jim Thorpe. Ted Coy of Yale was a great running, plunging and kicking back. Bronko Nagurski was named as a tackle in place of a fullback. Joesting was rated as the star Minnesota line breaker. But Nevers had everything a great fullback needs. He was also a brilliant defensive back. It seems strange to have an all-star backfield that doesn't include Mahan, Heston, Eckersall or Coy—just as it seems strange to name all-star ends without including Hinkey and Shevlin. But too many of these played before the forward pass was added to offensive play.

A towering effort by
the New York Giants'
defense fails to block
a field goal by the
Pittsburgh Steelers.

257

The St. Louis Cardinals sweep to the left.

Passer-punter Norm Van Brocklin of the Philadelphia Eagles works under fire.

Books have been written on how the Cleveland Browns dominated the old All-America Conference and later the National Football League in the years 1946 through 1955. But here, from The Pros *by Robert Riger and Tex Maule, is one quick reason for their success.*

THE BROWNS' PERFECT TRIANGLE

Robert Riger and Tex Maule

When World War II ended, pro football had just begun to grow heartily. Because of this growth, a new football league—the All-America Conference—was started. It lasted four years, from 1946 through 1949, and then it died from malnutrition of the box office. During those four years, the most notable contribution the A.A.C. made to pro football was the Cleveland Browns, a wonderfully conceived team, assembled, organized and operated by one of the real geniuses of pro football, a small, cold and brilliantly intelligent man named Paul Brown. The principal instrument of Brown's brilliance was a fine quarterback named Otto Graham, who can tell the story of the Browns—which is the story of the All-America Conference—better than anyone else:

"Paul approached me while I was in service in 1945 and offered me $250 a month for the rest of the war if I would sign with the Browns, which were still in the planning stage, so I did. I had been drafted by the Detroit Lions, but they didn't contact me. I was lucky to play with the Browns. All of us were new in pro football and I got the chance to play all the time right away. Paul at first wanted us to be a running

team, but that didn't work. So we changed to passing and we developed a lot of the passing techniques that are successful today. Paul's concept of a pass was the perfect triangle." (See diagram below.) "Our receiver would go straight downfield maybe 5 or 10 yards, then cut to the sideline, but instead of cutting at a right angle he would come back to the base of the triangle. That way he picked up a step or two on the defensive halfback and he was impossible to cover. We did it with ends or halfbacks and we really perfected it, although other teams used it too. And, of course, we used the trap with Motley to keep the defenses honest. I guess Marion Motley was the best fullback I ever saw. He could start like a rocket and run hard and was great on pass-protection blocking."

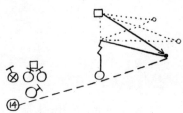

Campus and football were small-time at Notre Dame when Knute Rockne arrived to change it all. This excerpt from his autobiography takes Rock up to the first Army-Notre Dame game, which he helped win, 35–13.

FROM NORWAY TO NOTRE DAME

Knute Rockne

The first time I learned a football was not only something to kick, but something to think with, was when I saw a great football player in action for the first time. A sandlot youngster, who regarded football as a pleasantly rough recreation, I had no hero worship for any player and no interest in any team. But when the Eastern high school champions of thirty years ago challenged the Western champions, the meeting of the two teams in Chicago was a great event.

Brooklyn Poly Prep was the Eastern outfit and Hyde Park High in Chicago the Western. Crashing the gate—a habit of mine as a youngster—I sat spellbound through that game. It was one-sided: the final score was 105 to 0 in favor of the Chicago team. But the clearest picture remaining from that slaughter was not the overpowering might of the Western lads, who had among them the famous Hammond brothers, later Michigan stars. The striking feature was the brilliant, heady play of Hyde Park's quarterback—a lad named Walter Eckersall. He played prairie football, mainly wide sweeps around ends; but by instinctive timing he hit the heavier

Brooklyn linemen until they were dizzy. With no more than four fundamental plays he worked so quickly and coolly that he made his offense bewildering.

Eckersall's sharp, staccato calling of signals, his keen, handsome face, and the smooth precision with which he drove and countered and drove again, handling his players with the rhythm of an orchestra leader—all this gave football a new meaning to me.

After the game was over and the Western boys went cheering from the field, shouting the name Eckersall like a slogan over the defeated Easterners, I tried to get close to the hero of the day. Two or three thousand other youngsters were trying to do the same thing, so I had to go home without a handshake—yet, for the first time in a young and fairly crowded life, I went home with a hero. Dreams of how, some day, I might shine as Eckersall had shone that afternoon were my lonesome luxury. For years they were nothing but dreams. Eckersall went on to greater glory as the sensational star of the University of Chicago. My path took me from high school to nothing more athletic than being a mail dispatcher working nights, for years.

But there came an afternoon when the Notre Dame squad ran onto a Chicago field with the former sandlot boy, ex-mail dispatcher, as captain. The referee was Walter Eckersall. In his smart white togs, he looked hardly a day older than when he led Hyde Park in its overwhelming victory over Brooklyn.

Grasping his hand, I said, "I've been waiting years for this."

"For what?" said Eckersall.

"To shake your hand," I said, recounting how his brilliant performance for Hyde Park High had turned my mind seriously to football.

"Stop, stop," said Eckersall in the middle of the recital, "or Notre Dame will be penalized five yards for speech-making."

How a youngster from Voss, a hamlet in Norway that lies between Bergen and Oslo, could find himself in his mid-twenties captain of a typical, Midwestern American football team may require explaining. Perhaps it's sufficient explanation to say that this evolution is a typical American story—in business, athletics and politics. It has occurred so often that it's ordinary. The breaks came my way when I had sense enough to take them; and while that's an unromantic way of explaining a career, it has the advantage of being the truth.

Her celebrated majesty Queen Margaret of Norway had something to do with it. At least, there's the word of a student of Norse genealogy to that effect. It's on an elaborately inscribed piece of parchment that looks like a map outline of all the football plays ever invented. This, on close perusal, informs me that I'm descended—among others—from one Enidride Erlandson of Losna, Norway. He and his tribe were landowners of some consequence. When Queen Margaret merged the three kingdoms of Norway, Sweden and Denmark, she did not retain the best features of each. At least, my pride of ancestry won't permit me to believe that she did. For the Erlandsons of Losna refused to have anything to do with the merger, retiring, in a collective huff, to the town of Voss and there establishing themselves in the hills. Generations elapsed, the hills remained the same, but it became harder and harder to make a good living.

The traditional venturesomeness of the Norsemen, aided by infiltrations of Irish blood acquired when the earlier and hardier Vikings invaded Ireland looking for trouble and returned to Norway with colleens for wives, breaks out at intervals. With my father it broke

out when I was about five. The World's Fair was to be held in Chicago. Dad, by profession a stationary engineer and by avocation a carriage builder, wanted to show his wares at the World's Fair. He went to America. Later, he sent for his family. My mother took her three daughters and her only son to New York and we were duly admitted through Castle Garden. My only equipment for life in the new country was a Norwegian vocabulary, a fervent memory of home cooking combined with pleasant recollections of skiing and skating among the Voss Mountains.

How my mother ever managed that tedious voyage, which I still recall with qualms; how she guided us through the intricacies of entry, knowing nothing of English, and took us into the heart of a new, strange and bewildering country without mishap—how, in brief, she achieved the first step in our Americanization unaided by anybody, is one of the millions of minor miracles that are of the stuff and fabric of America.

Perhaps it was a trick of Fate that the first natives of the new country to register favorably with me were not only natives, but aborigines—Indians. In the Elysium of the World's Fair, with its glittering palaces, amazing crowds, a tow-headed Norwegian youngster was lost one day. Elated by an award of a medal for his exhibit of a carriage, Dad had failed to check my natural curiosity. So I wandered all over that paradise of sights and sounds and smells, having a glorious time on popcorn, pink lemonade and the new and delightful rite of the hot dog. At length—and it must have been a long time—I wound up before a reduced facsimile of an Indian reservation.

The contrast between me, a white-haired Nordic fresh from the original source of supply, and the jet-haired Indian papooses must have struck some minor Indian chief. When the fairgrounds police, in their nightly hunt for youngsters lost, stolen or strayed, came to item 181-B, specifying a Norwegian boy who knew no English but might respond to the name Knute Kenneth Rockne if pronounced with pressure on the K's, they gave it up. Until morning. Then a weary copper, passing the Indian reservation, beheld a blond head surmounted by feathers, bobbing through a scampering mob of Indian kids, wielding a wooden tomahawk and yelling for scalps.

They promptly collected me, stripped me of Indian finery and restored me to my puzzled parents. Ever since then I've held Indians in affection and esteem, unmodified even by collision on the football field with the greatest Indian athlete of them all. For when, as a professional player for Massillon, Ohio, I undertook the job of tackling Jim Thorpe and learned, while prostrate, following sudden and severe contact, that Mr. Thorpe was no respecter of even All-America persons—the Indian sign became more than an empty phrase.

We'll get back to that. Before I was to see and meet Indians again, a Chicago childhood and youth had to be gone through. It was not unpleasant going. The new, spacious city, with its endless corner lots and tolerant police, was a great place for a boy to grow up in, in the era B. C.—Before Capone. Our baseball and football games were undisturbed by rifle fire and the popping of pineapples. At that, there was excitement enough for everybody.

We lived in the Logan Square neighborhood —chiefly inhabited by Irish and Swedes. Chicago's broad ethnology called all Scandinavians "Swedes." The Irish were clubby, so were the Swedes. My lot was naturally with the latter. On a huge vacant corner boys of the two nationalities would meet on Wednesday and Saturday afternoons in impromptu and sometimes violent contests. A husky middle-aged copper named O'Goole kept a paternal eye on us. When the Irish lads were pounding us "Swedes," O'Goole strode up and down the sidelines grinning. To onlookers who protested that he should stop the free-for-all, he said, "Nonsense! It's an elegant game, good for the youngsters. Look at Patsy Regan there knock that Swede lad from under a punt."

A few of us, dissatisfied with constant lickings at the hands—and feet—of the Irish, scouted other neighborhoods for bigger Swedes. When bigger boys couldn't be found, we enrolled a couple of bruiserlike Italians on our side.

O'Goole strolled by while a bigger and better battle was in progress and the Irishers were getting a free and liberal taste of mud.

"This won't do at all," he said, striding to the midst of the battle and grabbing Swede boys by their necks. "The game is altogether brutal and unfit for small boys."

We could only even matters by appealing to the precinct captain to send us a Swede cop as well as O'Goole to supervise our games. Then mayhem was balanced for both sides.

My first real baptism of mire was received in one of those neighborhood corner lot games. I was an end on the Tricky Tigers—historic rivals of the Avondales—so called because we had a wow of a triple pass back of the line when we wanted to impress opponents and on-lookers. Our equipment wasn't elaborate. No helmets, one shinguard per player. We tied our ears with elastic tape to prevent spreading.

Many of us graduated to the Barefoot Athletic Club of older boys, mostly Irish. In a crucial game with the Hamburg A. C. for the district championship, trouble came in handfuls. Crowds lined the gridless gridiron and broke into it as the game progressed. Irish sympathizers were militant. Only seven policemen were there to hold back the mob. Things grew unpleasant as the more pugnacious spectators slipped away every now and then for refreshments at nearby saloons.

The game was held in a huge lot opposite the White Sox Ball Park. My part in it was not brilliant, but dramatic. In those early days I had spindly legs, which I've retained, and speedy feet, which left me long ago. When the call to carry the ball came, I'd lay back my ears and sprint. That afternoon the call came. Spurting in an end run with the Hamburg boys after me, my path to a touchdown was clear. Not a Hamburg player was in front. But Hamburg rooters came to the rescue. They threw me and swiped the ball. Minor riot ensued, players on both teams being pummeled impartially. There were so many players' noses punched that a police sergeant would only let players with nose guards wade into the crowd.

Most of us returned home that evening with evidence of a strenuous afternoon's sport. For me, this was a serious matter. As a football initiate, I played the game surreptitiously, my parents sharing the general belief that football was a system of modified massacre. My most prized possession, a pair of patched moleskin football pants, had to be smuggled in and out of the house. Scars of battle in the Hamburg game betrayed me. My football career was squelched. As it was nearing winter, this didn't matter much, for when spring arrived with the crack of baseballs on bats, I went out with the rest of the sandlot gang. The family approved of baseball. During a vicious, extra-inning game with the Maplewood boys, a hot argument developed. Being blessed or bothered by hidden strains of Irish ancestry, I found myself in the thick of it. Suddenly a bat bent on the bridge of my nose. I went home blinded, but uppermost in my mind was not sorrow, but logic. The family had banned football because it was dangerous.

"And I got this nose from baseball," was my triumphant reply.

With full parental approval, when high school days arrived for me, I went out for football, after making the high school track team as a half-miler. There occurred the inspirational picture of Walter Eckersall in action. Likewise, such prodigies of sport as Rube Waddell and Three-Finger Brown took niches in what there was of my mind.

Rube Waddell was a figure to inspire any athletically minded youngster with the easy glory of games. We knew something of his tradition: how he had jogged on to a crowded ball park in Harrisburg, driving a team of mules and a wagon, himself attired like a scarecrow; how, after parking mules and wagon by a players' bench, he took possession of the pitcher's box and struck out twelve men in a row.

The Rube always played up to the youngsters. He'd guide droves of us into the ball park free, and we'd even follow him miles and miles in his eccentricities. He'd take French leave from his club, go to Libertyville or some other town and pitch for a local semi-pro outfit. The man was a great showman. I remember once in a semi-pro game he turned dramatically in the box, waved in all the outfielders, sent them to the bench, and struck out every batter.

In those days, I yearned to follow in the footsteps of Waddell, or that other fine pitcher, Three-Finger Brown. That meant having exceedingly sizable feet, which may be one reason why I never became a pitcher, but an outfielder. When the football bug bit me after seeing Eckersall, the diamond's luster dimmed.

The first big thrill of my life came when, at thirteen years of age and weighing 110 pounds, I was put on the scrubs of the Northwest Division High, now Tuley High, in Chicago. In the scrubs we had some slight coaching. Our sandlot football was what the professors call eclectic: we pinched whatever plays we had seen and could remember.

We were keen for signals. Half the fun of the game was the solemnity with which our corner lot quarterbacks would shout, and we would receive, the long litany of signals. Only colored players excel sandlot boys in love of signals. Two teams of Negro footballers I once umpired for devised a baffling code. Both named their plays after dishes. Pork chops meant a smash through right tackle, pigs' feet a run around right end, fried chicken a split buck, and so on. Very confusing to spectators and hardly less confusing to the players. The only worthwhile thing I recall about that strange game is that one side, led by a quarterback yelling items off a menu, marched down the field and paused on the one-yard line for the team pilot to scream in final challenge: "Now, boys, over that line with the whole blame' dining car!"

High school football in those days had all the enthusiasm but none of the finesse of today. Coaches were few. Two professors, Peters and Ellis, volunteered to teach our school squad. They did a good job of it, if only by holding me back and making me realize there was something more to football than the ball. It took me until my senior year to get on the team. Chicago followed our high school games in huge crowds. In those days our team—Northwest Division— beat the powerful Marshall High, tied with Crane, and bowed only to North Division High, whose second team licked us. The first-string players, led by Wally Steffens, now Carnegie Tech coach, joshed us from the sidelines.

Then the name of Alonzo Stagg rose on my horizon. Not in connection with football, although I knew something of his fame. It was a favorite trick of the crowd I played with to hook into the Chicago U. football field through the motor-car gates, guarded less closely than the turnstiles. We saw Eckersall run his team against squads whose names were almost mythically great to us—teams like Northwestern, Haskell and Michigan. My ambition then was to become a quarterback. When Eckersall wasn't on the field, Wally Steffens or Lee Maxwell directed the Chicago plays; each had a snap to his style that made the quarterback's job the focal point in the football drama. That was right. But a good quarterback needed all of many qualities, only a few of which I had— the principal one being speed.

Coach Stagg supervised an annual series of interscholastic meets around Chicago. The half-mile was my specialty. With the fondness for coincidence that all of us share, many have asked me whether or not Stagg and I met in those days. If we did, it must have been under the stands when I dropped out of long-distance foot races, as invariably occurred. But persistence at track meets won me a small reputation, and when a whimsical switch to pole vaulting brought me in the news by making an indoor record of 12 ft. 4 in.—which today wouldn't qualify a boy to be a mascot—I began to think I'd arrived.

While in high school, I got on the Chicago A. A. junior team, after making the grade in one of the numerous athletic clubs dotted around Chicago. In minor meets, the chance to win depended as much on quick wits as stopwatches. Youngsters were quickly initiated into the tricks of the athletic trade. One official timer was known for his distaste for continuous Irish victories. When he was officiating and our teams faced stiff and conquering competition, somebody on our side would always stand near this official and holler of a winning opponent named Schmidt, "Watch that O'Brien come," or of a Thorgensen, "Look at that Reilly jump." But chickens came home to roost. Once when I was bold enough to sub for an absent teammate in an 880-yard sprint for what I thought was record time, some malicious bird yelled, "Come on, Kelly," as I dashed down the lane. The non-Hibernian official overheard: the record was not mine.

The interim between finishing high school and entering college—four years, to be exact— was the principal period of my not-too-celebrated career as a track athlete. I carried the colors of Irving Park A. C. and the Central Y. M. C. A., for which I managed to win the half-mile in 2.2, a good mark then, and graduated to the Illinois Athletic Club. In various meets, I ran against old-time stars like Lindberg, Harvey Blair, Ward and Belot. Martin Delaney and Dad Butler were our coaches, and we newcomers were able to touch shoulders with Olympic stars like Ralph Rose, Lightbody, Hogenson and Irons—and even the great Johnny Hayes, winner of the classic Olympic Marathon over Dorando, came to Chicago to fraternize but not to compete with us—because Johnny had turned pro.

If anybody wonders why it took so long for me to get from high school to college, the answer's easy. I was obliged to earn a living. Football, save as a spectator sport, was neglected, and I relied on track competition to keep in physical shape.

I had hoped, at high school, to make my way in college. To that end, I learned how to earn more money and save it. A Hebrew boy and I got the summertime job of cleaning our high school windows at good pay. But other boys, possibly jealous over our appointments, would break windows, invade the school, switch door signs from doors with coarsely diabolical wit and commit other sabotage for which the amateur window cleaners were blamed. Naturally, we were fired.

But with an urge for the public weal, I took civil service exams for the mail service and received appointment as a mail dispatcher. At this time, I was ambitious to go to Illinois U. and I set in my mind a goal—to save one thousand dollars and march on Illinois for an education. Athletic fame was secondary, for, to me, college players loomed as supermen to whose heights I could never aspire.

It seemed more and more unlikely that any college would have the opportunity to matriculate or reject me, as years of night work ensued, my prep school being the sorting room of the post office.

About the most a clerk could earn was $100 a month. He could make his job soft or hard by taking simple or complicated routines. I took the hard routine of dispatcher to have something to do in a temple of loafing. If a clerk took Southern territory, he wouldn't have much to remember because few railroads fed the South from Chicago. But if he took the dispatching job in Illinois or Eastern territory, he had to memorize every main-line and branch-line train and amend that knowledge with all the timetable changes made by the railroads.

It took me a full year to learn the dispatching scheme or routine. Most of the old-timers called me a fool to tackle a tough job. But there was excellent memory training in it. This has been a good investment in mental energy, for if a football coach needs one thing more than any other, it's a memory for the swarming details of plays and combinations of plays—especially the personal styles of coaches and players in executing them.

For the rest, civil service taught me little save its unevenness and unfairness. Going on the job with a zeal to make good and get promoted, you wondered at first why veterans smiled at youthful ardor and industry. Enthusiasm could hardly survive the discovery that a dispatcher who worked hard, eight hours a night, received less than a henchman who did nothing more arduous for eight hours a day than sell stamps from an irremovable seat on a stool.

I was on the way to develop into the smartest shirker of all, having reached a point of lethargy where it took me an hour to distribute as many pieces of mail as in the first enthusiastic days would have only taken me ten minutes; but, fortunately, I had garnered my thousand dollars by then.

Notre Dame was hardly a name to me. Football, by that time, had been eclipsed by track and field. Much as I should like to profess being animated by a burning zeal to go out and conquer in the name of pigskin and be acclaimed a mighty player and a coach of massive intellect, the cold, unembellished fact is that a sister of mine was more ambitious for me than I was for myself. She insisted that a college education would mean more to me and the family than anything else. Also, that I'd be able to waste my time to better advantage as a college track athlete than as a part-time wonder of the campus called the Loop. Two friends of mine, Johnny Devine and Johnny Plant, both runners of more than local note, were going to Notre Dame. When we discussed our plans during a Chicago meet, and I told them I was bound for Illinois, they suggested I go along with them to the Indiana school.

"Why," I remember exclaiming, "who ever heard of Notre Dame? They've never won a football game in their lives."

What swung me to go there was the argument that I could probably get a job, and certainly get by cheaper than at Illinois.

So I went down to South Bend with a suitcase and a thousand dollars. I'd hardly seen more than two trees at one time anywhere, so the first impression on me was the sylvan beauty of Notre Dame. The Fathers of the Holy Cross who operate the university received a grant of twenty-three hundred acres in the early pre-pioneer days when Indiana was a territory and not a state. By industry and intelligence they made it an ideal site for a university.

Notre Dame University, in 1910, when I felt the strangeness of being a lone Norse Protestant —if the word must be used—invader of a Catholic stronghold, comprised six halls, in one of which, Brownson Dormitory, I was installed. There were 400 undergraduates, physical training was compulsory, and a fellow wasn't thought much of unless he went out to try and make his hall team for football.

Shorty Longman, an end on Michigan's famous point-a-minute team, was Notre Dame's head coach—the first college coach I ever knew. He was a snappy, belligerent figure who affected a shock of hair after the manner of McCullough, the actor.

The university gave me a chance to work off my board and room as janitor of the chemical laboratory, cleaning out the slop buckets and doing minor chores. Somebody stole a gallon of experimental wine from the pharmacy laboratory; I was blamed, and ran risks of expulsion. So my reputation was not glamorous. When, therefore, Joe Collins, a varsity squad man, recommended me for a chance with the big boys, Longman wasn't enthusiastic.

But he gave me the chance. Freshmen were played in those days, and with a small enrollment we needed them. Longman sent me out with the scrubs in a test game with the regulars. He made me fullback. They should have changed my position to drawback. Never on any football field was there so dismal a flop. Trying to spear my first punt I had frozen fingers and the ball rolled everywhere it wasn't wanted.

Longman kept me in that agonizing game. Finally, I tried a punt. Nothing happened. I might have been a statue of a player trying to punt. Nothing was coordinated. I was half paralyzed. A 200-pound tackle smashed into me. My 145 pounds went back for a 15-yard loss.

Longman yanked me out of the scrubs and sent me back to Brownson Hall. I was a dub, a washout, not even good enough for the scrubs.

But the fact remained that I could run, and running was important to a football player. Perhaps, I reasoned, if I tried for a job at end, my old spot on the sandlot and high-school teams, I'd have better luck. The first step was to get on the varsity track team, which I did. A track letter gave me the prestige to try once more for the football squad.

In the meantime I had sat at the feet of a learned tramp athlete whose name then was Foley, although he had played for many schools under aliases. He was typical of young men who roamed the country, overflowing with college spirit, regardless of the college. His tongue teemed with professional jargon. He knew all the technique and practiced none of it; yet so glib was he that it invariably took a shrewd coach half a season to get wise to the fact that this tramp athlete had only one principle in football, which he pithily expressed: "Avoid 'em." He opened my eyes to a state of affairs in college football which has since been reformed —of the journeymen players who'd leave new names behind them wherever they went and live to a ripe old age, from foot to mouth, so to speak, taking loyalty and sometimes talent with them to whichever Alma Mater would give them the best break.

We played teams whose purity of enrollment was not quite ninety-nine and three quarters per cent. The Indian schools were careless in that respect, several Indian players changing legal names to Indian names as they switched from one Indian school to another. The famous back, Emil Hauser of Haskell, became Chief Waseka at Carlisle; another lad I knew named Dietz blossomed into Chief Long Star, and I always called the celebrated back, Pete Hauser, Chief Long Time Eat when I met him playing for his third or fourth Alma Mater—he shone brightly at the training table.

Although a growing youngster, I had the advantage of not being too green when I broke into big football company. I was twenty-three and able to wear a lettered sweater without too much intoxication. There were natural hurdles to be jumped in a social sense, for a lone Norwegian, always mistakenly dubbed a Swede, had difficulties among so many Hibernians. These were largely dissipated when, blushing furiously, I was called on to talk at a football rally and having heard somebody call somebody else just a dumb Irishman I had the good fortune to remark:

"There's only one thing dumber than a dumb Irishman." Before the bricks could fly, I explained: "A smart Swede."

Notre Dame was struggling to establish itself in football circles. Its schedules were not strong —Ohio Northern, Marquette and Pittsburgh were "big games." Our equipment was poor. In the first game I played in—against Ohio Northern—a guard was so severely injured that we had to use up our lone roll of tape. Later, his substitute in the line cracked up, so we had to take tape off the first boy to bind up the second.

Shorty Longman knew much about football, but he talked much more. Our offense was principally a punt and a prayer—varied with an occasional line plunge.

Longman's method was that of the old-fashioned oratorical coach. Before a game, he would enter the dressing room dramatically, toss back his shock of black hair and burst into rhetoric.

"Boys," he declaimed, "today is the day. The honor of the old school is at stake. Now or never, we must fight the battle of our lives. I don't want any man with a streak of yellow to move from this room. You've all got to be heroes—HEROES, or I never want to see you again. Go out and conquer. It's the crisis of your lives!"

When I heard that for the first time, I was tremendously impressed. The team went out and all but pushed the opposing team—Olivet— over the fence. The next Saturday, as we lay resting in the dressing room, Coach Longman entered:

"Boys," he detonated, "today is *the* day of days. The honor of the old school is at stake. The eyes of the world are on you. Go out and bleed for the old school, and if anybody has a yellow streak let him——"

I sat there awestricken. Then I saw Dorais and Bergman, two veterans, yawn.

"What do you think of the act today?" asked Bergman.

"Not so good," said Dorais. "I thought he was better last week."

One oration a season is quite enough for any football squad. Action brings reaction, and if the coach talks too much, his words lose weight.

From my first coach, Longman, came another valuable lesson. A sturdy man and useful with his fists, he believed that the best way to impress his charges was to demonstrate that he was physically their master. With this in mind, he prescribed boxing lessons which he himself would give, beginning with the lightweights and working his way through to the heavies of the Philbrook displacement.

Respectfully the squad gathered to see the first demonstration. Several of the less heavy boys, myself included, were to be operated on with boxing gloves. Shorty selected a mild-mannered chap named Matthews, a light end, for the first object lesson. That was a bad break. Matthews stepped out expertly, ducked and weaved and hooked and jabbed. After three minutes Shorty had enough. There were no boxing lessons for the rest of us.

Our next coach was Jack Marks, the Dartmouth back. He made us over from a green, aggressive squad into a slashing, driving outfit. The first time that he looked over Eichenlaub, the Notre Dame 200-pound torpedo, Marks showed he knew his stuff.

"We're playing Wabash this afternoon, Eichenlaub," Marks said. "Jones, Feeney and the rest will make the holes. You tear through them."

"But I'm only a poor high-school boy," said Eichenlaub.

Marks turned on his heel. That afternoon Eichenlaub ripped through Wabash for total gains of more than 400 yards. The Wabash squad piled on a streetcar for the depot, badly licked. The car stopped for a feeble old lady carrying parcels. She worked her way through the limping Wabash players while a wag cried:

"One side! Here comes Eichenlaub's mother."

Marks was always a quiet mentor: but he liked to pile up scores. Once we led Adrian by 81–0, and the Adrian coach said he'd used up all his substitutes and would we agree to let him send men back who had already played? Marks agreed. He returned to the sidelines. Some time later he saw a strange player on our bench.

"You're on the wrong bench," he said.

"I know it," said the lad. "I've been in that scrap four times already, and they're not going to send me back if I can help it. I've had enough."

Marks laughed quietly, and let the lad remain. Again, during a game with Butler, a big halfback named Meyers, strong but shy, was missing.

"You've only got ten men on the field," the umpire cried to the Notre Dame coach. Marks looked over the field in anger.

"Where in heck is Meyers?" he demanded.

"Here I am, coach," sang Meyers from his blanket. "I got bumped right on my knee."

Marks smiled quietly, said nothing. But Meyers played no more. That was his method. The team stepped out under his leadership so that gradually we came to be noticed a little beyond the Midwest. I won a regular berth as end under Marks and had the pleasant surprise of seeing myself discussed as an All-America possibility toward the end of the 1912 season. Almost imperceptibly, it seemed to me, I was established in football. One year, practically abandoning the idea of continuing the game; the next, being talked of—never mind by whom— as an All-America prospect.

Then the end of football and college career impended. My father died, and it seemed imperative that I quit school, although it's on the record that I passed my special subject, chemistry, *cum laude*. A wise sister interposed.

"If you quit," she said, "all right. You may earn a living, but it will be as a mail dispatcher."

So I went back, and I had hardly got off the train at South Bend that autumn when I was greeted by a cordial voice.

"You're Rockne?" its owner asked.

"Well," he went on, after having introduced himself as Jess Harper, Notre Dame's new coach, "I'm grabbing you football men off the trains as fast as I can. We've got to work our heads and legs off."

"What's the excitement?" I said, trying to be calm.

"They're letting us play in the East," he exclaimed. "The Army has agreed to play Notre Dame."

One of the most famous pieces in sports fiction, Rackety Rax, *is a delightful prohibition brew of farce and satire. Its title became part of the language; its college (dear old Canarsie U.), a national institution; and its main characters—the Chief (Francis X. "Knucks" McGloin), his lieutenant, Mike, his lawyer, Councilor, and P. R. Man Schatz —were four of the best known heroes of the Gang Wars. As we pick up the story, the Chief, who controls all the other worthwhile rackets in town, is about to muscle into the football business.*

RACKETY RAX

Joel Sayre

Mike and the Councilor were there, too, and both of them were looking happy. Mike smiled and nodded his great red head and made a little flip of greeting with an enormous right paw, while the Councilor rubbed his hands together and said: "Hah, Mr. Schatz, a pleasure." They were sitting at the big teak table on which stood a bottle of rye, plenty of glasses and a large pitcher of ice water.

The Chief didn't say a word, but I could tell from his eyes and the way he panthered around that he was all smoked up. I got a glass from the sideboard, poured myself a shot, drew a chair up to the table and sat down.

"You tell him," said the Chief over his shoulder to the Councilor.

"I should tell him, when it's your inspiration," said the Councilor, beginning to wave his arms. "Why—"

"Tell him, tell him!" said the Chief, pacing up and down.

"All right"—the Councilor shrugged—"but you shouldn't be so modest." He turned to me. "Before you, Mister Schatz, you see the founders of a great educational institution, the layers of a cornerstone that shall prevail down the corridors of time, that shall—"

"It's a gag to muscle into this here football racket," interrupted the Chief, sitting down on the arm of his big chair. "Since you and me had that talk last year I been figuring angles and now I think I got a way. And with all the headaches this year, we got to try *something*. You say it ain't possible to go up to Columbia or N.Y.U. or Fordham or Harvard or Yale and just muscle right in. I still don't see why, but if you say it means more headaches, why we got plenty right now. Well, see if here ain't a way to do ourself some good."

The Chief slipped into the seat of his chair, put his left elbow on the table and brought his hand gently over the scar. He didn't look straight at me, but out of the corner of his eye. His voice got soft and sleeply.

"What do you say we open a university of our own?" he said, shooting his eyes away and then back at me again. "The Councilor tells me that opening a university ain't much different to opening a speakeasy. All you do is send a couple bucks to Albany and the guy sends your incorporation papers back just like it was a gin mill." (All of the Chief's joints were incorporated as clubs and on all their walls were the framed papers signed and sealed by the Secretary of State.) "Well, we think up some name for our university and get the papers from Albany. Hahzat?"

The terrible eyes crept round to me again.

269

"That's swell," I said, "but where are you going to get the team?"

"Team!" he said. "Why, the team ain't no trouble at all. It's a wonderful chancet to get some use out of that mob of palooka fighters and wrasslers I got eating their heads off. And it don't make no difference how many of 'em gets killed, 'because there's more coming up from the amachers every day. Do you think maybe that would work out?"

"Hmmm . . . well, I guess they'd make wonderful material all right. You could use the wrestlers for your line and the fighters for your backfield, although they'd have to be taught to run forward instead of backward. You'll need a coach. But what about a stadium?"

"Well," said the Chief, "we thought the first season we'd play all our games away from home."

"Hmm, that's a good gag. Notre Dame, the place where the best football in the country is played, didn't play a home game for the first forty years. They used to call 'em the Ramblers before they got a stadium of their own—in the early days they traveled around the country with their toothbrushes and spare collars parked in their derby hats. But you'll have to have a place to practice in. It's going to be quite a chore to get these mugs into shape, or rather to teach 'em the game."

"What's all the gyms for?" said Mike just prior to tossing off a shot.

"No, you've got to have dirt. Football players wear cleats in their shoes and Stillman wouldn't like to have his floor scratched up."

"Well, what about one of the cavalry armories? We can have our pick of them."

I thought this over a moment.

"Well, an armory might do in a pinch, but those wrestlers tumbling around would tear such holes in the dirt the horses might fall in and bust their legs. What you've got to have is a field somewhere, and as I guess we don't want the New York sports writers to nose around too much at first, the field ought to be somewhere they can't get at."

Everybody pondered for a while.

"I got it," said Mike, "that place back of the warehouse in Canarsie. It's out of the way, and nobody to bother us. The ground is kinda swampy, so nobody could hurt theirself if they took a bad fall. Mebbe we could clear out the warehouse and make it a regular training camp."

In case you don't know, Canarsie is a section over on the Long Island waterfront that everybody has heard about but nobody has ever been able to find the way to. Consequently, it makes a wonderful place to land booze, and that's how the Chief happened to have the warehouse over there. It's a terribly lonely place; there is a lunch wagon, and the cop house is a rose-covered white frame cottage. I once fell asleep on a subway train and landed there at the end of the line; but I couldn't do it again in a million years.

The Councilor was smiling up at the ceiling. "You got a wonderful name for the university right there," he said. "Canarsie, Canarsie University. It sounds swell. Good old Canarsie."

Everybody said Canarsie over to himself a couple of times to see how it sounded, and it sounded fine.

"Now, what about games?" said the Chief finally.

"Well, that's going to be tough," I said. "In the first place, most schools have already made their schedules up long ago. And in the second place, nobody ever heard of us, so we can't have our pick of the schools we play. But I'll look around and see what open dates there are and get in touch with anybody I can, and I'll hunt us up a coach, and as soon as I get him lined up he can have a talk with you and let you know how much you'll need for equipment. We won't know what our traveling expenses will be until we get our schedule made up. But this is going to take a lot of my time. What'll I do about the fight and wrestling ballyhoo?"

"Oh, to hell with that," said the Chief. "Get some good guy you know is all right and turn it over to him. I'll pay him whatever you think he ought to have. You bear down on this here football. You'll have to front for us, knowin' the collegiate racket and all. I guess you better be that guy you told me about last fall, you know, the main mug in the racket?"

"The graduate manager of athletics? All right, I'll have to do some traveling around making connections and I'll need some dough."

"How do you want this university incorporated?" the Councilor put in. "You'll be president, of course. What'll I and Mike be?"

The Chief turned to me.

"What monikers would youse give 'em?"

"Well, let's see. Mike can be dean of the College of Liberal Arts and the Councilor, mmm, the Councilor can be—uh—dean of women."

"Why can't *I* be dean of women?" said Mike.

"Shut up," said the Chief. "Okay, kid. Draw on me for whatever dough you'll need. You take care of it so's it's all legitimate, Councilor. You better use the usual monikers, Smith, Jones and Brown, hey?"

"One thing more," I said. "What colors do you want? Every college has got to have its colors. What are old Canarsie's? Most places have two."

"Well, so long as one of 'em's green, I don't care about the other," said the Chief.

There was a long silence.

"I seen some mighty pretty stockings on a little lady at the Suzette the other night," said the Councilor. "They were kind of a, uh, eggplant color and looked fine. I wonder what they call that shade?"

"Puce," I said. My girl friend was the fashion editor of the *Times,* and one Sunday I was reading her stuff and I came across "puce." It struck me as a funny word and when I asked her what it meant she said it meant eggplant color.

"Puce! Geez. Puce, eh? Puce and green. Well, maybe you know what it's all about. Puce!"

The bottle was passed around.

"Gentlemen, I give you old Canarsie," proposed the Councilor. "May the puce and green never falter."

Everybody drank.

"I think this education is gonna be quite a gag," said the Chief. . . . "Puce . . . puce . . . geez . . . !"

Well, I got Canarsie University a coach and I fixed her up with her first schedule.

The coach was Brick Gilligan, the old Michigan tackle, who turned out some fine teams on the Coast until he got in a little trouble. Poor Brick tried to saw a streetcar in half early one morning with his car. And when the cops came they found a coed with him and some bottles. The whole thing was hushed up, but Brick had to resign "for business reasons." I heard from a sports writer that he was in town and when I tracked him down he was selling typewriter ribbons and accessories from office to office in the financial district. Of course, he was delighted to get the job at ten grand the first year.

I'll never forget that August when the candidates for the Varsity answered the call. Brick and I had spent the last two weeks in July superintending carpenters, painters and plumbers in the conversion of the ramshackle building in Canarsie from a booze drop to a field house with showers, lockers and rubbing tables. We set up a tackling dummy and charging machines and laid out a field that would do to practice on, although it was pretty swampy and full of gulleys, and we never did get the busted bottles and old barrel hoops and dornicks out of it.

It was the strangest array of gridiron material ever assembled: fighters running all the way from world's champions, in the best clothes that Billie Taub turns out, to palookas just graduated from the Golden Gloves with hardly any seats to their pants; heavyweights, light heavies, middleweights, welters, lightweights, feathers, bantams and even little Shrimp Stein, the king of the flies. There were cauliflower ears, squashed noses and swollen cheekbones. Save for the lumbering heavies, they all moved with superb grace.

And the wrestlers! All heavyweights, all around 300, great, fat, good-natured guys, most of them bohunks or grease-balls whose only English was an obliging: "Sure, boss!" There was Nick Tossilitis, world's champion of the week, wearing the gargantuan diamond which unscrewed from his championship belt and could be fitted easily into either ring or stick pin; Hazos, the Horrible Hun, a middle-aged Slav with old-fashioned side whiskers; Baliban, the Neckless Wonder; and dozens of others, panting and sweating. Like faithful domestic animals, they wondered what it was all about, but were eager to perform any task ordered by their masters.

The Chief, Mike and the Councilor stood in the background to see that everything started O.K. Brick, dressed in baseball pants and cap and a sweat shirt, was in command.

Brick had coached teams on the Coast where they produce plenty of Paul Bunyans for football players, but, he told me afterward, he had never seen such material. However, he thought he'd better begin in the usual way by showing them what was what.

"Siddown, everybody, and get the wax outa your ears," he began with a nasty bark. "You've all answered the call to play football for Canarsie, and that's what you're gonna do—play football. Now, in the first place, while you're playin' football for me you're gonna play it the way I want it played, not the way you played it before you come here. And while you're learnin' to play it you're gonna learn it the way I give it to you. Where you come from you may a been the world's champion of this and that and I dunno what all. But now you're gonna start from the bottom. The first thing you gotta do is learn to *use your head!* It don't matter how big you are or how fast you are. If you don't *use your head,* you won't ever be a football player.

"And the first thing about usin' your head you gotta learn is *pay attention to what I say.* Now look at those two men over there. One's pickin' bananas and the other's pickin' his nose while I'm *talking. Hey, you!*"

He was addressing two Hungarian wrestlers, who, not understanding a word of his discourse, had begun amiable conversation with each other in Magyar. As he shouted at them they looked in his direction and smiled like children. Somebody among the boxers let fly a long juicy razzberry, which started the wrestlers laughing, and in a second there was a whole migration of birds in the air. It looked very bad for the general's introduction to his troops until the Chief cuffed a few of the ringleaders, and said a few words, and restored order.

"Get this, you mugs," he shouted, "this here genneman is representing me, see, and anything he tells ya to do, you do it, see, same as if it was me telling ya, see? Go ahead, Mac, and any of 'em gives you any trouble when I ain't here, jest lemme know."

There was a deep silence and a lowering of eyes all around.

"Well, report to Mr. Schatz in the storeroom for your suits," Brick resumed, trying to keep his voice hard, but not quite succeding, "and leave your names with him. When you get dressed, report to me at the field."

It was quite a chore issuing suits to the squad of sixty-one on account of all the different lengths and contours in it, and we ran short of outsize pants for the wrestlers and shoes for the heavyweight fighters. But when they all assembled on the field there were fifty-two players completely outfitted with headguards ($15 each), jerseys ($10 each), shoulder pads ($14 each), hip and kidney pads ($15 each), pants ($17 each), shoes with screw-on cleats ($16 a pair), and stockings ($4.50 a pair). As it was August I had not issued any blankets ($13.50 each) or side-line shirts with hoods ($12 each).

The first thing that Brick found out was that he had three former college players among the wrestlers on his squad: Switz, of Notre Dame, a fullback; Oolaafsen, of Dartmouth, a tackle; and Schwulkopf, of Nebraska, a guard. After some calisthenics and duck-waddling up and down the field a couple of times by the whole squad, Brick divided his candidates into three groups and set them to falling on the ball.

The boxers took to it right away, being so used to fake fouls, but I wish you could have seen those wrestlers putting the divots in that swampland! It looked like Flanders Field after they were finished. The people that lived out that way must have thought they were blasting for a new subway.

After that they all worked out on the dummy,

and Brick had a terrible time explaining to some of the grease-ball wrestlers that they mustn't put the scissors on it. There were more reverberations when they worked out on the charging machines. I don't know if you ever saw a charging machine, but it's a kind of a frame on wheels with a platform in back of it. A bunch of guys stand on the platform and the linemen put their hands on the top bar of the frame and push the whole contraption at a signal from the coach. When they get to the end of their push, they all fall flat at full length—*bam.* Then up, charge and *bam,* all the way up and down the field and over and over again. When you get about half a dozen wrestlers at 300 pounds each all hitting the dirt at once it makes quite a shake.

Well, there was plenty of trouble with that squad. The fighters couldn't be taught at first not to sock instead of using the open hand, and the wrestlers would grab and hold. Brick divided them into Varsity, Second and Third Teams and had them scrimmage every afternoon with the three collegiate wrestlers helping him as assistants. At first, the boxers wouldn't play on the same teams as the wrestlers, having such a mean opinion of them; and they wanted us to put up another field house for the wrestlers on a kind of Jim Crow system, so that they wouldn't even have to look at them. You know, most fighters are very swell-headed and consider themselves above wrestlers. The wrestlers, however, have no false pride and are willing to take whatever comes their way with no complaints. That is why they all look well fed, while fighters nearly starve to death most of the time.

Although of course he never let them know it, Brick was enthusiastic about the possibilities of the squad.

"I think we can get a great club out of this bunch, Mr. Schatz," he used to say to me after practice. "We'll get a club this year that'll do all right, but just wait till I've had 'em a couple of seasons. There's awful power there, Mr. Schatz, awful power. God, if they could just learn not to use their hands on the offensive! But we'll see, we'll see."

I had terrible trouble and a couple of breaks, but here is the schedule I drew up for old Canarsie for its first year on the gridiron. The Navy game came through one of those severing of relations it has with the Army every once in a while.

Sept. 27.—Alfred University at Alfred, N.Y.
Oct. 4.—Temple University at Philadelphia.
Oct. 11.—Duke University at Durham, N.C.
Oct. 18.—University of Buffalo at Buffalo.

Oct. 25.—University of Detroit at Detroit.
Nov. 1.—Case School of Applied Science at Cleveland.
Nov. 8.—U.S. Naval Academy at Annapolis.
Nov. 15.—St. Mary's College at Oakland, Cal.

"There ain't no harm in trying," said the Chief when I showed him the schedule, "we're all aiming to make a buck, but if we don't do nothing but get off the nut this first year, it's eggs in the coffee."

That was the starting lineup of our first game. We had some debate about whether we should give out fake names for the team, making them all 100% Anglo-Saxon or Celtic, but I pointed out that football players all over the United States have the goofiest names ever heard of anyway, and nobody would think Switz, Radeswicz and Woola anything out of the ordinary. So I sent out the lineup to all the New York papers, and each of them gave us an inch or two, while three upstate sheets ran as a box a phony interview in which Coach Gilligan said he expected a terrible battle with Alfred. I remember I was kind of ashamed when I sent them out: we averaged 285.8 pounds from tackle to tackle.

CANARSIE		ALFRED
Oolaafsen	L.E.	Angley
Radeswicz	L.T.	Matoon
Hazos	L.G.	Porter
Tossilitis	C.	Schmidt
Baliban	R.G.	Haggerty
Schwulkopf	R.T.	Sessions (c)
Woola	R.E.	Priestley
McGloin	Q.B.	Santorello
Cello	L.H.	Fellowes
Flanahan	R.H.	Stein
Switz (c)	F.B.	Hardell

Switz was our threat man; he could run and pass, and as he had learned football under Rockne you can imagine what his blocking and tackling were like; but he couldn't punt, not more than twenty yards. Nobody on the whole squad could, as a matter of fact. Schwulkopf was a pretty good place-kicker and was all right for kickoffs. Oolaafsen, the old Dartmouth tackle, a product of the great Doc Spears, we had to make into an end to catch forward passes and turn in the opposing backfields. Woola, the other end, was a professional basketball player Brick dug up in a moment of desperation when he found so few of his players could catch a

ball. Woola could catch anything thrown anywhere in the park, but he was afraid to tackle; so they made big Schwulkopf play defensive end and go down under punts; while Woola, as a defensive half, was great at intercepting passes. The guards, Hazos and Baliban, the center, Chomp Tossilitis, and big Radeswicz, the other tackle, were all wrestlers.

Cello and Flanahan, the halfbacks, were two middleweights, famous for their speed and footwork. McGloin, the quarterback, was a nephew of the Chief's, a little rat-faced guy that used to stand on corners. Brick figured him as the best possibility for a field general.

Signals, early in the team's training, had to be given up as totally unintelligible to the vast majority of the members of the squad. The huddle system of communication was substituted. It used to look very funny from the sidelines with all those wrestlers' cabooses sticking out.

I will say this for Brick Gilligan: he was a smart coach. He realized that with the material he had he couldn't turn out for the first game any N.Y.U. Violets, all doing the Meehan military shift like so many Prussian Guards. What he aimed for was something simple and elemental. Knute Rockne used to say that if every man did his duty perfectly on every play, a touchdown would result. Well, for that first game with Alfred, Brick pointed for an uncomplicated application of that principle. He figured that if those wrestlers could just be made to squat down and push, and then, after they'd waddled forward a few steps, to lean against Alfred's secondary defense and lie on them for a few seconds, somebody in the backfield could carry the ball for a gain. Which wasn't such a bad idea.

Switz won the toss and Schwulkopf kicked off to Santorello, who was downed in his tracks on the 30-yard line by Flanahan. On the first play Hardell bucked center and gained 30 yards through no fault of his own, for Tossilitis seized him by the waist as soon as he had reached the line, twirled him thrice about his head just as he used to do before he pinned an opponent to the mat, and then slammed him to the ground, knocking him cold. Hardell was removed on a stretcher, Tossilitis, weeping, was banished from the game, and old Canarsie was penalized half the distance to the goal for unnecessary roughness. Tossilitis's place was taken by Nixi, the Finnish champion, a formidable matman, but less showy.

As far as I am concerned there ought to be a law against football games in which one team outweighs the other more than ten pounds to a man, so I hasten to say that we took 80 points off Alfred, making three touchdowns each quarter. The Alfred boys were plenty game, but they didn't have a chance, because in every American sport but murder a good big man is always better than a good little man.

What Gilligan knew after the game was that he had the possibilities of an impregnable defense against everything but a forward passing attack. There were possibilties there, too, of a marvelous offense; for if most of your opponents are lying on their backs and looking up at the sky, why you don't need to worry much about losing ground.

The Chief sat on the bench with the squad and was greatly interested in the Alfred cheering section. Outside of the roars of our own squad, we had had no one to cheer us on.

After the game I took him for a walk around the Alfred campus. He was impressed by the buildings.

"Geez, ain't they got a plant here!" he said. "This here is quite a jernt. . . . Say, about them scholars there today with their barks and all . . . we got to have something like that if we're gonna be in this racket. I'll try to figure out some gag this week when I get back to town."

"Oh, don't bother about that, Chief," I told him. "If you get a good team and some decent publicity, you'll have plenty of following. Look at Notre Dame. In the old days they were always playing away from home and couldn't bring their own mob with them; yet whenever they played in New York they always had plenty out there pulling for them to win."

"Well, mebbe so, but we got to have our own mob next week down in Philly. That's Boo Boo Hoff's town, and I wouldn't want him to get the idea we was a bunch of pikers or no class D mob. You leave it to me. I'll figure out some gag. What else do we need beside a mob of scholars to get out there and bark?"

"Well, the big schools usually have a band, too."

"Oh, they have a band, do they? Well, I guess we can pull a connection on a band, all right. A band, eh?"

So I was not surprised the next Saturday when a band appeared on the field clad in puce uniforms and green shakos. It marched out playing "The Maine Stein Song," and playing it surprisingly well for a college band. There was something vaguely familiar about the sways and wiggles of the drum major twirling his baton, but his enormous bearskin busby was so far down over his face that I couldn't make him out. Curious, I went from the press box down to where the Chief was sitting with Mike and the Councilor.

"Swell, but who's the drum major?" I asked. "I've seen him somewhere from the cut of his jib."

"Sure, you have," said the Chief. "It's Ernie Norvelle from the Suzette, and them's the bands from all the clubs and hotels massed into one. We tried to get Paul Whiteman, but he's playing a date in Chicago. Ernie's been working out on the boys all week."

The Councilor beamed and rubbed his hands together.

"Fine like silk," he purred.

"Get a load of our scholars," said Mike, motioning over his left shoulder.

I looked into the stands behind me. There, row upon row, were fat, bland, blue-chinned faces—each with a set of large, slightly protruding horse-chestnut brown eyeballs. On each head was a soft hat with the brim turned up in front, and overhead floated Canarsie's puce and green pennants on canes. Our student body, all smoking cigars, was mostly inclined to portliness and seemed between thirty-eight and fifty years of age. Presumably many of them were old alumni. Scattered among them were many metallically pretty girls, also waving Canarsie pennants on canes. Our student body looked strangely familiar. I turned inquiringly to Mike.

"The boys wanted to come down and lay a little bet with the Philly mob," he explained, "so I made 'em all go around to Sizzbaum's and get fixed up."

Sizzbaum was the customer who outfitted all the floor shows of our night clubs.

"I hope everything's O.K.?" Mike continued anxiously.

"And co-heds we got!" purred the Councilor.

"Yeah," said Mike. "I thought it wouldn't do no harm to give the gals the trip down for the day, so I sent them along to Sizzbaum's to get fixed up, too."

Evidently our entire entertainment staff had been enlisted to help out with our appearance in the City of Brotherly Love; for a few minutes later six masters of ceremonies appeared in sweaters and with megaphones and began calling for "a locomotive for Temple and get hot, folks!"

The gamblers removed their cigars and the girls took reefs in their gum, and the cheer was given, given with quite a respectable volume, considering our numbers and lack of practice. Mike nudged me: "Get a load of the little specialty we got between rounds," he said with a wink as the Temple stands roared back a cheer for Canarsie. The band struck up "The Maine Stein Song" again.

Temple had a good club that year, built around McNaboe, their caveman end. McNaboe weighed 196, was five feet seven inches tall and uglier than a wrestler. He could punt 75 or 80 yards, drop or place-kick 45 from any angle, forward pass 60, and when he tackled, it hurt. They used him as fullback on the offensive, and there wasn't anything he couldn't do in the way of running with the ball.

All right. We kicked off. Their left halfback ran the ball back 20 yards, for we hadn't yet learned to get down under kickoffs as fast as we should. Oolaafsen smeared an end run. On the next play, McNaboe tried an off-tackle buck. They picked him up with both hips dislocated. Don't ask me how. It just happened, that's all. And we won another ball game: 29–0. They couldn't stand that terrible pounding our line gave them.

The big feature of the Temple game was what Mike called the between-rounds specialty, which occurred between halves. Ernie Norvelle blew his whistle, spun his baton and the band, playing "The Maine Stein Song" paraded out on to the field and spelled out: "TAKE TEMPLE." After this pretty effect, Ernie again blew his whistle and the band started back toward our stands. Mike, very much excited, nudged me and said: "Let's scram around to the other side so we can catch this right," and led the way, with the Chief and the Councilor and the gorillas following, to a position in front of the Temple bench. I noticed a great shifting and moving among our loyal student body. The band kept pumping out "The Maine Stein Song" softly. Ernie blew his whistle and held his baton, with both hands high above his head, parallel to the ground. The music ceased in the middle of "To the gods, to the fates, to the—"

A double row of coeds, all in white dresses, stood up and formed a very fancy giant C. Ernie blew his whistle. They sat down. He blew his whistle. All the coeds crossed right knees over left and the C turned to puce. Ernie blew his whistle. The C turned to green as the coeds crossed left knees over right. It seemed that each was wearing a puce right stocking and a green left.

Ernie again blew his whistle and the afternoon sun emblazoned a giant C that kaleido-scopically shifted from puce to green to puce to green and back again scores of times, so fast that it dazzled the eyes. The effect was tremendous, and the Temple supporters seemed almost reconciled for the loss of their great McNaboe, so loudly did they cheer.

"A nifty little novelty," was the Chief comment.

The Duke game, which we won 64–0, in spite of the heat, was notable only in that the entire Duke backfield was removed from the game with dislocated hips, and our new anthem, "Dear old Canarsie o' Mine," was introduced. It was a little thing that Ernie Norvelle had worked out during the week. The tune was a waltz, and, by turns, strongly reminiscent of "When It's Moonlight in Kaluha" and "The Merry Widow." The words were:

Alma, Alma, Alma Mater,
Every son of yours and daughter
Far above Canarsie's water
Looks to thee,
Sweet Varsity.
As underneath these stars
We pledge this loyalty of ours
To
Oh, oh say Can-ar-sie,
Old Canarsie o' mine!

After the student body had finished singing it (and it was a little strange to observe the large number of bald pates among our undergraduates as they stood with their hats off in the Southern sun), Ernie led a double quartette of crooners from the band over in front of the Duke stands where they cooed it through little megaphones, and on the second chorus the tenors rendered it in double time with plenty of "dooden-deepum-boden-eaten" and spasmodic wagglings of the hips. It made a great hit with the Southern crowd, as, of course, did our coeds with their pretty letter effects.

Buffalo is a great sporting town and the Chief had his betting commissioners foraging through the pool parlors as early as Monday, taking all the local dough in sight, and there was plenty. Football was a kind of new gag to the Buffalo boys, at least our team was, and by playing on local pride the commissioners were able to line up plenty of even money. Our club took 112 points off Buffalo without even getting up a sweat, and the local smarten-heimers swore off football for life.

I told Ernie early in the week that every college had not only an alma mater but a special football song as well, so this is the little number he dashed off:

FIGHT-CHA

As the Puce and Green sweeps down the field
To that five-yard line;
Can we make our groaning rivals yield
To a touchdown sure this time?
You will hear Canarsie's rooters yell
For their team to do or die:
"Fight-cha, fight-cha,
They won't hoit nor bite-cha."
[Spoken] "Get in there, you mugs!"
                    RAH, RAH, RAH!

The University of Detroit was the first tough game on our schedule, and one we had to win. The Chief doubled his flying squadron of commissioners and sent them ahead with a roll of about 250 grand, so it looked as though there would be a lot of dead wrestlers if we came out on the short end. Gus Dorais, the old Notre Dame quarterback who used to throw passes to Rockne, had a big, fast team, brilliantly coached in the Notre Dame system, seasoned and well balanced. Brick was worried.

"We'll win if we can get some breaks," was the best he would predict as he saw me off on the Wolverine early in the week.

It was our first attempt at bigtime football, so I bore down on the advance publicity; and as the town is very proud of the university's team, the Detroit papers gave me a nice play. Every college football aggregation that amounts to anything must have a zoological or meteorological name, such as Bulldogs, Tigers, Panthers, or the Golden Tornado, the Crimson Tide, the Mason Monsoon. I christened our boys the Thundering Pachyderms, making rather a neat combination of both schools, I prided myself.

Brick had scouted the Detroit club thoroughly. Their first-string backfield, Dugan, Wachtmeister, Nalti and Joyce, was another set of Four Horsemen; they could do anything and were lightning fast. What's more, Dorais had two other backfields almost as good as his first stringers that he could run in there. For fear that he would recognize Switz as a former Notre Dame player, we changed his name to Murphy and made him wear a nose guard so big that his own mother would have been doubtful about him.

After Brick had given the squad a long dressing-room harangue on watching out for the Detroit hidden-ball plays, and how to meet their shifts and overhead attack, the Chief, who had been sitting there listening, got up and glared around at the assemblage.

"Which is the five mugs?" he asked Brick.

"Schwulkopf, Hazos, Tossilitis, Radeswicz, Baliban, stand up," barked Brick at the line from tackle to tackle. The five monsters rose abashed.

"Listen, youse," said the Chief, putting the bad eye on them, "I want ten tackles this half from each of youse, and if I don't get 'em . . . well, it'll be just too bad, unnastand, just too bad."

Brick said, "Let's go," and the Thundering Pachyderms rushed out of the locker room, eager to die for the old Puce and Green.

Detroit won the toss and kicked. In about nine seconds they wished they hadn't, because little McGloin caught the ball on our 20-yard line and made a touchdown. It was the damnedest thing I ever saw, although later on it became famous all over the country as the Canarsie Funnel. It seems that Brick had been working the boys at it all week.

The flying wedge was abolished in 1905, after a disastrous season in which eighteen players were killed; but what Brick uncorked that day on the first play against Detroit was nothing more or less than the old flying wedge, only executed with perfect legality. The idea was simply that as soon as the other side put a boot to the ball, big Tossilitis, our center and world's champion of the week, ran back to a few yards in front of where the ball was to come down and the whole team formed in a wedge behind him. Flanking him to the rear were the guards, Baliban the Neckless, and Hazos the Horrible, with his whiskers tucked into his headguard; back of them the tackles, Radeswicz and Schwulkopf; back of them the ends, Woola and Oolaafsen; and back of them the backs, the whole forming an enormous V, several tons in weight, that moved like a giant tank. Into the mouth of the funnel dashed little McGloin with the ball. None of the ten men touched one another, but so Gibraltar-like was their ability to keep their feet that the Detroit tacklers bounced off like food shot from guns. Oolaafsen kicked goal.

Then we kicked off to them and they ran the ball back to their 40-yard line. Right away they started to hammer the tackles with that marvelous hidden-ball play of theirs, and the first thing we knew it was their first down in midfield. What a beautiful backfield Detroit had, and how perfectly their line functioned! Signal, shift, snapback, gain; signal, shift, snapback, gain; signal, shift, snapback, gain. Short punches, but the ball kept moving up the field. The shifts were running our wrestlers dizzy.

Brick began biting his nails when the referee

signaled to the head linesman and they measured on our 5-yard line. The referee blew his
whistle, waved toward our goal. First down,
goal to gain. Just then the quarter ended, and
they started to move the ball to the other end.

As the two teams followed the officials down
the field, it was easy to note the difference in
morale; the Detroit players bridled and ca-
pered, eager for a score; our boys dragged
slowly along with bowed heads, unresponsive
to the back-slappings and pants-kickings of
little McGloin.

Detroit would have had a dozen touchdowns,
had it not been for the omnipresent Switz-
Murphy. He plugged up holes in the line. He
knifed through perfect interference and ended
end runs. He dragged down off-tackle bucks,
and, on our 10-yard line, he intercepted a short
lob, aimed at their left end, when the De-
troiter all but had his nails dug into the ball.

By this time, our line was on the ropes, and
the Detroit forwards rushed through and hurried poor little McGloin so that his punt went
only 25 yards.

I looked at Brick inquiringly, wondering
why he didn't rush in some subs; but he was
still at work on his nails and had got them practically down to the moons. Then the referee
blew his whistle. Time out: one of our wrestlers
was lying on his back.

Doc Dreen, the Chief's chiropractor and
physician to the team, doubled out on the
field with his little black bag, the water boy
after him. It seemed that Tossilitis was hurt.
Our other linemen lay on their backs exhausted.
I could see Doc bending over the huge Greek.
The water boy was swiftly carrying his bucket
from player to player, plying his sponge.

Something queer was happening out there.
Our exhausted linemen seemed suddenly elec-
trified with energy. They had leaped up from
the ground and were pounding one another on
the backs and kicking one another's vast pants;
they hopped up and down and several of them
began shadow-boxing. When the referee blew
his whistle for time in, they lined up in a flash.
A miracle had happened. Doc and the water
boy doubled off the field. I looked more closely
at the water boy and a great light dawned; beneath the cap pulled far down over the ears I
saw the long, wicked knife-lash that somebody
had given the Chief in his early days. Doubtless,
he had been telling the boys it would be just
too bad.

And on the next play Dugan was carried off
the field with his left leg broken, after a ferocious tackle by Tossilitis.

From then on, bones began snapping like
popcorn. Joyce was taken out a few minutes
later with a broken wrist, and it was our ball.
This time McGloin didn't have to hurry to get
his punt off, and the kick sailed 38 yards. The
ends got down under it, neck and neck, and
when the Detroit safety man came to, a
couple of his ribs wouldn't work.

We were out of danger, and when the whistle
blew for the end of the half, Baliban, Hazos,
and Tossilitis were about to put headlocks on
one another in a dispute over who should get
credit for the tackle which had just dislocated
both of the Detroit quarterback's hips.

We made four more touchdowns the next
half, two in each quarter; for the Chief crouched
on the side lines in his water-boy makeup the
whole time, and whenever a puce-and-green
warrior looked his way, there he was shaking
his sponge at him as though it were a pineapple.
The leg drive produced by this simple gesture
was enormous. Score 33–0.

No sooner were we back home than Brick
started to point for the Navy game by spreading
anti-Navy propaganda. By the middle of the
week, so many sailors, innocently walking along
the streets and minding their own business, had
been suddenly slugged, that Brick had to de-
clare a three-mile limit around the Navy Yard
and put Riverside drive out of bounds to the
entire squad.

Tossilitis was particularly bitter, as he
claimed his sister had been betrayed in Athens
by a sailor during the war. That this sister's
betrayer was probably some able-bodied seaman from the Dutch herring fleet, and that the
approaching game was to be against American
naval cadets made no difference to the world's
champion of the week; sailors were sailors,
whatever their nationality or rank. His sister
had been betrayed and, with his left hand on
his heart and his right whipping many times
back and forth across his throat in simulation
of a shivaree, he swore a great oath that she
would be avenged.

That Saturday we went to Cleveland and
played the Case School of Applied Science.
Case didn't have a particularly strong team,
and the Navy had beaten them 47 to 13 in
the second game of the season. Well, after a
few minutes of play, we marched down the field
to their 1-yard line and McGloin sent Switz
into the heap for the scoring play. The game
was such a foregone conclusion that I began
to wish I had brought a good book along. There

was a pile-up and then the referee's whistle. Switz had fumbled and Case had recovered on their 1-yard line. Hawkes, their halfback, tried to punt from back of their goal line, but he was flattened in his tracks by practically everything on the field in a puce-and-green jersey. We were off to a 2-point lead.

And that, to the amazement of the football world, was the score at the end of the game. The Case team fought like tigers, and got to within our 10-yard line four times, once in the second quarter, twice in the third and once in the last. We, on the other hand, seemed to have lost our leg drive after that safety at the start of the game: there were so many fumbles and incomplete forward passes that I got sick counting. McGloin, a remarkably smart field general for (so to speak) a freshman quarterback, seemed to have gone completely daffy. When it was third down on our own 10-yard line he himself tried to buck center. Another time we lost the ball to Case on our 25-yard line after two straight tries at forward passes that went nowhere.

Gilligan sat on the bench chawing his nails, as usual, and making horrible faces; while the Chief, in his water-boy makeup, squatted on the side lines shaking his sponge. The entire squad was sent in the game, but we couldn't score. After the game, the Case team was carried off the field on the shoulders of their rooters, a snake dance was held and their own goal posts were pulled up in celebration of a more than moral victory.

As the game ended I turned to Mike and groaned: "Oh, those poor mugs!"

"What poor mugs?"

"Why, the team. Lake Erie's gonna be strewn with corpses of murdered wrestlers. Can't you do something with the Chief?"

"Why, what's wrong with the Chief? It all come out like he wanted, didn't it? Two to nothin's the lowest score we could win by. Ain't that O.K.?"

"The lowest score? I don't get you."

Mike looked at me curiously.

"You don't figure angles, do you? Well, the Chief does. We play Navy next Saturday, don't we? Well, the Navy win from these here Cases 47 to 13 early in the season. Here we are, s'posed to be at the top of our form, and we look lucky to take two points off of 'em. What do you s'pose all these here football experts in the papers is gonna say about our chancet of hanging it on the Navy next Saturday?"

It began to glimmer into the old skull.

"They'll say we haven't got a chance, and the Navy will look on us as something soft."

"Sure they will, and it'll blow the odds higher'n a kite. The Chief's got guys in Washington and in the Navy yards and as far as the Pacific fleet, and on Monday as soon as all the sports sections get read, they'll start layin' out our dough. After we finish playin' the Navy next Saturday, the Chief'll have a first mortgage on all the battleships Uncle Sam owns. The Councilor has picked out the submarine fleet to throw parties in, and I got my eye on that *Akron* airship."

"And so the Chief issued orders for the team not to bear down on Case?"

"Sure. That's why he was on the side lines there, threatening to take anybody for a ride that made a touchdown. And the word was passed around to let the Cases have the ball all the time, so's it wouldn't look like we was stalling."

"God," I said, "what a man!"

"Yeah," said Mike, "he sure is. Always in there, figuring angles."

And sure enough, the sports writers doped the game just as Mike predicted. As we had played all of our games on the road with comparatively unimportant teams, none of the New York experts had seen the team play; and as Admiral Byrd himself would have a tough time finding Canarsie, none of the experts had seen us practice. So they all picked Navy.

As I said before, the only reason the Navy had given us a game was because they had had one of their periodic rows with the Army. When they canceled their annual classic with the Kaydets, they shifted Pennsylvania up to the last game of the season and substituted us in the Saturday originally scheduled for Penn. When I thought what swell people the Navy had been to deal with, and then listened to our baboons planning to give them the works, I kind of felt ashamed of myself.

Because the Navy was the classiest team on our schedule, the Chief was anxious to make as good a showing in the stands as on the field, so a chorus call was put in all the want-ad sections of the papers, and Ernie Norvelle worked for two weeks with 300 chorines in puce and green stockings, teaching them to make the giant C.

Then one night the Chief happened to drop into the Newsreel Theater, and there was a shot of the middies' cheering section at one of their games. Each midshipman had a piece of colored cardboard and went through a regular drill with it, so that the whole cheering section made those monster pictures. When the Chief saw that, he decided right away we had to have something like it ourselves.

On the morning of the day of the game four special trains were run out of the Penn Station to Baltimore: the Nick the Greek and the Gigantic Ginsberg Specials hauled all the gamblers; the Texas Guinan Special hauled all the coeds; while the Puce and Green Special carried the squad and the board of strategy.

I figured we'd win all right, although the Navy had a swell team, big and fast, that had already beaten Princeton, Georgetown and Ohio State, all ace clubs that year; but I was sure they'd be overconfident after that Case game. And in football, when two teams are pretty evenly matched, the one that's out for blood can always hang it on an opponent looking for something soft. And were we out for blood!

However, Brick surprised me with his dressing-room talk. Instead of the usual fifteen minutes of liquid fire, he pulled the old hearts-and-flowers; and in place of that man-eating-shark sneer it generally wore, his face looked like a politician's at the tomb of the Unknown Soldier. His voice got all choked up.

"Fellows," he began, and the baboons all looked at each other in amazement, "fellows, we're here on the threshold of our big chance. This is the day we do or die. Today we're fighting for the future of old Canarsie—your future, my future, the future of all of us.

"Now, the first thing I want to insist on is clean play. The Seckatary of the Navy and plenty more Washanun big shots is gonna be out there in the stands looking us over, and I don't want to see any dirty play. And that goes aspesh'ly for you linemen: no toeholds, no head locks, no dislocated hips. Do you get that, Tossilitis? No, never mind about your sister." (For the Greek had risen from his seat and begun to roll his eyes and saw his throat with his imaginary shiv.) "We want to play the Navy again next year, and if we don't show 'em plenty sportsmanship they'll cut us off their schedule. That don't mean, though, that you're not to hit *hard* when you do hit. I wanna see those *guards,* you, Hazos, and you, Baliban, swing out into that interference on those end runs and *take those tackles.* But when a Navy man is knocked cold, the man that did it, get over there and help him up. Pat him on the back and shake hands when he comes to. Remember, this is just a friendly game between two schools. . . . But lemme see lotsa *leg* drive.

"Well, fellows, our future is at stake. All Broadway, your Broadway and mine, is out there in the stands, watching you, praying for you. Your old Prexy here" (the Chief, leaning against a blackboard, glared around him) "is looking to you to win and will be *mighty disapp-oint-ed if you don't.* Mr. Dumphy, Councilor Sultsfeldt and Mr. Schatz here and I have given all our time and money, wearing ourselves to the bone, teaching you every l'il detail, to get you ready for this game. And we'll all be watching you and praying for you.

"But, fellows, never mind about old Canarsie, never mind Broadway, never mind the Prexy, never mind Mr. Dumphy or the Councilor or Mr. Schatz or I. Just listen to this."

He pulled a yellow envelope from his pocket.

"Fellows, I don't mind what Broadway would say, or the great disappointment it would mean to you and me and all of us. But just listen to this telegram I got here. It just now come and it's from my little six-year-ole girl and it says: 'Daddy, bring me back the Navy. Elsie.' 'Daddy . . . bring . . . me . . . back . . . the . . . Navy. . . .' There you see, fellows, the real reason why I don't want you to lose this game. I don't wanna break the heart of a li'l six-year-ole kiddie. Course, we can't bring her back the Navy like she says, but we can bring her back the football we'll take from the Navy, *if we win.* Can you break the heart of a li'l six-year-ole kiddie, fellows? It's for her I'm asking you. Are you gonna disappoint a li'l six-year-ole kiddie? Are you?"

There was a mighty roar of *"No!"* as the squad rose with wet eyes and rushed out of the room. I was the last to leave. I noticed that Brick had left Elsie's telegram lying on the table. I glanced at it.

"Nosegay in the fourth Belmont," was all it said.

Our band made a great hit before the game with its rendition of "The Maine Stein Song" and "Anchors Aweigh" and the spelling out of "Hahzit, Navy?" complete, with comma and question mark.

It was terrible the way we took the Navy—58–0. That score, I guess, is the worst they've ever been licked by since they've had a football team. McGloin caught the kickoff and was funneled over for an immediate touchdown. Not a Navy tackler laid a finger on him; and from then on it was a rout. Our plays—we had only about ten that first season—clicked perfectly almost every time; and our wrestlers tore huge holes in the Navy line and cleaned out their secondary with such regularity that a paralytic could have rolled his wheel chair through for touchdowns behind them. The Navy team seemed in a terrible daze, and the score at the end of the first half was 30–0.

When the whistle blew and the two teams went to their dressing rooms, the midshipmen in the stands got out their colored cardboard rectangles and started to make pictures. First they made the Stars and Stripes fluttering in the breeze. We gave them a great hand on that, and our band favored with a quick refrain of "The Maine Stein Song." Then they made a gigantic anchor. More applause and "Anchors Aweigh" from our band. Then the left half of their cheering section made an enormous puce elephant which got up on its hind legs and waved its green trunk. Our stands went crazy. Then the right half of their cheering section made a field gun out of which spurted a cloud of smoke.

As the score was then 30–0 in our favor, the stunt that Ernie Norvelle had worked out for our cardboard wielders seemed all the more appropriate. He blew his whistle. There was a frantic shifting and stirring. And then our rooters spelled out in colossal puce and green letters very rapidly: "NUTS, NAVY! NUTS, NAVY! NUTS, NAVY!"

An ominous growl came rumbling out of the Navy stands, but the spirit of good feeling was restored a few seconds later when our coeds made the old puce-and-green C.

As usual, I was sitting next to Mike on the bench.

"I thought we'd win all right," I told him some time in the third quarter as our apes were rushing up and down the field almost unimpeded, "but I didn't figure on anything like this. I've been watching Army and Navy teams play football for years, but I never saw one that looked like that one out there. The service teams are famous for their wonderful shape, and when they hit they hit, like a million dornicks. They've always got all the leg drive in the world. But those boys out there are stale, they're sluggish, and they haven't got any more leg drive than a plate of oysters. I can't figure it out."

Mike took a comb from his pocket and ran it through his curls.

"When Irish eyees are smileeeing," he sang under his breath.

"No, sir," I said, "it's a mystery to me. I don't see how that club out there ever hung it on Princeton and Georgetown."

Mike put his comb in his pocket and winked at me.

Later, I found out that two weeks before the game a little spade waiter at the Club Whambam turned up at the Naval Academy and got a job as scullion or something in the kitchen that prepared the steaks for the football squad. Whether he did anything to that food, I don't know. All I do know is that the Navy was incredibly sluggish that afternoon against us. I got the story from the Councilor at the Club Whambam one night when he was pretty cock-eyed. I know, also, that the little spade had been made headwaiter. And it was a Broadway proverb the way the Chief always took every precaution to insure his wagers.

We made four more touchdowns the next half. The way our mugs picked up the Navy boys and dusted them off after they had been knocked cold made a fine impression in the stands, and nearly all the sports writers commented on it the next day. We got a fine play, by the way, in all the New York papers; and in his Monday column in the *Sun* Grantland Rice said our line would recall to old followers of the sport the 1901–1905 point-a-minute juggernaut teams that Michigan put on the field.

After the game there was a big tea dance at the Belvedere Hotel in Baltimore, and eighteen of our coeds became engaged to midshipmen. What the Councilor did when he got full of that Maryland rye was plenty, too.

Brick pulled a fast one in the St. Mary's game. St. Mary's had a corking team which had come to New York earlier in the season and licked a fine Fordham eleven 28–12; but Brick figured he could beat them if all the odds were even. When an Eastern team goes out to the Coast for a game it has not only got a rival to lick but the change of climate as well.

So when the squad got back to town that night from Baltimore they were rushed right off the train to the hot room of the Turkish bath at the Argonne. The bath was cleared of customers, and the squad was put right to bed. The next day they were made to run through signals there; the day after that, all bundled up in sweaters and blankets, they were taxied in limousines to the Grand Central Terminal, where three specially heated Pullmans on the Twentieth Century were ready for the word. Every member of the squad had an electric hot-water bottle and extra blankets in his berth. Did those mugs sweat!

But when the train reached San Francisco, and they got out in the air, they were shivering. And sore! They took it out on St. Mary's. Bones snapped like garters on a Coney Island Saturday night, and there seemed a never-ending procession of stretcher-bearers interrupting the game. We won 46–0. It was the worst any Coast outfit had ever been beaten by an Eastern team since the war. All the New York papers sent staff men to cover the game, and there were play-by-play accounts in the late editions the same afternoon.

As a special treat for our undefeated, unscored-upon gladiators, the Chief threw a banquet at the St. Francis Hotel that night at which everybody down to the lowest sub made a speech. Brick talked of next year and spring training; Mike sang "Mother Machree"; while the Councilor brought tears to all eyes by his disquisition on "Football as a Character Builder." After the banquet he spent the rest of the night hunting for the Barbary Coast.

Altogether, it was a wonderful season for a first year. We had beaten the pants off three major teams and scored 426 points. Nobody had been able to cross our goal line or even score a safety against us. To be sure, 426 points weren't as many as those Michigan juggernaut teams used to run up. For five consecutive years they averaged 526 points a season. But they used to play ten- and eleven-game schedules, while we had played only eight.

Of course, blocking is the quintessence of winning football. And our wrestlers, with their tremendous strength and specialized knowledge of how to throw an opponent off his balance or on his back and even dislocate or break his bones, made probably the best linemen that ever played football. And the boxers, with their speed and wonderful sense of coordination, became excellent ball carriers. Of course, their defensive play, especially against a forward passing attack, was crude that first season. But whenever an opponent successfully executed a forward pass, the successful executants—the back who passed and the end who caught the ball—would be out of the game after the next play with dislocated hips, and there would be no more of *that* nonsense for a while.

But the actual end of the season was not yet. One night two weeks after the St. Mary's game I was at the Chief's suite when Mike and the Councilor came in. The Councilor was carrying a brief case.

"O.K.," said the Chief, glancing at the brief case.

He led the way into an adjoining room. The Councilor opened the brief case. And there on the bed before my goggling eyes were counted out one million, one hundred dollars in $5,000,

$1,000 and $100 bills, and the whole was cut up 50–25–25.

The Chief counted his cut once more, opened a little wall safe behind an oil painting, tossed the hippo-choking roll in, twirled the knob, and carefully set the picture straight.

"This here education is gonna be all right," he said. His face was very serious.

As soon as spring came Brick had the whole squad out plus about twenty young fighters who had turned pro that winter and a couple of dozen young wrestlers. The new arrivals he herded off into a freshman squad and began to break them in on fundamentals. Last season's players were drilled in kicking and passing.

Brick realized he'd have to teach his team something to vary the bone-crushing, slaughterhouse game that came to them so naturally. If he could develop a skillful, spectacular forward-passing attack, it would be a better draw at the gate, and something had to be done to cut down the terrible casualty lists we had left in our wake the first season, or the sports writers and the Rules Committee and the various college athletic authorities might get suspicious and mark us for lousy, as the boys say; that is, refuse to give us a game, and then we'd have to play the barber colleges or the Alexander Hamilton Institute.

So all that spring and summer, Brick had the squad catching and throwing passes. He taught the boys to grab the ball with their arms relaxed from the elbows down and their fingers limp; and he taught the passers to throw a few yards ahead of the receivers away to hell and gone down the field. Brick didn't believe in short, flat passes: what he liked were the ones that looked as though they came out of the Boche 70-mile gun and flew right over the heads of the secondary defense into the paws of some galloping end or half.

Those were the plays that made the turnstiles click, so we concentrated on them. By the time fall came around every member of the squad, even Tossilitis, could collar a 40- or 50-yard pass almost behind his back.

Then he concentrated on kicking. In the spring the Chief sent over to France and imported three *savate* fighters, Cocluche, Plon and Moustiquaire, figuring they ought to make great kickers. You know, the *savate* fighters do all their boxing with their feet. Well, the Chief's hunch was O.K.: they turned into swell kickers right off, averaging 60 and 70 yards each and Moustiquaire could sometimes stretch his punts to 80, but they were all such little guys that they were broken to pieces before the first week's scrimmaging was over and had to be shipped back to Paris. Anyway, they weren't needed, as Brick had developed both Switz and Flanahan, a left-footer, into a pair of fine punters by the time the season started.

Then the Chief decided that this season our opponents should be allowed to do some scoring, as it would make the games more exciting and benefit the gate. So it was agreed that every time one of the opponents threw a pass of fifteen yards or more he should be allowed to complete it (providing, of course, that it was not muffed or grounded) and we were ahead far enough so that a touchdown wouldn't matter.

This system led to almost uniform results. The Thundering Pachyderms would go to work and run up about four touchdowns in the first half. We still used the Canarsie Funnel, as it was a sure-fire gag to bring the customers to their feet; but after a while rival coaches warned their captains not to kick off to us if they won the toss, so we couldn't start the game with it unless the coin spun our way. (If we had made our four touchdowns in the first half, we didn't use it if it was our turn to receive.) Then, in the second quarter, we'd let our opponents run the ball up to midfield, if we had kicked to them, or purposely fumble the ball, if it were ours, and let them recover.

On or about the 50-yard line, however, we'd turn into a stone wall, so that they'd be forced to open up and start passing. Then we'd let them make about three touchdowns and all the customers went home with a warm glow, each satisfied that he'd got his money's worth.

I'd done a lot of traveling that winter and we had a fine schedule. Whenever a school didn't have a stadium of its own or wasn't in a big city where a good gate would be assured, we used the nearest big-league ball park. That New Year's Day we played Southern California in the Rose Bowl at Pasadena before 80,000, beat them 28–21 and won the Erskine trophy, emblematic of the National Intercollegiate Football Championship.

These were the scores of that second season:

Canarsie 28—Washington and Jefferson 21 (Polo Grounds)
Canarsie 28—Pittsburgh 21 (Forbes Field)
Canarsie 28—Colgate 20 (Yankee Stadium)
Canarsie 28—Michigan 26 (Ann Arbor)
Canarsie 28—Ohio State 18 (Columbus, O.)
Canarsie 28—Missouri 21 (Columbia, Mo.)
Canarsie 28—Navy 21 (Baltimore)
Canarsie 28—Army 21 (Polo Grounds)
Canarsie 28—Southern California 21 (Pasadena)

Some time in the middle of January we gathered around the Chief's bed, and on this occasion the roll they cut totaled $1,900,000, including gambling returns, or as the Chief put it: "With tips and all."

That winter and spring passed pretty uneventfully. There were the usual murders, but nothing outside the routine killings that always come along. Legs Diamond was shot for the eleventh time as thousands yawned. Professional boxing and wrestling were virtually nonexistent; but nobody seemed to notice. The only fights of any account that year were the finals in Paul Gallico's Golden Gloves Tournament, which were postponed until the summer and moved out to the Yankee Stadium and substituted for the usual Milk Fund Heavyweight Battle of the Century. Everyone was more pleased, including the Milk Fund.

The Councilor was doing a good deal of lushing. Most of his days were spent in his rooms, snoring off hangovers; at night he teetered about more or less in the gauze. It was certainly a break that there were no big cases up just then that required his personal attention, cases that couldn't be taken care of by his assistants —say the trial of some important members of the mob for murder—because there was no telling what might have happened. The guy was so irresistible to any dozen mugs he ever faced in a jury box. If he'd had a case, he probably would have pleaded with them to send his client to the electric chair. And it would have been curtains for the client, all right, if the Councilor had asked for it.

A funny thing happened that summer. The Chief had opened up a new joint, the Varsity Inn, on part of the take from that second season. It was decorated with more college seals than there are in the gents' only at the Paramount Theater and became a great hangout for gamblers and hustlers of all kinds. One day a big strapping apple-knocker with a straw suitcase came in and asked the bartender if he could direct him to Canarsie University. He said he was from some high school out in the sticks and wanted to enroll as a student. Mike, who happened to be there at the time, gave the bartender the office, and the apple-knocker was told to take the subway. All summer long, kids kept coming to the joint, wanting to know how to get to Canarsie. They'd looked in the telephone books and asked the Travelers' Aid, but although everyone had heard of the place, nobody had actually *been* there. We just told them to take the subway. Nothing was ever heard of them again. They're probably still wandering around, lost in that vast labyrinth.

I had arranged a great schedule for the coming season. Not only did we have games with the Army and Navy again and Notre Dame and Leland Stanford, but we were taking on Princeton, Yale and Harvard in the order named, merely for tune-ups at the start. We weren't going to wind up the season on the Coast again, but instead we were to finish off at Soldier Field in Chicago with Lake Shore Tech, a new school that had had a fine first season the year before. They were so anxious to get a game with us that they guaranteed us seven-tenths of the gate. Obviously they wanted to play us for the prestige.

The Chief jumped at the chance, as our troupe had never played Chicago; and ever since that Tunney-Dempsey fight back in '27 it had been his ambition to count the house there some day. The stadium was then still the largest in the country. So I wrote the Lake Shore graduate manager that we should be delighted.

The Councilor kept right on lushing. I was stopped one night at Forty-first Street and Seventh Avenue by a letter carrier who told me I'd better come along with him. We went over to the other side of Eighth, and he led the way up some stairs to a door and rang a bell. A peephole opened and he said: "O.K., Jerry."

It was one of those little neighborhood joints that smelled of yesterday's beer and had a bowl of cole slaw on the free-lunch counter. The cole slaw changed three colors if you forked it around a little. A knot of taxi drivers and laborers in shirt sleeves was gathered at one end of the bar. At the other was the Councilor. He was shaking his finger at his reflection in the mirror. It made your flesh creep as he began trying to break the reflection down, just as though it were a prosecution witness in a trial. Every now and then he would turn to the terrified bartender and speak to him as though he were the judge.

"You'll be open with me, won't you?" he said to himself with a horrible sneer on those thick lips. "Now, what do you do for a living, Mr. Julheim? Oh, a tailor, eh? A tailor. You don't mean a pants-presser, do you? No, never mind that, answer yes or no. Yes, you're just a pants-presser, aren't you? Not a tailor at all, are you? Isn't it a fact, Mr. Julheim, that you couldn't sew a button on, and as for a lapel—you'd be *lost, wouldn't you?* Answer yes or no. You would, wouldn't you? Yes, you're really not a

tailor at all, are you—just a pants-presser."

"Geez, Mac, take it easy," pleaded the bartender.

"All right, Your Honor, I'm just attacking the credibility of the witness. Very well, Your Honor, we respectfully except. . . . Now, Mr. Julheim, you say the defendant's face was white when you saw him come out of the room. You testified before Magistrate Wilson that his face was as white as a collar, didn't you? Well, did you or didn't you? Yes, you did. Well, was it *this white?*"

And the Councilor ripped off his starched collar and shook it at his reflection in the mirror. His big brown eyeballs rolled. *"Here's a collar! Was it this white? Was his face as white as this?"*

The postman and I led him out brandishing the ripped-off collar and jabbering about subornation of perjury. We finally got him back to the Argonne and in bed. The house physician gave him a stab.

It seemed the Councilor was cracking up.

The Chief, after looking over the team at the end of the summer workout and seeing what superb form it was in, decided on a new plan of strategy for the third season.

As I said before, during our second season we allowed our opponents to score three touchdowns in the last half after we had scored four in the first.

For the third season, the Chief thought it would improve showmanship if we allowed the other teams to score four touchdowns in the first half; and then we'd get in there and score five in the second. It is always more thrilling when a team comes from behind and wins out, especially if it is from 24 to 28 points behind. And it turned out to be a great gag. In addition, the system had wonderful gambling possibilities: between halves, with the score four touchdowns to nothing against us, the betting commissioners could get wonderful odds.

We opened the season with Princeton at the Palmer Memorial Stadium and took them 35–27, coming from behind in the last thirty seconds on a long pass, Switz to Woola. The following Saturday we beat the Elis in the Bowl 35–28. The next week Harvard fell 28–19. The score was lower than usual because the Crimson suffered from a bad epidemic of fumbling in the first half and couldn't score four touchdowns, no matter how hard we tried. Then we cleaned the Army (35–27) and the Navy (35–26).

Brick was taking no chances with Notre Dame, however, and we opened up with the old Canarsie Funnel right at the kickoff and ran up five touchdowns in the first half. Hunk Anderson had an unusually weak team that year, and they were able to score only a field goal. But what a field goal: a tremendous long boot from the 61-yard line and worthy of the immortal Gipp! Switz did not make the trip to South Bend.

On the next three Saturdays we restored the virility of the effete East by toying with Leland Stanford (35–0), Southern California (35–0) and Oregon (35–0) before vast crowds in the Yankee Stadium. The Chief figured that plenty of Eastern fans would be willing to pay dough to see some of those Coast teams take a good shellacking, for a change. And he was right.

The Sunday after we hung it on Oregon, Brick and I were at the Chief's, waiting for Mike, who had gone to Chicago to scout the Lake Shore-Nebraska game. The Chief was in his big chair. Voine, black-lace-pajamaed, was sitting on the arm. One of those goofy dolls with the squiggly legs she held snuggled up to her. Every now and then she would make a pass at the Chief, and he would duck and spar her off as though she were some kind of fly. He was discussing the future.

"I been figuring," he was saying, "if there ain't some way to make a buck out of these other college sports. It strikes me there ought to be something in this here basketball for us. I figure there is if we could get a big enough house, say if we could fill up the Garden oncet a week. They tell me basketball ain't made a dime since the rules was drawed up. Maybe, if we put on a swell floor show in between halves, or had a dance afterwards with plenty of our dames mixing in the crowd."

"Oo naughty sing," purred Voine, trying to muss his hair. "Oo wet dose dirls awone. Don't be finkin' about 'em so muts."

The Chief gave her a look and parried with his left. He pulled out his watch.

"What's keeping Mike?" he said. "He ought to show any minute now. It's ten after eight. The big loogan musta stooped somewheres to grab a few shots. Well, anyways, I'm trying to figure some new angles on this education racket. Basketball maybe, if the public will go for a side show. Hockey's all sewed up by the pros, and ain't no good anyways. College baseball's a laugh. There might be something to this foot racing, if you didn't have to cut the gate with so many people. When one school runs another, there ain't anybody there but the towel-holders.

When there's a big meet you got to cut the gate fifty ways. Now this rowing, maybe if you could fence off a couple miles of the Hudson on both sides—"

The ring of the door buzzer by the gorilla outside cut into this discourse. Voine got up and got a cigarette off the ebony table.

"There's Mike now," said the Chief. "Let him in, Kid."

Without bothering to ask over the phone who it was I opened the door.

On the threshold, swaying slightly, stood the Councilor. He was stiff as a plank. There was a wide smile on his face. On his arm, Fanny McGloin, presumably just back from her world tour.

"S'prise, s'prise!" the Councilor muttered.

Fanny took four steps into the room and then paused, unable to make up her mind whether to go to work on the Chief or Voine. Finally, she chose Voine, but during that brief pause Brick and I rushed and held her.

"I knew it'd be like this," she screamed, struggling fiercely. "I knew I'd fine that trollop here! Lemme at her till I pull that yeller mop offen her ugly head! Lemme at her!"

Voine had backed up against the table, frozen.

"Willya listen, Fanny," pleaded the Chief, "willya listen!"

Then she tractored her fingernails down my cheek as she tried to get at *him*.

"And as for *you*, you doidy bum, you," she squalled, "wait till I get my hands on you! You doidy bum, you! You come outa the gutter and that's where you belong, you doidy bum, you! I'll give you night goils, you doidy beast!"

She stopped her struggling for a little to catch her breath. Then she tried to spit on Voine. Women are lousy spitters. Suddenly Mike was in the room.

"Why, hahzit, Fanneee!" he roared, coming over to her and forcibly taking her hand and pumping it up and down. "Hahzit, bebee! Geez, it's great to see you. Whenja get in? How ya doin' in there, palleee?"

"You get outa my way, Mike Dumphy," Fanny yelled. "Lemme at that doidy bum. Him and that thing of his. I'll give 'em a honeymoon. Lemme at 'em!"

Mike was pumping her hand up and down and patting her shoulder.

"Why, there ain't nothin' wrong, is there, bebee?" he bellowed. "You ain't sore at the tomato here, are ya? Why, this here's Voine, my gal. I'm just after comin' up here to fetch her. I been outa town, same as you have, and she got lonesome and come upstairs here to wait for me, didn'ya bebee?"

He shot a tremendous burlesque-show wink at Voine, who rallied and managed to nod her head up and down, like a counting horse.

"Nobody got a girl frien' for me?" the Councilor put in thickly.

Mike went right on roaring.

"Did you think Voine was Frankie's tomato, Fanny? Geez, that's a laugh, ain't it, Voine? Why, Voine's my little gal, ain't you, bebee? You got Voine all wrong, Fanny. Why, say, if I caught a mug like Frankie McGloin foolin' with Voine I'd punch him right in the nose, wouldn't I, Voine? I'm levelin', Fanny, honest to God. Ain't that the truth, boys? Well Fanny, it's great to see you again. I know you got plenty to talk over with Frankie about your wonderful trip and all, so I'll say good night. We better scram, boys, and let the happy pair get together."

He walked over to Voine, grabbed a couple of arms and hands full of her, and gave her a long noisy kiss that ended with a bang.

"Glad to see me, bebee? Was you a good gal while I was out in Chi?"

Brick and I had let go of Fanny. She was looking at Mike and Voine with everything she had. Mike went into his act harder than ever, and used everything but a knife and fork on his partner.

"How'd you make out in Chicago?" asked Brick.

"O.K.," said Mike, pausing a moment. "Come on downstairs, bebee," he said to Voine, "I brought you a present."

He started for the door with her under his arm. She was afraid to look back at the Chief, for fear Fanny would see.

"What's the payoff on Lake Shore?" Brick yelled to him.

He stopped on the threshold and turned around.

"Geez, that's a pip," he said, and went into a loud laugh. The Councilor started to laugh, and we were all in such a state that we laughed, too. The Chief laughed and even Fanny smiled. It sounded crazy as hell.

"Yes, sir, that's a pip," said Mike. *The jernt belongs to Capone!* Well, good night, all."

He dragged Voine out with him.

It was like a quick first-act curtain.

There was a large solid block of gray-blue almost exactly in the middle of the Capone stands which I was trying to determine the cause of. Mike, beside me in our box on the 50-yard line, had brought a pair of binoculars, the kind the bookies carry at the tracks.

"Take a squint through your glasses, Mike, at those people over there. It looks like a bunch of French soldiers."

With great gravity Mike raised the binoculars to his eyes and adjusted the micrometer screw. He chuckled softly.

"It looks from here like they was mail carriers," he said. "Must be the boys from the Postal Workers' Union givin' their dogs a holiday."

"Aha, mail carriers!"

"Yeah, that's what it looks like from here they was. Must be havin' a convention or sumpen. And the little Doctor heard about it and sent 'em all to the ball game. That guy always did have a yen for the U.S. mail."

He passed me the glasses.

"Yeah, they're mail carriers, all right. But it doesn't look as though they were here on any outing. They all seem to have brought their leather bags along, and the bags look full."

"Mebbe they got sumpen for somebody. Get a load of the little Doctor."

The Chief was standing on his iron chair, carefully counting the house of 110,000, trying on his fingers to deduct the nonpaying customers from the paying.

There was a roar from the Capone side of the field as a long stream of black-helmeted, black-jerseyed, black-panted, black-hosed, black-booted players, most of them of swarthy complexion, flowed out onto the field from a tunnel under the stands, divided up into four teams and began running through signals. Their band struck up "Giovanezza, Primavera." But a moment later there were four puce-and-green teams on the field and our band was blaring the buttons off its instruments in a counter-rendition of "Old Canarsie o' Mine."

You could smell the stink of trouble beginning to spread as soon as those bands started to out-umpah each other. And matters weren't helped when the Lake Shore band spelled out: "Kill Kanarsie" in the middle of the field a few minutes later. Immediately after they had finished, Ernie Norvelle blew his whistle and our band came back with a bit of clever repartee: "Louse Up Lake Shore."

Our rivals had worked out a novel variation of the old skyrocket: instead of giving the long whistle rising to a crescendo and the conventional *Boom!—aaaaah!,* their rooters, teeth clenched and eyeballs wild, would slowly swell from their seats with horrible cries—half hiss,

half growl—saw their necks with imaginary
stilettos, à la Tossilitis, and then point to our
stands with wild yells of: "Canarsie, Canarsie,
tutti, tutti, tutti!"

Such black curses would have jelled our blood
had not the ingenious Ernie devised a sure
means of passing them off lightly by plucking
from the band half a dozen double-bass tuba
players and forming them into a battery which
greeted every massed Sicilian imprecation with
prehistoric birds.

The two captains were in the center of the
field. The referee spun a coin. Switz won the
toss and chose to kick with the wind. Oolaafsen
teed the ball; the team ranged itself on either
side of him along our 35-yard line; a whistle
beeped; there was a dull thump. The ball flew
in a beautiful high parabola straight to the arms
of the Lake Shore quarterback.

Imagaine our dismay when he ran 95 yards
for a touchdown behind a perfectly executed
Canarsie Funnel!

They kicked goal.

But then we received, and little McGloin was
funneled 100 yards just as perfectly for a touchdown in return, and Oolaafsen tied the score by
putting the ball straight between the posts.

This time, after a huddle in which apparently
Oolaafsen was instructed not to kick to the
Capone backs, the ball went to their left tackle
on their 30-yard line and he was down before
he had run three steps.

Lake Shore opened with a wide end run
around Oolaafsen, which he smeared; but before the next play began Tossilitis, world's
champion of the week three years ago, was
removed from the game with a pair of dislocated
hips. A little later, Hazos the Horrible was
similarly afflicted and had to be hauled off.

Mike whistled.

"The Capone mob always was famous for
stealin' the other guys' stuff, but I never expected nothin' like this. Well, I ain't surprised.
They got the whole Pacific Coast troupe of
wrasslers on their club, and all the fighters
around this here section. It's a laugh on the little
Doctor, at that. He give Gilligan orders before
the game, to hell with the customers, but give
them Capones the woiks. You know, plenty of
that old slugaroo, like we done the foist season.
It's all on account the way he hates Capone.
Capone ain't a bad guy, but the little Doctor's
been after him ever since he got outa Leving-
woith. He clipped the Doc in a deal. So he
orders the woiks from Gilligan, and here they
are lettin' us have it. Ain't that a laugh?"

But just then Lake Shore punted, and on the
next play we put their left tackle out of the
game with a broken instep. Two plays after
that the casualty list was neck and neck. The
Chief leaned over to Mike. His eyes were on
fire:

"Mike!" he yelled, cupping his mouth with a
hand, for the Canarsie cheering section was
roaring delightedly as the body of our enemy
was borne from the field, "scram down to Gilligan and tell him to take all them fighters outa
that game and put nothin' but wrasslers in there
'til I tell him to stop. And tell him to make
them wrasslers plenty big and tough. And tell
him to tell them mugs to get in there and give
them Capone guinzos the woiks or I'll be down
and cut their heads off. Tell 'em no holds
barred. Now, scram."

"O.K., Frankie," and Mike had disappeared.

So that was why, when the half ended,
twenty-nine of our baboons and thirty of theirs
(we put two out on the last play) had been
dragged wounded from the field. Stretcher-
bearers on both sides certainly earned their pay
that day. And that was why the football that
first half, after what the Chief ordered, was not
very interesting to watch. For with 300-pound
wrestlers carrying the ball and directing the field
generalship (Lake Shore had quickly followed
our lead in bringing out the mastodons) the
ball remained almost stationary in the middle
of the field. At the whistle the score was still
7–7.

We all went down to the dressing room between halves, so I don't know what unpleasantness took place in the stadium or how the cops
kept the rival factions from climbing out of the
stands and going to work on each other.

There was enough unpleasantness in our
dressing room, filled as it was with stretchers
of the groaning. Doc Dreen and a corps of trainers, rubbers and towel-swingers were rushing
about ministering to the patients. It was like a
base hospital after a heavy bombardment at the
Western front.

"Get all these mugs outa here and on the
train," was the Chief's first command.

Brick was standing in a corner, pale and
shaky.

"How we fixed?" The Chief looked him over
with a hard eye.

"God, Chief, I, uh, we're running outa wrasslers. That's hell on 'em out there."

"Nuts!"

It was the old Wiper war cry. You could feel
the voltage in the voice.

"All youse mugs 'at's in shape, c'mere."

He swept the quick and the able with those

terrible eyes as he began panthering up and down, his hands folded behind him.

"Now listen, youse. Foist of all, the fighters goes back in this half. Switz! Flanahan! Cello! McGloin! And you Oolaaf, you big screwy Swede, and you, Woola We're gonna pass 'em to death, see, pass 'em to death, right from the bell, see? And youse mugs inna line, give 'em plenty protection, see, or *it'll be jest too bad*. And 'at goes for youse ends and backs, too, see. The mug 'at muffs a pass or heaves one wild— well, *it'll be jest too—*"

The Chief broke off, scrambled to the top of a locker and clawed at a tiny wire cleated to the wall. There was a ripping and a banging of metal against metal, and then, up over the locker's top, he reeled in a little japanned box that looked like the bottom part of an electric bell.

"A dictygraph, hey, the doity, double-crossin' grease-ball rats! Well, let 'em get a load of it."

He began screaming frantically into the little box.

"Nuts! Nuts! Nuts! And 'at goes for you, too, Capone, you big guinzo grease-ball! This here's McGloin speakin'. Yeah, Knucks McGloin, you big Bohunk, you! And get this—"

Mike touched him on the arm and pointed to the broken-off end of the dictograph wire lying on the floor.

Brick looked at his stop watch and said in a weak voice that it was time to return to the field.

They kicked off to us, but a Canarsie Funnel failed to put the ball back farther than the middle of the field. We just didn't have the wrestlers for it. On the first play Switz whipped a short pass to McGloin which gained 8 yards. Another to Woola brought us 6 more and first down. A long heave to Flanahan was batted down by a Lake Shore halfback. Then McGloin tossed a short one to Cello that was good for 9. By way of variation, Swtiz went off tackle for 3, and it was first down again. Switz lobbed another to McGloin for 7.

Half a dozen consecutive plays without a single casualty! Evidently, they, too, were running out of wrestlers.

Switz cocked his arm and threw one a mile down the field to Oolaafsen, who caught it and had started for a touchdown with a clear field when two Lake Shore backs hit him at once— and he fumbled.

Up in the box we had to hold the Chief to keep him from climbing right out onto the field and cutting that Swede's head off.

Lake Shore got off a beautiful punt to our 20-yard line, and their ends nailed McGloin as soon as he touched the ball. The kick had come down near a side line, so on the first play McGloin ran himself straight across to the center of the field.

Switz was back with his arms outstretched, the ball was snapped, he cocked his arm, and there, clear, away down the field was Woola, good old basketball Woola, who could catch anything that stayed in the park. A sure touchdown!

And then, suddenly, like a wild goose shot in midflight, the ball stopped dead in its arc and dropped straight to the ground, right smack on the 50-yard line. It was as though it had struck an invisible wire. But when it hit the ground it neither bounced nor bobbed, just parked where it landed, like a coffee cake.

White-knickered officials and players had run up to it. There was much arm-waving. Mike was gazing through his binoculars.

"It's Switz," he said. "Switz has got it in his hands. He's stickin' his fingers right through it."

"Through what, you muzzler?"

"Right through the ball. They's a hole in it big enough to jump through."

The Chief's curses could be heard clearly above the roar of the crowd.

"We been jobbed!" he roared, ripping off his hat and tearing his hair. "Them lousy wops shot it down. They put it onna spot. It was inna bag for a touchdown and they put it onna spot. Oh, them lousy wop grease-balls!"

Down on the field the white-knickered puppets were fluttering rule books. Evidently they found no provision for assassinated footballs; for, after a great deal of argument they procured another from the side lines and the referee marched with it back to our 20-yard line. "Second down. 10 yards to gain. Incompleted forward pass," announced the scoreboard.

Lake Shore cheers were equaled by our boos.

"Maxim silencer?" I asked Mike, remembering there had been no report when the ball pancaked.

"Sure," he said. He was sweeping the Capone stands with the binoculars.

"Lookit! There's the mug done it. There, see? Right where I'm point at."

He handed me the glasses and, sure enough, in the top row about the center of the stands I saw a tall, slender man, dark and mustached, with a rifle to his shoulder at the ready. The rifle had a telescopic sight, I noticed. The dark sharpshooter turned to make some remark to a man beside him and when he smiled I noticed he had beautiful even teeth. Over the muzzle of the rifle was a pear-shaped silencer.

Three consecutive short passes brought the ball from our 20-yard line to the middle of the field. Switz tossed a beauty to Oolaafsen for 20 more.

Then the dark sharpshooter spoiled another sure touchdown when he murdered a long pass just before it reached Flanahan standing well over the goal line. It was a beautiful heave and a beautiful shot. After a terrific squabble, the referee ruled that the ball had grounded over the goal line, and therefore it was a touchback and Lake Shore's ball on their 25-yard line.

The Chief was fit to be tied, and I remember wondering why blue flames were not pouring from his palpitating noseholes.

"Mike," he bellowed, "go over there to that mob and tell them Capones, them bohunk so-and-so's, that if they don't lay off they get the woiks, see, the woiks!"

Mike looked at him curiously for a second, patted the armpit holster under his breast pocket, laughed, handed me the binoculars and departed, singing softly:

" 'Tis the most distressful country that I have ever seen."

Lake Shore punted immediately, long and high, and little McGloin was again flattened by their ends on our 20-yard line.

Once more three short flat passes brought us to the middle of the field.

I trained the glasses on the dark sharpshooter and caught him in the act of changing the rifle with a telescopic sight for what appeared to be a double-barreled shotgun.

Switz had cocked his arm. There was Woola loose again and running as though all the fiends of hell were chasing him. And there went the ball after him as though all the fiends of hell were in its leather casing.

I saw the dark sharpshooter aim, and I saw the fingers of his right hand contract as though he were slowly squeezing a sponge.

The ball in mid-flight had suddenly vanished. He had scored a direct hit with both barrels!

I turned in horror to look at the Chief. He had disappeared.

After much puzzled gazing up into the sky, followed by a molten debate between the rival captains, the officials decided to penalize us for unsportsmanlike conduct in having concealed the ball.

Our winded warriors lay on their backs panting, while the referee with the new pigskin under his arm began pacing off the 15-yard penalty. The Lake Shore team was drawn up in a huddle.

Suddenly, a dumpy figure in an old black sweater and battered cap darted out from our bench onto the field with a water bucket. Instead, however, of making for the spent forces of old Canarsie he hared straight for the huddle. A few paces from it, he groped in his bucket for his sponge, found it, seemed to give it a squeeze and then tossed it straight in the hub of the human wheel.

There was a flash, and a terrific explosion went echoing through the stadium. The little water carrier was tearing back toward our bench. It was the Chief.

"Scraaaam! Scraaaam!" he screamed, waving the bucket he was still holding by the handle. "Scraaaam!"

The field was strewn with black-helmeted heads, black-jerseyed torsos, black-hosed legs.

Another moment and the Capone machine guns had opened on the puce-and-green figures on the field which had suddenly sat up when the bomb went off. One after another they all lay down again.

Then the block of blue figures in the middle of the Lake Shore stands rose as one man and began to bomb all points of the compass.

The crowd stampeded.

Don't ask me how I ever got out of that thing alive. Somehow I did, but just how I couldn't tell you. I remember being carried all the way out of the stands to the ground without once putting a foot down. I remember the dames screaming and the yells of the wounded and I remember the furious ringing of ambulance bells and the bombs roaring and the machine guns rattling away like riveting hammers. I remember the cops losing their heads and starting to club anybody they could reach. One big bull reached over and caught me one on the head with his billy and I went out like a light.

When I came to I was standing outside the stadium, wondering how I got there and supposing I had been sardined out in the crowd. The Chief was standing in front me. He was drenched with sweat and dirt, and most of the old sweater and shirt were torn off, and the peak of his cap was around 'way to one side. He was helping two letter carriers load some big canvas sacks into a black car with the curtains up. The Councilor was parked in the back seat.

"Hahzit, Kid?" he said. "You O.K.? We're just after kicking in the main box office. This here's the gate. I'm taking it on the lam to Deetroit 'til this blows over. Tell the boys I'm O.K. and I'll be back in about a month."

He opened a back door of the car and put a foot on the running board.

"Listen," he said, "it looks like Canarsie University was all washed up for a while. Did you know they got Mike, them lousy Bohunks?"

"They did? God, that's terrible."

"We'll see 'em for it. Tell the mob I'm O.K."

"Sure, Chief. Geez, I'm sorry about poor old Mike."

"Yeah, 'at was tough. Tell Voine I'll drop her a card. All set, boys?"

"O.K., Chief," said one of the gorillas as the last of the day's gross proceeds were swung into the tonneau over the Councilor's feet. "You wanna drive?"

"Yeah, I'll drive," said the Chief, climbing in behind the steering wheel. "We ain't got room for you, Kid. Tell you what you do. Ed Grogan is just leaving over there, look, by that ambulance. See where I'm pointing at? Scram over there, now, and he'll give you a lift. So long, Kid. Hurry up, now."

I started to run over to where the Grogan car was just starting, waving over my shoulder to the Chief.

He stepped on the starter. There was a flash and a terrible explosion. Some of the heavy metal work of the car came down, but they never found a button of the Chief or the Councilor or the letter carriers. The Capones had fastened an extra-special bomb on the starting mechanism of the car. An old gag, but effective. So that's why Canarsie University hasn't had a team in the field for the last couple of seasons.

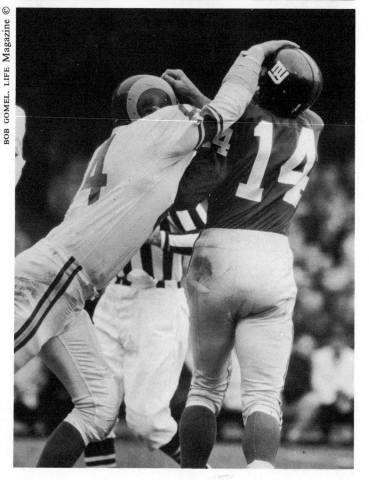

One of the surest, quickest ways to a touchdown in football is to let Tittle do the pitching. Y. A. Tittle, former Baltimore Colt and San Francisco 49er, has led the New York Giants to three consecutive championship playoffs with the best-developed pass offense in the game. To achieve his rank as the pros' No. 1 passer, Tittle spent years of learning, throwing—and taking it.

PROFESSIONAL PITCH . . .

. . . **AND PUNCH**

Around, over and through the enemy ranks, All-Pro Fullback Jimmy Brown
of Cleveland has run up the greatest total yardage of any back
in pro football. On his own or behind a screen of blockers,
Brown offers the defense the ultimate challenge: first, try
to reach me and *then* try to bring me down!

UPI   BOB GOMEL. LIFE Magazine ©

THE EIGHTY-YARD RUN

Irwin Shaw

The pass was high and wide and he jumped for it, feeling it slap flatly against his hands, as he shook his hips to throw off the halfback who was driving at him. The center floated by, his hands desperately brushing Darling's knee as Darling picked his feet up high and delicately ran over a blocker and an opposing linesman in a jumble on the ground near the scrimmage line. He had 10 yards in the clear and picked up speed, breathing easily, feeling his thigh pads rising and falling against his legs, listening to the sound of cleats behind him, pulling away from them, watching the other backs heading him off toward the sideline, the whole picture, the men closing in on him, the blockers fighting for position, the ground he had to cross, all suddenly clear in his head, for the first time in his life not a meaningless confusion of men, sound, speed. He smiled a little to himself as he ran, holding the ball lightly in front of him with his two hands, his knees pumping high, his hips twisting in the almost girlish run of a back in a broken field. The first halfback came at him and he fed him his leg, then swung at the last moment, took the shock of the man's shoulder without breaking stride, ran right through him, his cleats biting securely into the turf. There was only the safety man now, coming warily at him, his arms crooked, hands spread. Darling tucked the ball in, spurted at him, driving hard, hurling himself along, all 200 pounds bunched into controlled attack. He was sure he was going to get past the safety man. Without thought, his arms and legs working beautifully together, he headed right for the safety man, stiff-armed him, feeling blood spurt instantaneously from the man's nose onto his hand, seeing his face go awry, head turned, mouth pulled to one side. He pivoted away, keeping the arm locked, dropping the safety man as he ran easily toward the goal line, with the drumming of cleats diminishing behind him.

How long ago? It was autumn then, and the ground was getting hard because the nights were cold and leaves from the maples around the stadium blew across the practice fields in gusts of wind, and the girls were beginning to put polo coats over their sweaters when they came to watch practice in the afternoons . . . Fifteen years. Darling walked slowly over the same ground in the spring twilight, in his neat shoes, a man of thirty-five dressed in a double-breasted suit, ten pounds heavier in the fifteen years, but not fat, with the years between 1925 and 1940 showing in his face.

The coach was smiling quietly to himself and the assistant coaches were looking at each other with pleasure the way they always did when one of the second stringers suddenly did something fine, bringing credit to them, making their $2,000 a year a tiny bit more secure.

Darling trotted back, smiling, breathing

deeply but easily, feeling wonderful, not tired, though this was the tail end of practice and he'd run 80 yards. The sweat poured off his face and soaked his jersey and he liked the feeling, the warm moistness lubricating his skin like oil. Off in a corner of the field some players were punting and the smack of leather against the ball came pleasantly through the afternoon air. The freshmen were running signals on the next field and the quarterback's sharp voice, the pound of the eleven pairs of cleats, the "Dig, now *dig!*" of the coaches, the laughter of the players all somehow made him feel happy as he trotted back to midfield listening to the applause and shouts of the students along the sidelines, knowing that after that run the coach would have to start him Saturday against Illinois.

Fifteen years, Darling thought, remembering the shower after the workout, the hot water steaming off his skin and the deep soapsuds and all the young voices singing with the water streaming down and towels going and managers running in and out and the sharp sweet smell of oil of wintergreen and everybody clapping him on the back as he dressed and Packard, the captain, who took being captain very seriously, coming over to him and shaking his hand and saying, "Darling, you're going to go places in the next two years."

The assistant manager fussed over him, wiping a cut on his leg with alcohol and iodine, the little sting making him realize suddenly how fresh and whole and solid his body felt. The manager slapped a piece of adhesive tape over the cut, and Darling noticed the sharp clean white of the tape against the ruddiness of the skin, fresh from the shower.

He dressed slowly, the softness of his shirt and the soft warmth of his wool socks and his flannel trousers a reward against his skin after the harsh pressure of the shoulder harness and thigh and hip pads. He drank three glasses of cold water, the liquid reaching down coldly inside of him, soothing the harsh dry places in his throat and belly left by the sweat and running and shouting of practice.

Fifteen years.

The sun had gone down and the sky was green behind the stadium and he laughed quietly to himself as he looked at the stadium, rearing above the trees, and knew that on Saturday when the 70,000 voices roared as the team came running out onto the field, part of that enormous salute would be for him. He walked slowly, listening to the gravel crunch satisfactorily under his shoes in the still twilight, feeling his clothes swing lightly against his skin, breathing the thin evening air, feeling the wind move softly in his damp hair, wonderfully cool behind his ears and at the nape of his neck.

Louise was waiting for him at the road, in her car. The top was down and he noticed all over again, as he always did when he saw her, how pretty she was, the rough blond hair and the large, inquiring eyes and the bright mouth, smiling now.

She threw the door open. "Were you good today?" she asked.

"Pretty good," he said. He climbed in, sank luxuriously into the soft leather, stretched his legs far out. He smiled, thinking of the 80 yards. "Pretty damn good."

She looked at him seriously for a moment, then scrambled around, like a little girl, kneeling on the seat next to him, grabbed him, her hands along his ears, and kissed him as he sprawled, head back, on the seat cushion. She let go of him, but kept her head close to his, over his. Darling reached up slowly and rubbed the back of his hand against her cheek, lit softly by a street lamp a hundred feet away. They looked at each other, smiling.

Louise drove down to the lake and they sat there silently, watching the moon rise behind the hills on the other side. Finally he reached over, pulled her gently to him, kissed her. Her lips grew soft, her body sank into his, tears formed slowly in her eyes. He knew, for the first time, that he could do whatever he wanted with her.

"Tonight," he said. "I'll call for you at seven-thirty. Can you get out?"

She looked at him. She was smiling, but the tears were still full in her eyes. "All right," she said. "I'll get out. How about you? Won't the coach raise hell?"

Darling grinned. "I got the coach in the palm of my hand," he said. "Can you wait till seven-thirty?"

She grinned back at him. "No," she said.

They kissed and she started the car and they went back to town for dinner. He sang on the way home.

Christian Darling, thirty-five years old, sat on the frail spring grass, greener now than it ever would be again on the practice field, looked thoughtfully up at the stadium, a deserted ruin in the twilight. He had started on the first team that Saturday and every Saturday after that for the next two years, but it had never been as satisfactory as it should have been. He never had broken away, the longest run he'd ever made was 35 yards, and that in a game that was already won, and then that kid had come up from the third team, Diederich, a blank-faced German kid from Wisconsin, who ran like a bull, ripping lines to pieces Saturday after Saturday, plowing through, never getting hurt, never changing his expression, scoring more points, gaining more ground than all the rest of the team put together, making everybody's All-America, carrying the ball three times out of four, keeping everybody else out of the headlines. Darling was a good blocker and he spent his Saturday afternoons working on the big Swedes and Polacks who played tackle and end for Michigan, Illinois, Purdue, hurling into huge pile-ups, bobbing his head wildly to elude the great raw hands swinging like meat cleavers at him as he went charging in to open up holes for Diederich coming through like a locomotive behind him. Still, it wasn't so bad. Everybody liked him and he did his job and he was pointed out on the campus and boys always felt important when they introduced their girls to him at their proms, and Louise loved him and watched him faithfully in the games, even in the mud, when your own mother wouldn't know you, and drove him around in her car keeping the top down because she was proud of him and wanted to show everybody that she was Christian Darling's girl. She bought him crazy presents because her father was rich, watches, pipes, humidors, an icebox for beer for his room, curtains, wallets, a fifty-dollar dictionary.

"You'll spend every cent your old man owns," Darling protested once when she showed up at his rooms with seven different packages in her arms and tossed them onto the couch.

"Kiss me," Louise said, "and shut up."

"Do you want to break your poor old man?"

"I don't mind. I want to buy you presents."

"Why?"

"It makes me feel good. Kiss me. I don't know why. Did you know that you're an important figure?"

"Yes," Darling said gravely.

"When I was waiting for you at the library yesterday two girls saw you coming and one of them said to the other, 'That's Christian Darling. He's an important figure.'"

"You're a liar."

"I'm in love with an important figure."

"Still, why the hell did you have to give me a forty-pound dictionary?"

"I wanted to make sure," Louise said, "that you had a token of my esteem. I want to smother you in tokens of my esteem."

Fifteen years ago.

They'd married when they got out of college. There'd been other women for him, but all casual and secret, more for curiosity's sake, and vanity, women who'd thrown themselves at him and flattered him, a pretty mother at a summer camp for boys, an old girl from his home town who'd suddenly blossomed into a coquette, a friend of Louise's who had dogged him grimly for six months and had taken advantage of the two weeks that Louise went home when her mother died. Perhaps Louise had known, but she'd kept quiet, loving him completely, filling his rooms with presents, religiously watching him battling with the big Swedes and Polacks on the line of scrimmage on Saturday afternoons, making plans for marrying him and living with him in New York and going with him there to the night clubs, the theaters, the good restaurants, being proud of him in advance, tall, white-teethed, smiling, large, yet moving lightly, with an athlete's grace, dressed in evening clothes, approvingly eyed by magnificently dressed and famous women in theater lobbies, with Louise adoringly at his side.

Her father, who manufactured inks, set up a New York office for Darling to manage and presented him with three hundred accounts, and they lived on Beekman Place with a view of the river, with fifteen thousand dollars a year between them, because everybody was buying everything in those days, including ink. They saw all the shows and went to all the speakeasies and spent their fifteen thousand dollars a year and in the afternoons Louise went to the art galleries and the matinees of the more serious plays that Darling didn't like to sit through, and Darling slept with a girl who danced in the chorus of *Rosalie* and with the wife of a man who owned three copper mines. Darling played squash three times a week and remained as solid as a stone barn and Louise never took her eyes off him when they were in the same room together, watching him with a secret, miser's smile, with a trick of coming over to him in the middle of a crowded room and saying gravely, in a low voice, "You're the handsomest man I've ever seen in my whole life. Want a drink?"

Nineteen twenty-nine came to Darling and to his wife and father-in-law, the maker of inks, just as it came to everyone else. The father-in-law waited until 1933 and then blew his brains out, and when Darling went to Chicago to see what the books of the firm looked like he found out all that was left were debts and three or four gallons of unbought ink.

"Please, Christian," Louise said, sitting in

their neat Beekman Place apartment, with a view of the river and prints of paintings by Dufy and Braque and Picasso on the wall, "please, why do you want to start drinking at two o'clock in the afternoon?"

"I have nothing else to do," Darling said, putting down his glass, emptied of its fourth drink. "Please pass the whisky."

Louise filled his glass. "Come take a walk with me," she said. "We'll walk along the river."

"I don't want to walk along the river," Darling said, squinting intensely at the prints of paintings by Dufy, Braque and Picasso.

"We'll walk along Fifth Avenue."

"I don't want to walk along Fifth Avenue."

"Maybe," Louise said gently, "you'd like to come with me to some art galleries. There's an exhibition by a man named Klee . . ."

"I don't want to go to any art galleries. I want to sit here and drink Scotch whisky," Darling said. "Who the hell hung these goddam pictures up on the wall?"

"I did," Louise said.

"I hate them."

"I'll take them down," Louise said.

"Leave them there. It gives me something to do in the afternoon. I can hate them." Darling took a long swallow. "Is that the way people paint these days?"

"Yes, Christian. Please don't drink any more."

"Do you like painting like that?"

"Yes, dear."

"Really?"

"Really."

Darling looked carefully at the prints once more. "Little Louise Tucker. The Middle-Western beauty. I like pictures with horses in them. Why should you like pictures like that?"

"I just happen to have gone to a lot of galleries in the last few years . . ."

"Is that what you do in the afternoon?"

"That's what I do in the afternoon," Louise said.

"I drink in the afternoon."

Louise kissed him lightly on the top of his head as he sat there squinting at the pictures on the wall, the glass of whisky held firmly in his hand. She put on her coat and went out without saying another word. When she came back in the early evening, she had a job on a woman's fashion magazine.

They moved downtown and Louise went out to work every morning and Darling sat home and drank and Louise paid the bills as they came up. She made believe she was going to quit work as soon as Darling found a job, even though she was taking over more responsibility day by day at the magazine, interviewing authors, picking painters for the illustrations and covers, getting actresses to pose for pictures, going out for drinks with the right people, making a thousand new friends whom she loyally introduced to Darling.

"I don't like your hat," Darling said, once, when she came in in the evening and kissed him, her breath rich with Martinis.

"What's the matter with my hat, Baby?" she asked, running her fingers through his hair. "Everybody says it's very smart."

"It's too damned smart," he said. "It's not for you. It's for a rich, sophisticated woman of thirty-five with admirers."

Louise laughed. "I'm practicing to be a rich, sophisticated woman of thirty-five with admirers," she said. He stared soberly at her. "Now, don't look so grim, Baby. It's still the same simple little wife under the hat." She took the hat off, threw it into a corner, sat on his lap. "See? Homebody Number One."

"Your breath could run a train," Darling said, not wanting to be mean, but talking out of boredom, and sudden shock at seeing his wife curiously a stranger in a new hat, with a new expression in her eyes under the little brim, secret, confident, knowing.

Louise tucked her head under his chin so he couldn't smell her breath. "I had to take an author out for cocktails," she said. "He's a boy from the Ozark Mountains and he drinks like a fish. He's a Communist."

"What the hell is a Communist from the Ozarks doing writing for a woman's fashion magazine?"

Louise chuckled. "The magazine business is getting all mixed up these days. The publishers want to have a foot in every camp. And anyway, you can't find an author under seventy these days who isn't a Communist."

"I don't think I like you to associate with all those people, Louise," Darling said. "Drinking with them."

"He's a very nice gentle boy," Louise said. "He reads Ernest Dowson."

"Who's Ernest Dowson?"

Louise patted his arm, stood up, fixed her hair. "He's an English poet."

Darling felt that somehow he had disappointed her. "Am I supposed to know who Ernest Dowson is?"

"No, dear. I'd better go in and take a bath."

After she had gone, Darling went over to the corner where the hat was lying and picked it up. It was nothing, a scrap of straw, a red flower, a veil, meaningless on his big hand, but on his wife's head a signal of something . . . big city, smart and knowing women drinking and dining with men other than their husbands, conversation about things a normal man wouldn't know much about, Frenchmen who painted as though they used their elbows instead of brushes, composers who wrote whole symphonies without a single melody in them, writers who knew all about politics and women who knew all about writers, the movement of the proletariat, Marx, somehow mixed up with five-dollar dinners and the best-looking women in America and fairies who made them laugh and half-sentences immediately understood and secretly hilarious and wives who called their husbands "Baby." He put the hat down, a scrap of straw and a red flower and a little veil. He drank some whisky straight and went into the bathroom where his wife was lying in her bath, singing to herself and smiling from time to time like a little girl, paddling the water gently with her hands, sending up a slightly spicy fragrance from the bath salts she used.

He stood over her, looking down at her. She smiled at him, her eyes half closed, her body pink and shimmering in the warm, scented water. All over again, with all the old suddenness, he was hit deep inside him with the knowledge of how beautiful she was, how much he needed her.

"I came in here," he said, "to tell you I wish you wouldn't call me 'Baby.' "

She looked up at him from the bath, her eyes quickly full of sorrow, half understanding what he meant. He knelt and put his arms around her, his sleeves plunged heedlessly in the water, his shirt and jacket soaking wet as he clutched her wordlessly, holding her crazily tight, crushing her breath from her, kissing her desperately, searchingly, regretfully.

He got jobs after that, selling real estate and automobiles, but somehow, although he had a desk with his name on a wooden wedge on it, and he went to the office religiously at nine each morning, he never managed to sell anything and he never made any money.

Louise was made assistant editor and the house was always full of strange men and women who talked fast and got angry on abstract subjects like mural painting, novelists, labor unions. Negro short-story writers drank Louise's liquor, and a lot of Jews, and big solemn men with scarred faces and knotted hands who talked slowly but clearly about picket lines and battles with guns and lead pipe at mine shaftheads and in front of factory gates.

And Louise moved among them all, confidently, knowing what they were talking about, with opinions that they listened to and argued about just as though she were a man. She knew everybody, condescended to no one, devoured books that Darling had never heard of, walked along the streets of the city, excited, at home, soaking in all the million of tides of New York without fear, with constant wonder.

Her friends liked Darling and sometimes he found a man who wanted to get off in the corner and talk about the new boy who played fullback for Princeton, and the decline of the double wing-back, or even the state of the stock market, but for the most part he sat on the edge of things, solid and quiet in the high storm of words. "The dialectics of the situation . . . The theater has been given over to expert jugglers . . . Picasso? What man has a right to paint old bones and collect $10,000 for them? . . . I stand firmly behind Trotsky . . . Poe was the last American critic. When he died they put lilies on the grave of American criticism. I don't say this because they panned my last book, but . . . ."

Once in a while he caught Louise looking soberly and consideringly at him through the cigarette smoke and the noise and he avoided her eyes and found an excuse to get up and go into the kitchen for more ice or to open another bottle.

"Come on," Cathal Flaherty was saying, standing at the door with a girl, "you've got to come down and see this. It's down on Fourteenth Street, in the old Civic Repertory, and you can only see it on Sunday nights and I'll guarantee you'll come out of the theater singing." Flaherty was a big young Irishman with a broken nose who was the lawyer for a longshoreman's union, and he had been hanging around the house for six months on and off, roaring and shutting everybody else up when he got in an argument. "It's a new play, *Waiting for Lefty;* it's about taxi drivers."

"Odets," the girl with Flaherty said. "It's by a guy named Odets."

"I never heard of him," Darling said.

"He's a new one," the girl said.

"It's like watching a bombardment," Flaherty said. "I saw it last Sunday night. You've got to see it."

"Come on, Baby," Louise said to Darling, excitement in her eyes already. "We've been sitting in the Sunday *Times* all day, this'll be a great change."

"I see enough taxi drivers every day," Darling said, not because he meant that, but because he didn't like to be around Flaherty, who said things that made Louise laugh a lot and whose judgment she accepted on almost every subject. "Let's go to the movies."

"You've never seen anything like this before," Flaherty said. "He wrote this play with a baseball bat."

"Come on," Louise coaxed, "I bet it's wonderful."

"He has long hair," the girl with Flaherty said. "Odets. I met him at a party. He's an actor. He didn't say a goddam thing all night."

"I don't feel like going down to Fourteenth Street," Darling said, wishing Flaherty and his girl would get out. "It's gloomy."

"Oh, hell!" Louise said loudly. She looked coolly at Darling, as though she'd just been introduced to him and was making up her mind about him, and not very favorably. He saw her looking at him, knowing there was something new and dangerous in her face and he wanted to say something but Flaherty was there and his damned girl, and anyway, he didn't know what to say.

"I'm going," Louise said, getting her coat. "I don't think Fourteenth Street is gloomy."

"I'm telling you," Flaherty was saying, helping her on with her coat, "it's the Battle of Gettysburg, in Brooklynese."

"Nobody could get a word out of him," Flaherty's girl was saying as they went through the door. "He just sat there all night."

The door closed. Louise hadn't said good night to him. Darling walked around the room four times, then sprawled out on the sofa, on top of the Sunday *Times*. He lay there for five minutes looking at the ceiling, thinking of Flaherty walking down the street talking in that booming voice between the girls, holding their arms.

Louise had looked wonderful. She'd washed her hair in the afternoon and it had been very soft and light and clung close to her head as she stood there angrily putting her coat on. Louise was getting prettier every year, partly because she knew by now how pretty she was and made the most of it.

"Nuts," Darling said, standing up. "Oh, nuts."

He put on his coat and went down to the nearest bar and had five drinks off by himself before his money ran out.

The years since then had been foggy and downhill. Louise had been nice to him, and in a way, loving and kind, and they'd fought only once, when he said he was going to vote for Landon. ("Oh, Christ," she'd said, "doesn't *anything* happen inside your head? Don't you read the papers? The penniless Republican!") She'd been sorry later and apologized for hurting him, but apologized as she might to a child. He'd tried hard, had gone grimly to the art galleries, the concert halls, the bookshops, trying to gain on the trail of his wife, but it was no use. He was bored, and none of what he saw or heard or dutifully read made much sense to him and finally he gave it up. He had thought, many nights as he ate dinner alone, knowing that Louise would come home late and drop silently into bed without explanation, of getting a divorce, but he knew the loneliness, the hopelessness, of not seeing her again would be too much to take. So he was good, completely devoted, ready at all times to go any place with her, do anything she wanted. He even got a small job, in a broker's office, and paid his own way, bought his own liquor.

Then he'd been offered the job of going from college to college as a tailor's representative. "We want a man," Mr. Rosenberg had said, "who as soon as you look at him, you say, 'There's a university man'" Rosenberg had looked approvingly at Darling's broad shoulders and well-kept waist, at his carefully brushed hair and his honest, wrinkleless face. "Frankly, Mr. Darling, I am willing to make you a proposition. I have inquired about you, you are favorably known on your old campus, I understand you were in the backfield with Alfred Diederich."

Darling nodded. "Whatever happened to him?"

"He is walking around in a cast for seven years now. An iron brace. He played professional football and they broke his neck for him."

Darling smiled. That, at least, had turned out well.

"Our suits are an easy product to sell, Mr. Darling," Rosenberg said. "We have a handsome, custom-made garment. What has Brooks Brothers got that we haven't got? A name. No more."

"I can make fifty–sixty dollars a week," Darling said to Louise that night. "And expenses. I can save some money and then come back to New York and really get started here."

"Yes, Baby," Louise said.

"As it is," Darling said carefully, "I can make it back here once a month, and holidays and the summer. We can see each other often."

"Yes, Baby." He looked at her face, lovelier now at thirty-five than it had ever been before, but fogged over now as it had been for five years with a kind of patient, kindly, remote boredom.

"What do you say?" he asked. "Should I take it?" Deep within him he hoped fiercely, longingly, for her to say, "No, Baby, you stay right here," but she said, as he knew she'd say, "I think you'd better take it."

He nodded. He had to get up and stand with his back to her, looking out the window, because there were things plain on his face that she had never seen in the fifteen years she'd known him. "Fifty dollars is a lot of money," he said. "I never thought I'd ever see fifty dollars again." He laughed. Louise laughed, too.

Christian Darling sat on the frail green grass of the practice field. The shadow of the stadium had reached out and covered him. In the distance the lights of the university shone a little mistily in the light haze of evening. Fifteen years. Flaherty even now was calling for his wife, buying her a drink, filling whatever bar they were in with that voice of his and that easy laugh. Darling half-closed his eyes, almost saw the boy fifteen years ago reach for the pass, slip the halfback, go skittering lightly down the field, his knees high and fast and graceful, smiling to himself because he knew he was going to get past the safety man. That was the high point, Darling thought, fifteen years ago, on an autumn afternoon, twenty years old and far from death, with the air coming easily into his lungs, and a deep feeling inside him that he could do anything, knock over anybody, outrun whatever had to be outrun. And the shower after and the three glasses of water and the cool night air on his damp head and Louise sitting hatless in the open car with a smile and the first kiss she ever really meant. The high point, an eighty-yard run in the practice, and a girl's kiss and everything after that a decline. Darling laughed. He had practiced the wrong thing, perhaps. He hadn't practiced for 1929 and New York City and a girl who would turn into a woman. Somewhere, he thought, there must have been a point where she moved up to me, was even with me for a moment, when I could have held her hand, if I'd known, held tight, gone with her. Well, he'd never known. Here he was on a playing field that was fifteen years away and his wife was in another city having dinner with another and better man, speaking with him a different, new language, a language nobody had ever taught him.

Darling stood up, smiled a little, because if he didn't smile he knew the tears would come. He looked around him. This was the spot. O'Connor's pass had come sliding out just to here . . . the high point. Darling put up his hands, felt all over again the flat slap of the ball. He shook his hips to throw off the halfback, cut back inside the center, picked his knees high as he ran gracefully over two men jumbled on the ground at the line of scrimmage, ran easily, gaining speed, for 10 yards, holding the ball lightly in his two hands, swung away from the halfback diving at him, ran, swinging his hips in the almost girlish manner of a back in a broken field, tore into the safety man, his shoes drumming heavily on the turf, stiff-armed, elbow locked, pivoted, raced lightly and exultantly for the goal line.

It was only after he had sped over the goal line and slowed to a trot that he saw the boy and girl sitting together on the turf, looking at him wonderingly.

He stopped short, dropping his arms. "I . . ." he said, gasping a little, though his condition was fine and the run hadn't winded him. "I—once I played here."

The boy and the girl said nothing. Darling laughed embarrassedly, looked hard at them sitting there, close to each other, shrugged, turned and went toward his hotel, the sweat breaking out on his face and running down into his collar.

"Fight, team, fight!!"

CARTOON BY GEORGE GATELY

Every Saturday afternoon in the fall there are hundreds of college games—and more of them resemble this one between Middlebury and the U. of Vermont than, say, Illinois vs. Michigan. The rustic scene is described by columnist Red Smith, a Notre Dame man.

BIG GAME, MOUNTAIN STYLE

Red Smith

It poured rain on the eve of battle and plans were abandoned for a bonfire and snake dance after the pep rally in the gym. The weather, however, didn't discourage the rooters of the University of Vermont, come down to Middlebury for the last and biggest game of the football season in the Green Mountain country.

It takes a great deal to dismay either side in this annual meeting. Last year, for instance, Vermont wasn't conceded much chance, yet brought off a monumental upset, 34–7. This year, Middlebury was the favorite again, having won three times in seven starts. Vermont had played six and lost six but the young men from Burlington had scored twice, making 7 points against St. Michael's while St. Michael's was making 41, and 6 against New Hampshire, who scored 54.

Late into Friday night, jalopies prowled the campus. Spotlights played upon dormitory windows. There were shouts in the rainy darkness. In the morning there were big yellow V's pained on the trees and buildings and mailboxes. In theory, freshman task forces combat such attacks by mechanized cavalry, but the Middlebury war machine is imperfect. Another season on the eve of the Vermont game, an enterprising but inconsiderate photographer made a picture that subsequently appeared in the Middlebury *Campus*. It showed two sentries sound asleep on the chapel steps, their nightsticks dangling from nerveless hands.

Snow fell Saturday in big, wet flakes. Spectators waded squishily to the box office, bought general admission tickets—Middlebury doesn't bother with reserve seats—and spread newspapers or blankets where they chose on the muddy planks of the bleachers flanking Porter Field. A wind whipped across the field, plucked overcoat collars open and stuffed melting snow into the apertures.

Grayness blotted out horizons. This far valley between Green Mountains and the Adirondacks was shut off in a world of its own. A million light-years away, 45,000 people were cheering Princeton's Dick Kazmaier, 80,000 were watching Ohio State and Illinois, almost 60,000 sat in Michigan Stadium.

Only the players seemed unaware of the mud,

the snow and the cold. They went down wallowing in the primeval ooze, got up shaking big gobs of muck from their paws, and hustled back into another scrimmage. Middlebury made a touchdown the first time it got the ball. The home forces added another, then Vermont went across, making the score, 13–6. This looked closer than anticipated and excitement mounted, but a pretty fourth-down pass play made it 19–6 one second before the half ended.

Everybody seemed to know everybody else. Between halves they wandered around visiting, stomping the cold from their feet. Toddlers in bright snow suits and galoshes paddled through puddles on the sidelines. Nobody herded them back when the teams came out for the second half. A man pushing a baby carriage through the mud followed the play, hurrying along the sideline as the Middlebury team ran up the score.

Every few minutes a kid named Worthington or Allen or Zabriskie would break loose and the Middlebury stands would rise in a shouting confusion of bright color. Gals of the senior class carried canes to the Vermont game, replicas of the walking stick favored by Gamaliel Painter, who founded the college in 1850. Whenever Middlebury scored they brandished the canes ferociously. They did a lot of brandishing. The final score was 51–12. After its two touchdowns Vermont kept unsullied its record of missing every extra point against Middlebury since 1942.

There was some remarkable running in the treacherous bog and some astonishing passing with a greasy ball. A tall Middlebury end named Sonny Dennis leaped for passes and when the ball spurted away from him like wet soap in the bathtub he juggled it and caught it again on the run. Vermont played the T-formation; Middlebury's coach, Duke Nelson, employed the single-wing attack with buck lateral sequences favored by his friend Charley Caldwell of Princeton.

"But," Nelson said, "Charley runs it with Kazmaier. We use the same book but we're still on page three. This is about like intramural football except that the varsity players get to put in a little more time at it. Not an awful lot more time at that. Our kids aren't real football players physically. But we ask them to think. If you can get 'em started thinking, then they play better football and it becomes a game and they have some fun. That's my notion anyway."

Across the campus the bell in the old chapel started to ring. Because Middlebury had won, it would ring for three hours, with a detail of freshmen pulling the rope.

Arthur Brown, the athletic director, was telling of the days when Middlebury regularly played opponents like Harvard, Yale, Army and Penn State. One year the opener was lost to Harvard by something like 55–0, the game to Yale by about 60–0, and about that time an idea took shape that Middlebury was out of its class. Still and all, they do remember the year Harvard was tied.

"Our president then was Dwight Moody," Mr. Brown said. "He telephoned to ask the score. '6–6,' I told him. 'Sixty-six to what?' he asked."

The cliché expert gets out his crystal ball and gazes at the season ahead.

GRID GANDER

Frank Sullivan

With the tang of autumn in the air, the thoughts of sports-lovers naturally turn to football, and it becomes the task of the expert to see what gives on the nation's gridirons this fall. I return to my annual football prophecies bloody but unbowed. Of the ten elevens I predicted last September would reap top honors, only one, the Georgia Varmints, made the grade. I was also wrong on eleven of my selections for the All-America team, but I was one hundred per cent correct when I predicted that young Brian O'Halloran, of Upsala, would win the assistant managership of football there. He did, nosing out a Psi U named Wagstaff in the last week of the season. So here goes for a gander at the 1950 grid prospects!

The game itself remains substantially as it was last year. There have been a few changes in the rules, designed chiefly to throw the alumni off the scent. The number of players remains eleven to a side, pending final figures on the 1950 census. Reapportionment following the increase in population may cause the addition of a twelfth player, but that is something to worry about next year.

Although it has been criticized in some circles, the new rule about broadcasting will probably simplify football games for the stay-at-home fans. This rule provides that any play that has been misunderstood and/or incorrectly described by a radio and/or television broadcaster is automatically void and must be played over.

The proposal to change the officials' shirt stripes from vertical to horizontal did not find favor with the Intercollegiate Conference of Intercollegiate Football, but at the April meeting the I.C.I.F. did O.K. the so-called Marshall Plan rule. This requires powerhouse outfits with a surfeit of crack, hard-hitting players to share their excess triple-threat men with less fortunate, fifty-watt colleges. The rule was passed over the veto of Notre Dame.

The classic grid tilts will take place as usual, but there have been some schedule changes. Northwestern will not meet Southeastern this fall, for the first time in as many years, and Southwestern will not play Northeastern.

College teams have suffered the usual losses from graduation, falls in slippery bathtubs, and other mishaps. Holy Cross loses its star back, Doak McCloskey. Wesleyan loses *its* star back, Doak McMaster. North Carolina loses its triple-threat star, Doak Justice, and Army's Doak Davis is a pro. Colorado School of Mines loses its great passer, Doak Doolittle. What the Beetles will do without Doolittle is one of the posers football offers this fall.

Southern Aggie is going to feel the loss of its crack, triple-threat, hard-hitting, strapping, speedy, crack back, Froggie Beltravers, Sr. Beltravers entered Southern Aggie in 1931 but, because of repeated conditions in poultry husbandry, did not gain his degree until last June. Through the years, as his sons reached college age and joined him, the Beltravers backfield became a force to be reckoned with. It will be interesting to see what Froggie, Jr., and Buster Beltravers will accomplish this fall without Dad.

In the Ivy League, the eyes of fans and experts will be on Yale's promising new passer, Azenbrodt Teele, who will be making his first varsity appearance in the game with Southern Trappist next month. Teele is a strapping, hard-hitting, crack 200-pounder with the advantage, always handy to a passer, of having three arms. He prepped with Ringling's sideshow. There was doubt among League officials as to whether Teele was eligible to play. It has been more or less the tradition in the Ivy League that players should not have more than the usual complement of arms and legs, though other conferences have winked at such departures from the norm. However, it was pointed out that a two-headed boy from the medical museum played quarterback quite successfully for Harvard in 1871, and in view of this precedent no objection to Teele was raised. Yale has done a characteristically sporting thing by offering to knock off 2 yards from any 10 yards gained by Teele while using more than two arms.

Eyes this fall will also be on Boff Dostoievsky, Union Theological's highly touted, strapping, hard-hitting, crack center. This remarkable 340-pound youngster, standing 5 feet 2 in his stocking feet, will get a chance to show his mettle in the Vicars' game with Purdue. A senior, Boff has never yet played in a game, although he has made every All-America team except mine for the past two years. A succession of mishaps has dogged his footsteps. Last year, on the eve of the game with Tulane, in which the Vicars counted on him to even old scores with the Louisiana Sugar Cookies, he came down with scarlet fever, and did not finish desquamating until Little Christmas, by which date basketball had supplanted football. In the previous year, Boff was hailed as a soph whizz, but hard luck crossed him then, too. On the first day of fall practice, he tripped over an assistant manager someone had carelessly left lying in an end zone and strained all the ligaments in his and the assistant manager's back. The latter, who was a pledge of the Dekes at the time, was dropped by that frat for his costly blunder.

Texas Poly will be itself again this season after the vicissitudes that beset it last year, when all seventy-two of its squad, the coaching staff, and the mascot fell in love. Every coach knows that of all mishaps that can throw a team or a coach into the doldrums none is more to be dreaded than love in midseason. Oddly enough, it was with the same girl, a Miss Daisy LaTouche, that they were one and all enamored, and old-time sportswriters say that this coincidence has not happened since the days of Frank Merriwell and Brown of Harvard. Texas Poly fans will rejoice to hear that Miss LaTouche moved away from Texas, last April, to Princeton, New Jersey.

The T formation will, of course, play an important part in grid success or failure this fall, but I have been hearing quite a lot of talk about the sensational new J formation, which Southern Baptist used for the first time last November in the now historic game with Minneapolis Poly. You can count on it that from now on the J formation will be stressed in all chalk talks given by the smarter coaches. It can be used with either 6–2–2–1 defense or the 5–3–2–1 defense, or in a pinch, with the 4–3–3–1 defense. Roughly, it works as follows: The receiver pivots, feints in one direction with the head and in the opposite direction with the shoulders, and then does a fake feint at an angle of 180° followed by a fake pivot, and then a fake lateral, a fake cutback, a fake bunt, and to top all, a fake bid of three spades. The defender then takes one or two steps to the right or left and executes another quick pivot and a fake dribble. The cheerleaders for the receiver call for a fake cheer. Then the wingback executes a cutback and the receiver fakes a block and follows up with a quick kick, and there you are.

It marks the first time that the principles of canasta have been applied to football, and it has the merit of being simpler in its essentials than the T formation. Its success depends on two of the tackles being disguised as officials. So, all things considered, we may look for crowded stadiums from now until snowfall.

Extensive improvements have been made in the stands at Baker Field, Columbia's home arena. Last spring, when Mr. Little examined the field, it was discovered that several alumni had been left in the stands all winter, and had worked considerable havoc. They had got into the woodwork and everything. New stanchions had to be installed throughout, but things are now shipshape, and the word is—you guessed it —"Play ball!"

Between halves at the 1961 Rose Bowl game—Washington vs. Minnesota—the capacity crowd of 100,000 and a national TV audience watched the Washington rooting section of 2,300 go through its animated card tricks. Much to the confusion of spectators—and to the horror of Husky cheerleaders—the section's effort to spell WASHINGTON in glittering capital letters came out CAL TECH. The next stunt, which was supposed to produce HUSKIES in flowing script, turned into gibberish and the dismayed Washington cheerleaders called it quits. Behind the embarrassing disorder was a practical joke concocted in the lively minds of a few students at California Institute of Technology. Lance Taylor, Class of '62, writing in the undergraduate magazine, Engineering and Science, *unravels the details of the plot.*

HOAX AT HALFTIME

Lance Taylor

Undergraduate pranks are nothing new. In fact, freshman knowledge of English literature reveals that pranks have been around as long as the Reeve's Tale—and they probably have a long antiquity before that.

Certainly, at Caltech, undergraduate pranks are as old as the Institute. Hardly a day goes by that some Tech students aren't outtalking soapbox lecturers at Pershing Square, or engaging in some other moderately interesting frolic. Every so often, however, a truly noble stunt is pulled off—a stunt involving untold man-hours of preparation and imagination above and beyond the call of reasonable likelihood. (Caltech students, so somebody said, are above and beyond reasonable likelihood anyway, so they appreciate noble stunts.)

One of these occurred this month, before a national television audience, during the halftime ceremonies at Pasadena's annual Rose Bowl football game.

On this occasion a group of Techmen undertook to "rewrite the scenario" for the University of Washington's halftime card demonstrations. This was a task involving Brobdingnagian dedication. Football game card-sections usually involve upwards of 1,000 students who sit *en masse* and hold up colored cards to form

patterns—words and mascots' pictures are favorites. The Caltech pranksters completely changed three of Washington's patterns.

First they made the unwitting Northerners spell out "CALTECH" instead of "WASHINGTON."

Then, when the card-section was supposed to spell out "Huskies" in flowing script, they arranged things so that, instead of the "h," the dot over the "i" appeared first. The tail of the "s" showed up next. And then, flowing inexorably backwards, the cards went from "s" to "e" to "i" to "k" to "s" to "u" to "h."

Then the pranksters had the card-section depict a Caltech Beaver in place of the Washington mascot.

These surprising substitutions came in numbers 10, 11, and 12 of a projected 14-trick sequence. As a result, the frustrated Husky card-section went out of business after pattern 12.

This noble prank was undertaken by 14 members of Lloyd House at Caltech. Most of them are in the class of 1962, and most of them belonged to the freshman section "K," which was notorious in its year for wacky stunts. Obviously, they've kept their fondness for folderol. (In fact, looking to the future, they

304

have approximately 50 prank plans carefully filed away in two overstuffed boxes of IBM cards.)

The Fourteen started work on the great Rose Bowl hoax before Christmas by making a series of telephone calls to various Rose Bowl officials. They learned that the Washington and Minnesota card-section students would arrive on December 29, and would stay at Long Beach State and Occidental Colleges, respectively.

The Fourteen sent one of their number to Long Beach State, posing as a reporter for the Los Angeles Dorsey High School *Dorseygram*. He arrived 15 minutes after the Washington band and card-section had arrived, and asked for the card-demonstration director. He was sent to Room 105 of a Long Beach State dormitory, where he found the director stashing away his precious cards until New Year's Day. Room 105, the Techman noted, was located only two doors away from an easily lock-picked entrance to the dormitory.

Approaching his prey and offering him a cigarette, the Techman began his interview and asked just how his card-section worked. The director obligingly told him, down to the minutest detail.

Each of Washington's 2,232 card-section members, said the director, gets his own stack of colored cards to hold up, as well as an instruction sheet that looks something like this:

1. PURPLE   4. VIOLET
2. PINK   5. AQUAMARINE
3. POLKA DOTS   6. ZAFFER

The card-section is divided into numbered subsections. On each stunt, the director calls out section numbers, sounding a little like a deliberate quarterback. When a subsection number is called, each of its numbers holds up his cards. For example, a director will call out 1–2–3–4–5, and the whole card section will spell out H–Y–M–I–E with each subsection holding up its letter when its number is called.

The reporter also found out that the section director planned to eat dinner about an hour later. One of the Techmen came back at that time, picked his way into the room, and took an instruction sheet from the middle of the heap the director had hidden behind a table. "They'd never miss one," said the lock-picker.

They didn't miss one, either, as the Fourteen discovered after they had made a hurried trip to a nearby printer to have approximately 2,300 near-duplicates of the instruction sheets run off for about $30.

They also discovered that their printer had furnished them with *manila* sheets to replace Washington's *white* ones, but after some futile attempts at dyeing, they gave up and hoped that the gods would mask the difference.

The next day, Saturday, the Techmen again arrived at Long Beach State when the Washingtonians weren't there. (The intrepid reporter had discovered that everybody was going to Disneyland that day.) Picking the lock again, they stole the master plans—large pieces of graph paper colored the way the stunts were to appear—from the director's satchel. They then decamped for the Lloyd House lounge.

There, they spread their 2,232 substitute instruction sheets over the tables and floor, and set about stamping them with "correct" instructions—changing the words in demonstrations 10 and 11, and rounding off the Husky's ears and giving him buck teeth to turn him into a Beaver in demonstration 12. Ten hours later, the project finished, five of the Fourteen and 2,232 new cards left once more for Long Beach and Room 105.

Knowing that Washington was elsewhere, celebrating New Year's Eve, the Techmen picked their way into the room once again, replaced the master plans, and substituted the altered instruction sheets for the original ones. Then they returned to Pasadena for a day-and-a-half wait.

Nobody knows whether Washington discovered the substitutions ahead of time—because there would have been no time for re-substitutions anyway. As it stood, the card-section director was observed riding contentedly in the Rose Parade on the morning of the game—and standing open-mouthed in the afternoon when 10, 11, and 12 came up.

Which is all the Techmen wanted anyway. As one of the Fourteen explained: "We did it to see if it could be done."

"Welcome to the fall term and football de-emphasis, Jablonowicz."

CARTOON BY GALLAGHER

In his humorous novel, Professor Fodorski, *Robert Lewis Taylor plays a merry game of satire with football. His professor is a member of the faculty at Southern Baptist Institute of Technology, where he has put his scientific mind to work to help the Unicorn football team become a major power. This selection—the broadcast of a vital game for S.B.I.T.—offers some familiar sounds.*

From *PROFESSOR FODORSKI*

Robert Lewis Taylor

"Picture if you will," said Bill Stern, "a bright, sunshiny day, a perfect football day here in old New Orleans, and 82,000 football-mad partisans jam-packing these stands, for this unique gridiron classic, one of the uniquest of this or any other year, between the Green Wave of Tulane and the Unicorns of S.B.I.T. Except for a few puddles, and I mean a very few, the field is almost completely dry—the rain has stopped. I will repeat that for those of you who have just joined the network for this gridiron classic—the rain has stopped and the field is comparatively, or relatively, dry. The big question on the lips of everyone in these seats today is—can—they—do—it—this—year? I needn't go into details of what was without a doubt one of the most heartbreaking, or most fortunate, depending on your allegiance, or partisanship— and let me say here that I am strictly neutral, it is only my job to give the facts—struggles in all the annals of football history. I refer of course to last year's struggle between these ancient, traditional rivals at Memorial Stadium in Varsity Commons, South Carolina. With a minute and thirty seconds to go and the Unicorns knocking at the golden gate, within the very shadow of the Tulane goalposts, Cuttlebone Perkins, carrying the mail around his own right end, fumbled on the 3-yard line and averted what would have been a certain Unicorn victory, unless of course the Green Wave of Tulane had been able to get back in that ball game, and that might well have happened, for no team of Hurry-up Hanson, no team in my experience as an announcer, and if you will forgive the personal note, ladies and gentlemen, that has been extensive, has ever been defeated until the final whistle has blown. And let me add that the same may be said for the Unicorns of S.B.I.T. and that very fine gentleman and my personal friend of several years' standing, Hulk Stockworth. And now for a few statistics—"

"It's going to be a dandy," said Dr. Cartwright, tuning up the radio in the sunroom of the Cartwright house, where he and his wife and Professor Fodorski were assembled. "I think we'll stick with Stern—he makes these things come to life."

"Tune it down just slightly," said Mrs. Cartwright. "The Everetts have a radio of their own."

"—stung by their defeat of last year, in which victory was snatched by a two-point margin, can—these—Unicorns—come—back—to—

307

even—up—this—traditional—series? Well, that's in the lap of the gods, ladies and gentlemen, *but here comes the Green Wave of Tulane out on the playing field!* They are entering from the north end, that is the goalpost to the left of our broadcasting booth as we face the east, and the Unicorns will enter from the other, or south end, with the west behind them. I give you these positions, ladies and gentlemen, to clarify in your mind, as in the minds of those of you who have been here before, the relative positions on the field. I am facing the opposite side of the field, and the wind is to my left. A slight wind is blowing diagonally across the field, from the Tulane side angling down to the south, or right-hand end, and that wind will be an ever-increasing factor as these teams line up to toss that coin."

"It's as good as being there," said Dr. Cartwright. "I've got the whole thing in my mind's eye."

Professor Fodorski removed his cutaway and rolled up his sleeves. He suddenly noticed, to his amazement, that he was perspiring.

"—happy to bring it to you, and don't forget. Ask yourself these simple questions: Do you ever feel hungry or out of sorts? Are you fatigued after a day's swimming, mountain climbing, or horseback riding? Do you lose your temper if telephoned by mistake at 3 A.M.? Are your nerves affected by a group of children beating on washtubs and pans? If the answer is yes, you are suffering from a deficiency of bleurium. Try Japalac, a magic new formula, rich in bleurium, discovered by a University of Illinois scientist working on his own time. Japalac is not one ingredient, like hydrogen or zinc; it is compounded of several ingredients, like a druggist's prescription. In a recent survey, four doctors were unable to trace a single case of fatal illness directly to Japalac. Yes, Japalac— 'It puts your intestines back on the right track.' Yes—"

"Japalac," said Professor Fodorski, pondering. "Now what do you suppose is the derivation of that excellent name?"

"Simple as ABC," replied Dr. Cartwright. "It's Calapaj spelled backward."

"Of course," said Professor Fodorski, looking sheepish.

"—and the family size for an eight years' supply. And now back to Bill Stern."

"Thank you, Ed Cheevers—the co-captains

are meeting in the center of the field for that all-important toss of the coin. For Tulane we have Hank Du Bois, Two-ton Perregaux, Merl Bronski, R. Bradford, and Chug Chug Stewart, and representing the Unicorns are Allen, Oglethorpe, Hoskins, Meathammer, and Wisely—"

"I wonder why they have so many co-captains," said Mrs. Cartwright.

"I inquired about that," replied her husband. "There isn't any reason, actually. It just reflects the growth of red tape in general. The ailment started in bureaucracy, and has finally worked its way down to football."

"What will be the ultimate result?"

"Complete strangulation. Extinction of the race."

"Oh."

"—won the toss and will receive, defending the goal to our left as we face forward. They are lining up, the Green Wave of Tulane wearing, ah, green jerseys and the Unicorns of Southern Baptist in their traditional gold and silver, symbolic of their mining colleges, or rather, mining college, for I do not imagine that they have two colleges, or rather, one college each for gold and for silver. Ha, ha. THERE IT GOES! A long end-over-end—"

"By the way," said Mrs. Cartwright, "is there any other kind of a kickoff?"

"That's all," answered her husband. "Just the long end-over-end. It's in the rule book."

"—taken on the 15, fakes to his right and comes straight up the field. He's at the 20, the 25, the 30, hit hard at the 30 by two, three men, and falls forward to the 33. Make that the 42. But there's a man down; Tulane has a man down on the field—it's Du Bois, no, Bronski, and time is out. Picture if you will—"

"I hope he is not seriously injured," said Fodorski.

"It's always hard to tell. Stern tries to put people at their ease about these things."

"—can almost say with fair assurance that this boy is not critically hurt. They're helping him off the field; six of his teammates are helping, or carrying him off of the field—oh, ah! a man has gone back for his—no, it's his helmet. They're placing him in the ambulance, and I can assure you, Mr. and Mrs. Bronski, if you are listening, that your boy will receive the very best of care. A well-appointed ambulance is kept near the sidelines throughout the entirety of the game, and any injury, any injury whatsoever, will—receive—prompt—attention. This boy has an *excellent chance!* For no pains, and I mean none, and yes, I'll repeat that, *no* pains are spared to see that these boys are protected, and I mean very well protected indeed, in this traditional American sport. The ambulance is driving out of the stadium, in a hurry, and play is about to be resumed."

"I imagine the Bronskis feel relieved," said Mrs. Cartwright. "I'm glad they've got a well-appointed ambulance and don't have to carry him to the hospital by hand."

"—wait a minute! Southern Baptist is placing an entirely new team on the field. At fourth down, with Tulane on their own 40-yard line and forced to punt, S.B.I.T. is changing teams, to the last man. I am not in a position to say what's going on yet—that's in the lap of the gods—but we will hang on and find out. Yes, the Unicorns appear to be shifting an offensive team into the lineup. This is a radical departure, and we'll get some official word in just a minute as to whether it constitutes legal football procedure. Picture—"

"What's all this?" said Dr. Cartwright.

"Why, the truth is, I guess I'm responsible, in a way," said Professor Fodorski. "I was reading the rule book and mentioned to Mr. Stockworth the possibility of using offensive and defensive teams, changing as the ball changed hands."

"Why, I think that's wonderful!" cried Mrs. Cartwright.

"Perhaps we should see if it works."

"Ladies and gentlemen, we are seeing history made here today. S.B.I.T., stung by that narrow defeat of last year and the fact that they are a two-touchdown underdog in this game, has evolved or developed a system of offensive and defensive teams. And you may well believe that this will arouse plenty of discussion tomorrow in football circles. All right, you downtown quarterbacks—is this or is it not ethical football? What are the cros and pons, pros and cons, pardon me, if you will—"

Throughout the first half, Tulane's expected superiority was effectively nullified by the innovation Professor Fodorski had passed along to Stockworth. Though a warmhearted concert of boos greeted each hurrying cloud of players,

the Unicorn coach was not dissuaded from his plan. The green-jerseyed team, a pitiful minority of eleven, was held for downs five times in the first quarter and played the whole half without making a single serious threat. Southern's offense, while not functioning brilliantly, yet gave promise of developing into something interesting.

"They're getting the hang of it," said Mulligan, on the bench. "You'll have something there in a game or two, Flip."

In Fillipowitz, a working back of the old school, resistance to the new system was dying slowly. "Me, I like to see a halfback make a tackle once in a while. It knocks the conceit out of his guts."

When the half ended, the score was still 0–0, and Dr. Cartwright said, "Now we'll see what Stern and the boys make of it."

"—a man that I think needs no introduction to any of you," said Stern. "We're very fortunate in getting him up here in our broadcasting booth. Tell me, Coach Harvey Nickerson, head coach of the University of Southwestern California at San Pedro, what are you doing in New Orleans?"

"I came down here for the—"

"Right, you are attending the football game. Now, Harvey, you have, have you not, seen a lot of football in your time, am I right in that?"

"Why—"

"Exactly. Now what is your impression of this first half? How do you think these two teams stack up in a comparative way?"

"Well, this first half has seen some good, hard football, Bill. Both sides are playing hard and very good football."

"Defensive and offensive?"

"Why, yes, Bill. I'd say that the offensive play has been very good up to now and defensively, the play has been marked by hard, clean play."

"You'd say both sides were playing good, hard football, both offensively and defensively, would you, Harvey?"

"Yes, I would, Bill."

"That's great. Now would you mind telling our radio audience, Harvey, how you think this second half is likely to go? What do you look for in this second half?"

"Well, Bill, I look for plenty more action. I'd say that you'll see a lot of good, hard football out here today in this second half. Both teams are playing that kind of football."

"Thank you, Harvey Nickerson, for your rundown on the first half of this annual classic between the Green Wave of Tulane and the

Unicorns of S.B.I.T. It was a pleasure to have you with us."

"Pleasure to be here, Bill."

"And now for a few statistics. In the matter of fumbles recovered between the 10- and 20-yard lines, Tulane had a slight edge, with two to one. Ground gained on mousetrapping plays —Southern Baptist leads in total yardage, with 37 to 23, and I think, ladies and gentlemen, that that will go into the record books as a record for a partially rainy-day game played below the Mason Dixon line. I'm not sure, but I will check that and bring it up to date for you in just a very few minutes."

"Confound these statistics," said Dr. Cartwright. "I never have understood why they insist on keeping track of all these piddling triumphs. It gives the game about the same exciting quality as the annual report of the Bureau of Fisheries."

"But it's nowhere as bad as baseball," said Mrs. Cartwright. "*They* write it *all* down—who caught a left-handed fly within three feet of a center-field fence between 4 and 5 P.M. on any July 4, record number of steel-rimmed spectacles worn by a visiting outfield in a double-header, and so on. *Base*ball's the one. Comparatively speaking, this sounds like pretty essential stuff to me."

"Well, maybe you're right—oh, oh, did you get that one? Tulane also established a new record for a player with the worst twisted jockey strap in a conference game; word just came up from the dressing room. A fellow named Eubanks."

"I guess we've had enough statistics," said Mrs. Cartwright.

"—probably one of the greatest gatherings of celebrities ever to witness a ball game in any section of these United States. As I look around, I can see Hunter Galloway of the United Press, Dan Silberberg of the Nassau *Times,* Hannibal Coons of the Pacific Palisades *Courier,* Douglas Leigh of the New York *Journal-American,* Ollie Barbour of the Philadelphia *Inquirer,* Bill Riley of the St. Louis *Post-Dispatch,* and Red Hershon of the Atlanta *Journal,* to name but a few of the notables gathered here for this classic. Picture if you will—"

Professor Fodorski thrilled to the swelling uproar that inundated Stern when the teams reappeared. Statistically, the reappearance was an apparent failure, for the announcer added nothing to the newborn digits bearing on the first half; instead, he took up a directional message about the wind advantage; and the kickoff came simultaneously with his observation that "if the wind were descending from dead above, or overhead, there of course would be little advantage to either side, but the record books contain no mention of any such case."

The blowup came five minutes after the start of the third quarter. As reported by one of the New Orleans papers, "Due to the unfair tactics of wholesale substitution employed by Southern Baptist, a Tulane quick kick was accidentally blocked on the 15-yard line. Oglethorpe, one of a legion of S.B.I.T. tackles in transit throughout the afternoon, stumbled onto the ball in the end zone, recognized it, and fell on it, accounting for the first score. The attempted conversion fizzled weakly off into the mud."

This was a slightly pessimistic view of the incident. In fact, Stern saw it as "one of the greatest exhibitions of line play ever witnessed on a Southern or any other kind of gridiron, not that the Tulane line has not done equally fine work this afternoon, and always does."

This score, 6–0, stood until the last three minutes of play, when, with Tulane suddenly shaking free from midfield to the 20-yard line, Dr. Cartwright prone on the sofa, his wife commencing a vigorous dusting of things like curtains, wallpaper, and the undersides of ash trays, and Professor Fodorski making rapid notes on a pad, the aspect of the game shifted dangerously. In two line plays, Tulane picked up 7 yards. A deceptive sweep around left end added 5 yards and a first down on the 8-yard line.

Dr. Cartwright was beginning to breathe hoarsely and Professor Fodorski chewed the rubber out of his eraser, swallowed it, choked, and got it back up with difficulty.

"If they lose the thing at this stage, I'll resign my chair and get into another business," said Cartwright.

Fodorski, his wind returned, was working furiously at a defensive alignment that might, he thought, stave off the inevitable. Leaning forward, he shouted into the radio, "Perhaps an 8-man line, and substitute the—"

"—knocking at the golden gate," replied Stern. "The question is, will—Tulane—get—back—into—this ballgame? The clock shows two minutes and ten seconds and time is becoming an ever-increasing factor—"

Dr. Cartwright sprang from the sofa, picked up a copy of Burton's *Anatomy of Melancholy,* which he believed shaded a bound file of the *Southern Literary Messenger* by at least three ounces, and threatened the announcer with it.

"Put down that book," said Mrs. Cartwright, and she dusted his head and shoulders as the next play, a quarterback sneak, moved the ball to the 6-yard line. By now, the noise of the stands effaced Stern's disintegrating voice very effectively. In the background, they heard him urging his audience to try and "picture" something or other, but they were unable to identify it. Then the referees presumably waved the crowds to quiet, for in a slight lull, a reduction of the racket by perhaps five or six hundred decibels, the harassed announcer was heard to scream, "The old Statue of Liberty and it—"

The rest was swallowed up, engulfed by a wave of sound so thunderous that the radio's knobs jumped and hummed, and Fodorski scrambled back out of his chair like a foot soldier ducking a grenade.

Mrs. Cartwright, standing over her husband, said, "He seems to be turning blue."

"We lost," he replied. "You needn't tell me we didn't. I recognize that sound out of a home crowd."

"There is the matter of the extra point," said Fodorski.

"They won't miss, they never do."

"—Bradford dived for him at the 50, but he was straight-armed right smack in the kisser and Allen romped straight on to pay dirt. In all my experience as an announcer, ladies and gentlemen, and if you will forgive the personal intrusion, that has been extensive, I have never seen a play broken up with such effortless ease. As Bradford cocked his arm for the old Statue, Allen, who had just come into the ballgame with Southern's other offensive backs, knifed through and beat Tulane's right end to the ball. It was a perfectly executed Statue of Liberty play, in reverse. He picked it out of the quarterback's hand, tucked it under his left arm, and headed, if you will pardon me, for Ellis Island. Never, I am sure, has the old Statue looked as bright to an immigrant coming into these United States as it did to this Southern Baptist team. The extra point was missed and the clock shows nineteen seconds. Now the question is, can—

Tulane—get—back—into—this—ballgame, and it is by no means impossible. Trailing by 12 points—"

Dr. Cartwright lifted one hand weakly, but this time, Fodorski, anticipating a shovel pass with Burton's, leaned over and yanked out the plug. Then he threw his head back and cried, "Yeee-ow!" an expression almost unknown around Wittenberg.

Mrs. Cartwright was bending over her husband again. "He really is in bad shape."

"Do you think some ammonia?"

"Maybe an external application of water."

The stricken man's words, though faint, were audible to both his attendants. "Whisky. Get me a few pints of whisky. Hurry!"

Over their second highball, Fodorski said, "It's what I was calling into the radio. To substitute the offensive backfield. It seemed almost inevitable that the last series of downs would see passing or reckless plays."

"Fodorski," said Dr. Cartwright, "I have a feeling you're going to make history around this campus. If there's another secession, would you be available for the presidency?"

The professor gave his usual modest cough and said, "Well, to tell the truth a distant cousin of my mother's figured in the first separation."

"How do you mean?"

"Mr. Judah P. Benjamin, who was Attorney General and then Secretary of State in the cabinet of Mr. Jefferson Davis."

"What!"

"Oh, yes, a distant cousin."

Dr. Cartwright looked thunderstruck, as if he had just called to mind a long-forgotten fact. "Why, of course! Now, I wonder how many people that ever occurred to?"

"Pardon me?"

"I mean why the devil didn't you say so?"

"I would prefer not to engage in trading with my relations."

"Fodorski," said Dr. Cartwright, "you continue to amaze me."

"Up your leg," said the professor, lifting his glass, not displeased to ring in a toast he had acquired, but not entirely assimilated, only recently.

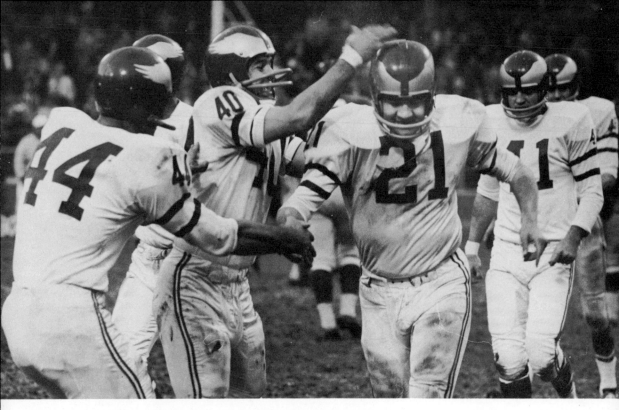

A show of hands for the Eagles' defensive halfback, Jimmy Carr,
after a fumble recovery.

Midweek movie review for the Giants in the locker room at Yankee Stadium.

A young admirer reaches for Rosey Brown of the Giants.

PAYOFF ON SUNDAY

313

The late George Trevor, a Yale Blue who wrote football for the New York Sun *for many years, turned out some of the most colorful and romanticized reports on the game ever written in a press box. In hurried longhand—he never used a typewriter—Trevor told of sunsets beyond the stadium walls, old grads wending their way home, glorious youthful efforts on the field below—and, only incidentally, of the tactics that succeeded or failed. His picture of Coach Bill Roper's last game at Princeton, in 1930, is a Trevor classic.*

SILENT TRIBUTE AT OLD NASSAU

George Trevor

The bronze chimes in the belfry atop the Colonial cupola of Nassau Hall did not toll Yale's knell as the yellow-gray fog of a rain-spattered dusk settled on the quiet walks of Princeton last Saturday evening—but they should have!

The ruddy glow of a bonfire at the famous cannon did not light the murk-shrouded Gothic towers of Old Nassau as a victorious memorial to Coach William Roper and the most courageous of the many gritty elevens that he has taught—but it should have!

Yale won the game on the wings of Tommy Taylor's left-handed heave to Pat Sullivan in the end zone—a cross-over pass very similar in conception to the Hoben-Fishwick toss that brought Yale up from behind to triumph in 1927—but to Princeton belongs the laurel wreath usually reserved for the victor. The Tigers, gloriously retrieving the drabbest season in Nassau football history, were greater in defeat than were the Elis in victory.

This blunt statement is not meant as a reflection upon a tenacious, tired Yale team which lost its form unaccountably under the nervous tension of a traditional climax game; it is simply the sentiment of 90 per cent of Yale partisans. As the Eli sympathizers sloshed into the Whistler-like mist toward the orange aura that hung above the distant train yard, you heard them telling each other: "We wanted our boys to win but it was a shame that Princeton had to lose the game after such a superb comeback."

Standing on the marshy soccer field and studying the faces of the 30,000 spectators who were squilching their muddy trail trainward, you saw no elation in the expressions of the violet-corsaged girls and their blue-feathered escorts. Glumly, moodily, the victors trudged along with not a trace of exuberance or hilarity. Their side had won a hairline decision but they felt that they had nothing to cheer about.

No Princeton defeat at Yale's hands has ever left so satisfying a taste in Nassau mouths. No Yale victory over Princeton has ever given Eli adherents so little cause to rejoice. For loyal Yale men the one rift of sunshine in this incongruous aftermath of success tinged by disappointment lay in the Homeric exploits of the Eli substitutes. Those inspired reserves, flung into the breach when the Yale regulars cracked wide open, carried the fight to Princeton's victory-frenzied first-stringers, scored the touchdown that won the game and were clawing their way to another when Coach Stevens decided to give his varsity a chance to redeem itself, a chance which was ingloriously foozled!

While Princeton, though beaten, richly deserves the major share of the day's honors, don't forget to drink a toast to the Yale substitutes, who, not content with smothering Princeton's savage attack, launched an aerial counterdrive that wrenched the game from Tiger claws in the third period. Give a long yell, with nine Yales on the end of it, for Avery, Rotan, Stewart, Sargent, Hawley, Hall, Walker, Taylor, Sullivan, Muhlfeld and Charley Heim, the unsung understudies who rescued the regulars from mortifying defeat!

Princeton, the jest of gridiron wisecrackers, uncovered the most devastating offense seen on any Big Three gridiron this year. "Fight!" alone can't explain this Tiger transformation from a tame tabby cat to a ravening Bengal mankiller. No amount of frenzy could have produced that clean-cut blocking, that technically perfect interfering, that smart cohesion between line and backs. Emphatically this wasn't the Princeton team that had disintegrated before Navy; which had bowed abjectly to Brown, Cornell and Lehigh.

We have deliberately refrained from employing the term "moral victory" in connection with Princeton's resurgence. Coach Roper never had any use for that phrase. His last team, playing its last game, pursued actual victory with a fixity of purpose, an unfaltering tenacity that was stirring to behold. Roper's last eleven epitomized its teacher's creed in its tactics. It went out to win, not to hold the score down. With the seconds slipping away, with the fog laying clammy fingers on its throat, this Princeton team disdained the tying field goal and thrust gloriously for the winning touchdown. It lost its gamble by four inches but in defeat it was true to the highest traditions of Princeton football—it didn't fear to put its fortune to the touch and win or lose on a single play.

William Roper's final season on the gridiron was not spent in vain. His reputation as a coach can rest on this 1930 Yale-Princeton game. He demonstrated to the skeptics that he is something more than a "whipper up," something more than an inspirational orator, something more than a psychologist with the gift of stimulating impressionable youngsters to one supreme effort. Only a master football coach could have produced an eleven that tackled, blocked, interfered and displayed such defensive cohesion and continuity of attack as did this Princeton team on Saturday.

Those last ten minutes will live in football saga. Yale, thanks to its gallant subs, leads, 10–7. It is Yale's ball on Princeton's 35-yard line. The orange-helmeted Tigers look drawn and tired. A dismal rain spatters down on 50,000 damp, disheveled spectators, a drab crowd in slickers, mackintoshes and improvised oilcloth capes.

Dr. Mal Stevens, pacing to and fro behind the Yale bench, senses that the time is ripe for the *coup de grâce*. He pats Francis Vincent on the shoulder and whispers into the Yale captain's ear.

A volcanic roar erupts from the Yale stands. The varsity is going in! The varsity is going in to atone for its wretched exhibition in the first half, when Princeton, with Bennett and James alternating as carriers, marched 50 yards to a touchdown, slicing inside Yale's widely spaced tackles. Watch the Yale varsity retrieve its faded laurels! Stand up and shout, you sons of Eli, the belated "slaughter" is about to begin!

This is the sentiment among Yale adherents as Vincent, Loeser, Barres, Flygare, Wilbur Hare, Booth, Crowley, Austen, and Dunn pull on their white helmets—gleaming like human skulls in the murky dusk—and gallop onto the rain-softened gridiron.

Booth cracks his little hands together. "Let's go, Yale!" You hear his resonant voice clear up in the press box. And Yale goes; a fluky pass, partially blocked, is deflected into Loeser's arms. Power House Pat Crowley crunches off tackle carrying two Tigers on his brontosaurian back; Albie himself, darting like a raindrop down a window pane, scoots to Princeton's 7-yard stripe.

"Touchdown!" shriek Yale rooters, who are to change their tune to "Hold 'em!" within five minutes. There is to be no touchdown by this Yale varsity. Princeton has Yale's number. Tightening resolutely in the pinch, the orange-crested black line submerges the Brobdingnagian Crowley and the Lilliputian Booth. On last down Booth's desperate pass, a long diagonal heave, flops harmlessly in the end zone.

And now it is Princeton's turn, the last mad surge to turn the tide. Now begins a march that will be enshrined in Princeton legend, that will be told and retold as often as the stories of Lamar's run, Poe's dash, DeWitt's place-kick, White's twin game thefts and Moffatt's four field goals. Princeton sons will hear from

Princeton fathers how Ricardo Mestres' men marched 78 yards through Yale's vaunted varsity in the last moments of the 1930 game; how they slashed, swooped, and bludgeoned their way to the Blue 2-yard mark only to lose the ball on downs, by 6 inches.

Garry Cochran's iron grenadiers of 1896, "Big Ed" McMillan's irresistibles of 1920, these never made a greater march than the derided "contemptibles" of 1930. Trix Bennett, scorning to favor the tender knee which was expected to give way at any moment, takes turns with burly Jack James at knifing through Yale's tackles.

James is a sophomore capitalizing his prep school reputation for the first time after a disappointing season. Bennett is a senior having his last fling at Yale. What a pair of yard eaters they are and what a line they have in front of them blotting out the Blue ends, trampling down the Blue guards, hamstringing the Blue tackles! It is a Princeton line that has found itself at the eleventh hour of a misspent season, a line which has suddenly been fused into a cohesive unit.

On and on rolls the Orange juggernaut, Bennett stabbing, James pounding. Whenever the rushing game stalls as Yale's frantic line stiffens Bennett flips a pass into the wingback zone. On one of these lancing air thrusts James reaches Yale's 4-yard line.

Only a Gustave Doré's pen could etch the climax scene. A humid mist partially obscures the milling players. Princeton's ball, fourth down—one yard to go for a first down on Yale's 2-yard mark. That yard is equivalent to the winning touchdown for there is just time to crowd in three more plays.

Suddenly a tousle-headed, tow-haired giant leaps from the Yale bench and hobbles laboriously onto the field, hand raised to signal the referee. By the map of Ireland on his pugnacious face you can see that it is Freddy Linehan. Crippled early in the game by a hip bruise, he alone of the Yale regulars has remained on the bench.

Freddy has only one leg under him, but a one-legged Linehan is worth two ordinary guards. He limps to his station, sags down on his bad leg in the mud. Trix Bennett, his lean face blood-smeared, his left jersey sleeve ripped off at the shoulder, takes the ball himself and dives over left tackle behind the bovine rush of Yeckley and Hockenbury, charging shoulder to shoulder.

Linehan meets that savage phalanx, grabbing legs. The wedge recoils, a tangled heap of bodies marks the spot where Nassau hopes lie buried. Just as Pickett's charge was the flood tide of the Confederacy at Gettysburg, so Bennett's vicious thrust represents high-water mark in Princeton's unforgettable advance.

Head Lineman Fisher runs out with his measuring stick. Referee Crowell, his foot planted where the ball stopped, studies the tape. Nobody speaks, nobody breathes.

The mud-stained pigskin is four inches short of the yard pole, chain stretched taut. That's why the big bronze bells in Nassau Hall are silent as the dazed crowd slowly trickles out of Palmer Stadium, but Yale can hear the ghostly echo of those muted chimes, and so can William Winston Roper. They never rang so loudly as the night they never rang at all!

In his excellent biography, Scott Fitzgerald, *Andrew Turnbull recalls their mutual interest in football when Fitzgerald was living on the Turnbull estate in Maryland in 1932.*

From *SCOTT FITZGERALD*

Andrew Turnbull

My friendship with him—I was eleven at the time—grew out of football. I too was a student of the game, though my horizons were limited to my Alma Mater, the Gilman Country School. Fitzgerald opened my eyes to Princeton, where a great new coach, Fritz Crisler, and a bumper crop of freshmen players foreshadowed the Tiger juggernauts of 1933–35. As it happened, Princeton had just received into its arms one of Gilman's immortals, a fullback named Pepper Constable. I remember running up the hill at top speed to get a Gilman yearbook wherein was an Achilles-like picture of Constable surrounded by his teammates. Fitzgerald took a polite interest in *my* interest, but I couldn't seem to persuade him that here was an authentic hero. Gilman sounded provincial to him; it lacked the authority of Exeter, say, or Kiski, or Lawrenceville. With prep school captains two and three deep in every position on this spectacular freshman squad. Fitzgerald held out little hope that Constable would ever be heard from again.

He bought a football which we tossed around the lawn when he was feeling athletic. Because I was small for my age and not a fast runner, he was going to make a passer out of me. (He was determined to make *something* out of me, for his instinct was always to mold, manipulate, cajole the human material around him— to get it to perform in one way or another.) He gave me a book by Barry Wood called *What Price Football?* and introduced me to the *Football Annual,* a marvelous publication full of swollen rhetoric and grimacing All-Americas.

That fall, when he took me to Princeton to see the Navy game, I was struck by his uncanny familiarity with the Princeton team. He knew so many details about each player that I suspected him of having memorized the programs of previous contests. His hopes that day were riding on a sophomore with the pungent name of "Katz" Kadlic—no ordinary quarterback according to Fitzgerald, but "a great field general," a kind of Stonewall Jackson with cleats on. Though Kadlic happened to be a pretty fair passer into the bargain, it was his tactical genius that concerned my host, who identified himself in some obscure way with the brains that leavened Princeton's brawn. The best Kadlic could manage that afternoon was a scoreless tie, but the following fall Fitzgerald and I saw him—plus the great freshman team, now sophomores and playing on the varsity—overthrow Columbia 20–0 (the same Columbia team that afterwards defeated Stanford in the Rose Bowl).

317

Unaccountably, my old friend Constable turned up at fullback, where he played the smashing brand of ball I had been telling Fitzgerald about. It was only the beginning of a splendid career, for Constable went on to captain Princeton's undefeated team of 1935 and to be mentioned for All-America.

By then Fitzgerald had left La Paix, but he wrote me a letter giving his version of how this Gilman peasant had risen to high estate. "So far as Constable is concerned," he said, "—*I don't want you to run him down*. He's all right —not as good as his substitute Rulon-Miller but *all right*. And I'm glad. In fact I got him elected Captain—I came into the room in a black-beard disguise during the conclave and pled with them. 'See here,' I said. 'A good back hasn't come out of Gilman since Slagle, & they're starving for somebody to admire, them kids are. Pretty soon they'll begin to turn to dolls like "Apples" Fitzpatrick & "Mozart" Hopney—' but I stopped myself at this juncture. I enclose Fritz Crisler's answer."

The enclosure, a bona fide letter from Crisler, contained a humorous postcript in Fitzgerald's handwriting, which said in part, "I have had Constable elected captain as a favor to your young friend Turnbull." Fitzgerald had ceded a point in his fashion, and yet I always thought it typical that on this Princeton team of glory he was excited by the peppery little climax runner, Gary LeVan, rather than the rugged workhorse Constable.

"You think we should tell him he's talking to the wrong team?"

CARTOON BY HUFFINE

© Fawcett Publications, Inc.

In case there are any doubts about it in New Haven: the author of this short story, a graduate of Miami University in Ohio, attended Yale for one year.

BOOLA BOOLA, BABE RUTH, AND A JUG OF WHISKEY SOURS

Milton White

I keep, among my Yale memorabilia, the New York *Times* Sunday sports section for November 20, 1932. The paper carries complete coverage of the Yale-Harvard game played the preceding day in one of the worst rainstorms in New Haven's history. Walter Levering ran 45 yards for a touchdown in the first period. Pat Sullivan earned the extra point when he carried the ball across on an ingenious run after finding it impossible to put the slippery ball in position for Curtin to kick from placement. Levering ran 55 yards for another touchdown in the third; and the last touchdown came on a 24-yard fourth-down pass from Lassiter to Marting on the first play of the final period. Yale beat Harvard, 19–0, the most decisive victory over the Crimson in thirty years.

I keep the copy of the sports section primarily because of a small news item on page 4, following the detailed account of the game. The item reads: "Babe Ruth sat in the downpour with Mrs. Ruth until even his massive physique could not stand it any longer. He left in the fourth quarter totally unnoticed. He was just

another bedraggled figure heading for the exits."

I have no quibble with the New York *Times,* but their report is inaccurate, and for a long time I meant to write to the editor. The truth is *I* noticed Babe Ruth leave the Yale Bowl. I sat next to him throughout most of the game. He invited me to share his gallon jug of whisky sours.

Marge Fulton missed all of that. Marge was to be my date for the game. Her father arranged it, early in November. I remember that I was walking back to Fayerweather after Freshman English class (*Henry IV, Part I*) when I saw Mr. Fulton, who is from Springfield, my home town, step out of a taxicab on Elm Street. Mr. Fulton hailed me, hurried toward me, and at the same time looked back, signaling the driver to wait. I braced myself—I was small, bespectacled, and weighed only 88 pounds. Mr. Fulton, tall, pot-bellied, with an enormous shock of white hair, seized my hand and pumped it.

"What luck!" he shouted at me. "I stopped over on my way back from New York just to see you." He clapped me on the shoulder. "So

320

you're a freshman at Yale!" he cried, sweeping his hand in the direction of the Old Campus. "You look all settled in."

He glanced up at the windows of the dormitories around Berkeley Oval and lowered his voice. "I might as well come to the point," he said. "How would you like to invite Margie to the Yale-Harvard game? Send her a letter. You don't have to say anything about my seeing you. And don't worry about the expense. I'll send you a check in a few days."

"Well," I said, embarrassed. I stared across the street, at Jerry selling his newspapers in front of Yale Station.

Mr. Fulton had five daughters—but I really liked Marge. I had taken her to my senior prom at Central High School.

"I'll write Marge," I said, "but you don't have to send me a check."

Mr. Fulton held up his hand. "I know how things are at home with your Dad. I'll send you fifteen dollars. I just want you and Margie to have a good time. Okay? Fine!" He looked down at me, clapped me on the shoulder, and tugged me along with him to the taxicab.

"You don't have to send me any money!" I cried, as the taxicab pulled away, but Mr. Fulton only winked.

At that time of morning most of Yale was in class. Berkeley Oval was quiet. The bright November sunlight pointed up the soot in the aged red brick of the buildings surrounding the open courtyard—White, Berkeley, Lampson, Haughton, and Fayerweather—all doomed to be torn down at the end of the schol year. *"Après nous, le déluge,"* we freshmen said.

As I stared at the morning sunlight on the red-brick Round House near the entrance to the Oval and at the six bare trees in the courtyard, it occurred to me that a fellow had only four Yale-Harvard games to attend in his lifetime as an undergraduate. I probably couldn't afford to go to the games played in Cambridge; that left me only the two games in New Haven.

I pushed open the door to the suite I shared with Mike Sayles. Mike stepped out of his bedroom wearing a shining new raccoon coat that reached almost to his ankles. He also wore a black derby. "Snazzy, eh?" he said, smiling. It was the first time I'd ever seen anyone Mike's age wearing a derby.

"I think I have a date for the Yale-Harvard game," I said to Mike.

"Swell. We'll have a party," Mike said. He'd already invited his girl, Jan Browning, down from Smith for the game.

In a burst of enthusiasm I said, "I'll pay for the gin if you get it." Mike knew a bootlegger on Temple Street.

That night Mike and Art Keyes went to the Paramount to see *Trouble in Paradise* with Miriam Hopkins and Herbert Marshall and Kay Francis. I liked Lubitsch's movies, but I didn't go. Instead I put 35 cents in an empty Lucky Strike tobacco tin and stayed in my room and read Plautus. Somehow I had the feeling that Mr. Fulton would forget to send a check. (I never did get one.)

For the next two weeks I saved every cent I could. *Roxanne,* the musical version of *Cyrano,* came to the Shubert, and William Lyon Phelps recommended it, but I didn't go. On Sundays, when Commons was closed, I ate only one meal: at eleven o'clock in the morning I went to the Waldorf Cafeteria on Chapel Street and ordered bacon and eggs and home-fried potatoes, then around six o'clock I ate an apple. That carried me until Monday morning when Commons opened.

I had just one letter from Marge, accepting my invitation to the game. She said she'd arrive in New Haven at 10:40 A.M. on Saturday, the nineteenth. She added that she'd arranged to stay overnight with her aunt, who lived out near the Yale Bowl.

On the Saturday of the Yale-Harvard game, after breakfast at Commons, I trudged through the rain to the La Belle Florists, way down Chapel Street a couple of blocks past Woolworth's. Earlier in the week I'd arranged with the lady florist who worked there to pick up a white chrysanthemum for only 35 cents. The rain dripped from my slicker as I waited in the shop for the woman to fasten a blue and white ribbon onto the chrysanthemum. "Beautiful!" she said, holding up the corsage.

The chrysanthemum looked small to me, but I didn't say anything.

The rain, when I stepped outside, had turned into a downpour. I debated whether to take a trolley car back to the campus, decided against it, and trotted across town, holding the box with Marge's corsage under my slicker. When I arrived at Fayerweather I found a telegram under the door. Marge had wired that she was fighting the grippe, but she'd try to get to New Haven, anyway. I was to meet the 10:40 train.

"Oh, fine!" I said to the bowl of guppies on the mantel.

The 10:40 was posted ten minutes late. Rain swept across the platform as I waited for Marge's train to arrive. At eleven o'clock I walked back into the station and stood in the wet and restless line at the information desk while the attendant explained to a white-haired lady carrying a Pomeranian that to get to Port Chester the lady would have to take the train coming in on Track 6 and then change to a local at Stamford. The station smelled of wet wool and chewing gum. The attendant told me at last that the train would be thirty-three minutes late.

Track 6, when I returned to it, was packed with Yale men waiting, glaring up at the rain. I had to stand at the edge of the platform, out from under the roof. By the time the Springfield train swung into sight around the bend, my trousers were soaked from the rain, and the cardboard box containing Marge's chrysanthemum had become soggy. The fellows on the platform stepped back as the train steamed past us, then they pushed forward, peering into the coach windows. The platform exploded into frantic waving and shouting, bodies thudding, heads ducking the rain. I saw Mrs. Fulton, Marge's mother, climb out of a coach near the end of the train and look around. She was alone and carried an overnight case. My heart sank as I elbowed my way through the crowd toward her. Mrs. Fulton, a round, ruddy woman in a black coat with a huge fox collar, saw me and raised a pudgy hand. "Margie couldn't come! Grippe!" she cried. "I've come instead."

"Oh," I said. I handed her the chrysanthemum.

"How sweet!" Mrs. Fulton said.

Two nuns under a large black umbrella stopped beside us. One of them leaned forward, tapped me on the shoulder, and told me that she was Sister Theresa. Her companion was Sister of the Nativity. "We have suitcases back in the coach, and it's impossible to find a porter," she said. Rain dribbled from her umbrella onto my head.

"You're dripping rain, Sister Theresa," said Sister of the Nativity. I thought she looked like Lillian Gish wearing steel-rimmed glasses.

Mrs. Fulton nodded at the nuns. "Of course he'll help," she said, pushing me.

Sister of the Nativity led me up the aisle of the coach. "Perhaps Sister Theresa and I should have asked someone else," she said, looking back at me. She pointed to two enormous Gladstone bags on the overhead rack.

"I can manage." I said.

Sister of the Nativity spread a copy of the Springfield *Republican* on the seat. I climbed up, lifted one of the suitcases off the rack, and tumbled into the aisle. My cap fell off. The man in the seat ahead sprang to his feet. With a sigh, he reached up to the rack, lifted off the remaining suitcase, and handed it to me.

Sister of the Nativity cleared the aisle for me. I staggered after her, lugging the two Gladstone bags. Mrs. Fulton and Sister Theresa stood far down on the platform under Sister Theresa's black umbrella, chatting. Mrs. Fulton peeked out from under the umbrella. "Here he comes," she called brightly, nodding in my direction. She stepped aside to allow the Pomeranian, its leash trailing free, to dart past her. The white-haired Port Chester lady hurried along the platform calling. "Fanfan! Fanfan!" The Pomeranian skidded to a halt beside me, looked up, barked twice at me, and sank its teeth into the cuff of my trousers.

"Good heavens!" cried Sister of the Nativity.

"Naughty!" the Port Chester lady cried, pulling Fanfan from me. The cuff of my trousers ripped. The lady pressed Fanfan to her breast. "He's *never* done that before!" she said, frowning at me accusingly. Fanfan licked her cheek, then barked at me. Mrs. Fulton and Sister Theresa hurried forward, mumbling sympathy. The Port Chester lady glanced at the blue and white ribbon on Mrs. Fulton's corsage, and turned to me. "Are you Yale?" she cried. "Oh, I *am* sorry."

At the corner of College and Elm. Mrs. Fulton and I got off the trolley car—taxicabs had been unobtainable at the railroad station—and, thoroughly drenched, we ran along Elm Street toward Berkeley Oval. A couple of white petals fluttered from the chrysanthemum on Mrs. Fulton's shoulder. In the entry to Fayerweather I tripped on the torn cuff of my trousers. Art Keyes, a towel over his shoulder, had come into the corridor on his way to the lavatory. I saw him glance at me, then at Mrs. Fulton. I shrugged and closed the door to the suite behind me.

"So this is Yale," Mrs. Fulton said, surveying the study. "Somehow I thought it would be fancier." She stared at the bowl of guppies on the mantel and the Yale 1936 banner on the wall. "You could call it homey," she said. She draped her coat over a chair, slipped out of her shoes, and examined her wet stockings.

"Gin?" I asked, pointing nonchalantly to the two bottles on the table. "There's grapefruit juice to go with it."

"You don't have whiskey?" Mrs. Fulton asked. "Well, gin will do." She competently opened a bottle, poured gin generously into the tumbler I handed her, and added a dash of grapefruit juice. "There," she said, sipping.

The shout "Fiiiyer! Fiiiyer!" resounded at

that moment throughout Berkeley Oval. "What in the world!" Mrs. Fulton cried. Glass in hand, she hastened toward the rain-streaked window and looked out at the two fellows and their girl friends dashing past in the rain, on their way to Haughton.

The gin had warmed me. "It's the sex-crazed onga-onga crying for its mate," I explained to Mrs. Fulton. "When any young female passes through Berkeley Oval, all the fellows lean out the dormitory windows and yell 'Fire.' It's a tradition." I threw open the window, stuck my head out into the rain, and yelled "Fiiiyer!"

"The onga-onga?" Mrs. Fulton said, finishing off her gin.

I nodded. Mrs. Fulton frowned, then shrugged, walked back to the table, and refilled her glass. She picked up her overnight case. "My stockings are wet. I'll have to change," she said. She looked down at the torn cuff of my trousers. "I'll sew up that tear for you."

I could hear Mrs. Fulton humming behind the closed door of my bedroom as she sewed the rip in my trousers. Staring out at the rain, I shifted my position on the study window seat so that my bathrobe covered my bare feet—I was drying my shoes and socks on the radiator. For want of anything better to do, I padded across the study and fed the guppies on the mantel.

The cry "Fiiiyer!" echoed once again in the Oval. "To the window, man!" Mrs. Fulton shouted to me, through the closed door of the bedroom.

Dutifully I flung open the window, wrapped my robe tight over my chest, leaned out into the rain, and shouted "Fiiiyer!" at the Yale man and his date who dashed past.

A taxicab pulled up to the curb on Elm Street and I saw my roommate, Mike Sayles, step out and start running toward Fayerweather. As he leaped up the entry steps, he saw me leaning out the window in my bathrobe. He looked startled.

"My roommate's coming," I shouted to Mrs. Fulton.

Mike burst in and stopped short in the center of the study.

"Hey!" I said to him.

"I'm finished!" Mrs. Fulton called. She opened the bedroom door and stepped into the study, smiling at Mike, holding my trousers out to me.

"This is Marge's *mother,* for heaven's sake," I said. I added quickly, "A dog bit me at the railroad station. At least he ripped my trousers."

"I see," Mike said. He inspected the two bottles of gin, and tucked the unopened bottle under his arm. "Well!" he said, still smiling.

"For heaven's sake," I said. I stalked into the bedroom to put on my trousers. Mike called to me, urging me to hurry: they were going to have lunch at the Taft—Jan had reserved a table—and after lunch they were all going to listen to the football game on the radio in Bill Callsen's room. Bill was a junior, with a room in Branford. "No one's going out to the Bowl," Mike said.

I opened the bedroom door. "*I'm* going to the game," I said.

"In this downpour?" Mike asked.

Mrs. Fulton sighed, lifted the depleted bottle of gin, and poured herself a drink. "It's misherable outside," she said.

Mike left a minute later. I watched him climb into the taxicab where Jan Browning waited. Mrs. Fulton stood beside me at the window, sipping her drink. "You're missing a good time with your young friends," she said.

"Fiiiyer! Fiiiyer!" shouted a fellow from a window in Berkeley.

Mrs. Fulton chuckled. Suddenly she turned on her heel, hurried to the door leading out to the corridor, and disappeared. By the time I stepped into the corridor, a commotion had already broken out in the lavatory. Mrs. Fulton, beaming, emerged, clutching two rolls of paper. Art Keyes, dripping from his shower, a towel wrapped around his midriff, peeked out the lavatory, his face incredulous. As Mrs. Fulton hurried past me, she chuckled again. She threw open the window in the study, leaned out, and yelled "Fiiiyer!" at two girls running across the Oval. Then, leaning far forward out the window, she sent a roll of tissue sailing high into the air. The tissue caught in the branch of a tree. The roll unfurled soggily in the rain. Voices across the Oval cheered. Mrs. Fulton shouted "Fiiiyer!" and tossed the second roll of tissue into the tree.

With horror, I heard the increase of intensity in the cries echoing throughout the Oval. A barrage of tissue soared from the windows of Berkeley, White, Fayerweather, and Haughton. Rain plastered the tissue against the bare branches of the trees in the yard. Mrs. Fulton lifted her glass in a gesture that encompassed all of Yale, then flung the glass into the Oval. The fellows leaning out the dormitory windows cheered her. Mrs. Fulton stepped back into the room and smiled at me. "There!" she said.

Five minutes later we stood on Elm Street, dodging the spray of the taxicabs that sped past us, unheeding our signals. Mrs. Fulton held a soaked copy of the Yale *Daily News* over her head. "You're too timid!" she shouted at me, over the downpour. A taxicab turned the corner at College Street. Mrs. Fulton stepped into the road and held up her hand. I caught the surprised look on the driver's face as he slammed on the brakes. Mrs. Fulton opened the door of the taxicab and smiled at the two men in the back seat. "Are you Yale?" she asked. "You won't mind dropping me off at my sister's, will you?" Without waiting for an answer she took her overnight case from me and climbed into the taxicab; then she leaned out and shook my hand. "It's been glorious!" she said. "Now, go and join your friends, have a wonderful time." She slammed shut the door and lowered the window. "Fiiiyer!" she cried, and the taxicab pulled away.

The bells in Harkness Tower tolled the hour. Determinedly, I sloshed across the campus to Chapel Street, rain dripping off the brim of my cap, streaking my glasses. In the Waldorf Cafeteria I gulped down a dish of macaroni and cheese and a glass of milk. I trudged through the rain again to the nearest trolley stop and boarded a trolley car marked Yale Bowl. The car was empty. Rain leaked in through the door. I took a seat far in back and tried to look out at the streets of New Haven (I'm on my way to the Yale-Harvard game, I told myself), but I could hardly see through the rain and steam that covered the windows.

At the end of the trolley line, soaked, I sloshed the remaining blocks to the Yale Bowl, hating the smell of wet wool. The Bowl lay surrounded by a sea of mud and water. The people around me, hurrying toward the ramps, wore slickers, rubber boots, sheepskin coats, and ponchos fashioned out of dime-store oilcloth, and they talked about rain, rain, rain.

Ten minutes before game time the Bowl seemed almost deserted. Wide pools of water covered the empty playing field. Most of the spectators had ignored their seat reservations and were huddled together in a section on the 50-yard line. I found myself all alone in the center of a section of seats on the 30-yard line. I could hear the rain beating down on my slicker, an awfully solitary sound. I didn't want to remember my first Yale-Harvard game like that, so I edged my way through the empty rows of benches toward the 50-yard line. I sat by myself a few feet away from most of the crowd.

In the row behind me a man and woman seated on the aisle held a large piece of linoleum over their heads as protection against the rain. The man beckoned. "Come on over," he called to me. "You don't want to sit alone!"

I climbed over the bench and moved across the aisle. The couple smiled up at me from under the linoleum. The man was Babe Ruth. He looked just like all the pictures I'd ever seen of him.

At that moment, heads lowered against the rain, the Yale and Harvard teams sloshed onto the playing field. The crowd stomped and cheered. The Yale Band struck up "Boola Boola."

"Sit down. Have a drink," Babe Ruth said to me, over the sound of the cheering. I sat down in a puddle on the bench. Mrs. Ruth shifted the piece of linoleum so that part of it covered me, too. Babe Ruth lifted a gallon jug from under the bench, poured something that looked like a whiskey sour into a paper cup, and handed it to me. "To Eli Yale," he said.

My hand was shaking. "Eli Yale," I said.

Babe Ruth grinned at me and raised his paper cup against the rain, and that is the way the moment has stopped for me, for all time.

How pro football scout Emlen Tunnell serves his team.

ON ANY GIVEN SUNDAY

Herbert Warren Wind

My interest in how a football team scouts its rivals was first whetted back in 1947, when I read a book by Dana X. Bible called *Championship Football*. Bible was then director of athletics at the University of Texas, after having spent more than thirty years coaching the game at such hard-hitting schools as Texas A. & M., Nebraska, and Texas itself. His exposition of how to mold a winning team was spelled out in unflagging detail, down to the last shoulder block by the weak-side tackle on an end sweep to the strong side. To my mind, though, no chapter was quite as impressive as the one on scouting. In that chapter, which I recently reread, Bible revealed that he could generally count on getting a good appraisal of a future opponent by having his scout answer forty-two mimeographed pages of questions and fill out eight more pages of comments and diagrams. The book supplied a sample of this scouting form, broken down into such logical divisions as Defensive Formation, Offensive Formations, Forward-Passing Attack, and the like. I have no idea how many eyes and hands Bible expected a scout to have, but the conventional number would hardly have sufficed. For example, under Kickoff, a rather minor subdivision, the scout was required to record the direction, height, and distance of each kick, the lineup of the kicking team, the players who were down first under the kick, the players who were down last, and the player (if any) who acted as the safety man, plus such additional data as whether the kick was made from the center of the field, whether a deliberately short kick was ever tried, whether the ends went straight downfield or cut toward the ball, and, finally, which players were the most consistent tacklers.

In the sixteen years since Bible's book appeared, some aspects of football have changed a good deal, principally in the direction of complexity. As far as scouting is concerned, there has been one significant change. Although motion pictures have long been used in both college and pro circles as an adjunct to the scouting report, until comparatively recently the practice of photographing a future opponent in action was generally considered unethical—a violation of the spirit of the game. In the middle 1950's, however, the National Football League, realizing that its teams had been informally supplying one another with films for many years on a private-agreement basis, decided that it would be much healthier to sanction an open exchange of films. Since that time, not only in the N.F.L. but among some colleges, "game films" have become increasingly important, and today many coaches have come to consider them, rather than the formal scouting report, the primary source of information; indeed, two N.F.L. teams—the St. Louis Cardinals and the Los Angeles Rams—depend almost entirely on films for scouting their opposition. Under the system of distribution that the N.F.L. set up when it gave the camera its official blessing, each team photographs its own game and is responsible for sending a print of the film to the team next on its schedule. For instance, last Monday the New York Giants, who meet the Pittsburgh Steelers this Sunday, dispatched to the Steelers a print of their game against the Washington Redskins last Sunday; in return, the Giants received from Pittsburgh a print of the Steelers' game against the Dallas Cowboys. Since most of the coaches in the league like to study their rivals "in depth," each team is also furnished with a print of its coming opponent's next-to-last game. Needless to say, the film of its own game the previous Sunday plays a prominent part in each team's weekly movie schedule. This is scrutinized as carefully as the film starring its coming opponent. It is nothing out of the ordinary for the coaches to rerun some segments a dozen times, in order to find out why their offense stalled on this or that play, and, as a corollary, why the other team moved the ball so well in specific situations. As befits the entrepreneurs of what has grown to be a multimillion-dollar business, the member clubs of the N.F.L. are cooperation itself when it comes to doing one another a reasonable favor in the film department. For example, when the Giants screened their own movie of their 35–24 loss to the Cleveland Browns on October 13, they discovered that their cameraman happened to have a very poor angle on the critical part of the 72-yard touchdown run that Jimmy Brown, the great Cleveland fullback, had reeled off against them; in the Giants' film, Brown appeared to sift like a specter through a mass of would-be-tacklers. Intent on finding out precisely how their defense had fallen down on that play, the Giants got in touch with the Browns, who immediately dispatched a copy of their own game film; in this one, Brown's gallop was clearly recorded in its full crunching efficiency. All in all, there is some ground for believing that a man like Vince Lombardi, the coach of the Green Bay Packers and a particularly insatiable viewer of films, sees more footage in a year than Louella Parsons and

Sidney Skolsky put together.

Despite all this reliance on the camera, the scout is regarded by most coaches today as being only a little less valuable than he was back in the Biblical era. In the N.F.L., where this kind of scout is called a game scout, to differentiate him from a talent scout, who combs the college ranks for likely material, the system of scouting varies slightly from team to team. Quite a few teams employ large scouting staffs, which fan out each weekend and cover several games. Other teams—the Cleveland Browns, for one—use a pair of scouts, who work in tandem, one charting the game play by play and the other feeding observations into a tape recorder. (Pete Halas, a nephew of the Chicago Bears' coach and a member of a Connecticut electronics firm, is credited with having introduced this wrinkle.) However, the setup that most pro teams use calls for the bulk of the work to be done by one man. The dean of the league scouts is Wally Cruice, a former Northwestern halfback who has worked for the Packers since 1946. The Giants' scout is Emlen Tunnell, an outstanding safety man for the team from 1948 through 1958, who finished out his playing career with the Packers in 1961 and returned to the Giants in his new capacity last year. Tunnell's predecessor was Frank Gifford, the Giants' veteran offensive back, who filled in as a scout during the 1961 season, when he was in temporary retirement. *His* most illustrious predecessor was Jack Lavelle, a huge, amiable sporting-goods salesman, who was named the team's first scout, in 1935, and stayed on until his death, in 1958. The story has it that when Lavelle, on the eve of his first assignment, protested to Steve Owen, the Giants' coach, that he didn't understand what he was expected to do, Owen told him, "Just go look at the game and write me a letter about it." Lavelle quickly became one of the most fluent letter writers in the business.

Tunnell acquired his extensive knowledge of N.F.L. football as a defensive back and a punt-return specialist. A tall Negro from Philadelphia who played his college football at Iowa, he first came to prominence in the early 1950's when he, Otto Schellbacher, Harmon Rowe, and Tom Landry (now the head coach of the Dallas Cowboys) formed the Giants' celebrated "umbrella defense"—the most accomplished anti-forward-pass unit of that day. During his fourteen seasons as a professional, Tunnell intercepted seventy-nine passes—an N.F.L. record. He also holds the league record for most punts returned—two hundred and fifty-eight, for a total of 2,209 yards. (He dropped only two punts that the other team recovered.) "A fellow like Tunnell gives you the extra dimension you can't get off of film," Allie Sherman, the Giants' pleasant, capable, and highly articulate coach, told me a short time ago. "Tunnell knows the mechanics of the game thoroughly. He knows the methods of the individual coaches. He knows the ballplayers, and he can evaluate their performances acutely. I think it helps that he played on defense. Small things— like how often a team will red-dog a linebacker, and in what situations—we can get from the films. And also large things, like how this team or that team aims to achieve continuity and consistency on the attack. What we can't get, and what Tunnell gives us, is, say, a defensive back's reaction speed under certain conditions, or a linebacker's pursuit on certain types of plays, or the spacing of the linemen up front when they defense different formations. Tunnell knows what we are looking for. He has vision. He has concept." Sherman is one of the livelier exponents of the modern football idiom, which has enriched the language with a host of new words, such as the verb "to defense" (to defend against), and has given new shades of meaning to old words, such as the noun "pursuit"—i.e., a player who has good pursuit doesn't stand around doing nothing when he has been fooled on a play, but turns and chases the ball carrier.

In order to learn a bit more about scouting, I arranged with Tunnell this fall to accompany him on an expedition he would be making to study and report on the St. Louis Cardinals, an up-and-coming young team that had started the season auspiciously. This trip took him to Washington on October 27—midseason, exactly— where the Cardinals were playing the Redskins the week before their first game with the Giants. On that last Sunday in October, the Giants were in Cleveland for a return meeting with the Browns. Going into the game, the Giants had a record of four victories and two defeats, compared to the Browns' record of six straight victories; to stay in the race, the Giants *had* to win—no two ways about it. From the moment I met Tunnell at noon in the railroad terminal in Washington—he had driven over from Princess Anne, Maryland, where, in his secondary capacity as a talent scout, he had watched Maryland State play North Carolina College on Saturday—it was clear that his mind was on the game in Cleveland. It was all he talked about while we had a bite to eat in the station dining room, along with Roscoe Barrick, a young

schoolteacher from Philadelphia (where Tunnell still lives), who was making the weekend swing with the scout. Halfway through the meal, Tunnell excused himself and went out to send the team a telegram. "I feel better now," he said when he returned. "I sent it to Jack Stroud, our offensive captain. 'Win this one for yourselves'—that's what I wired him. Not that you have to worry about veterans like old Stroud being up for a big game like this. It's the young kids I worry about. We can beat those Browns, I'm telling you." After his third cup of coffee, Tunnell seemed more collected, and around twelve-thirty we headed for the new D.C. Stadium, driving out in Barrick's car. "This is one of the real drawbacks of being a scout—you never get to see your own team play," Tunnell said as we climbed the ramps to the visiting scouts' booths, on the top rim of the enormous stadium. "Sherman thought of taking me along to Cleveland, you know. Counting exhibition games, I've seen those Browns play seven times this year. I know that team pretty well. At the last minute, he decided against it. I can see his reasoning. If we beat the Browns today, then our game with the Cards next week becomes a real big one for us, and we wouldn't be in very good shape if we didn't have them scouted, would we? Unless you're really ready, anybody in this league can beat you on any given Sunday."

Although kickoff time—two-fifteen—was more than an hour away when we arrived at our scouting booth, Tunnell immediately opened his attaché case and got his equipment neatly set up on a formica writing shelf that extended from wall to wall under a large plateglass window. His kit consisted of a dozen-odd pens, pencils, and colored pencils, along with three folders. The first held a stack of mimeographed forms for charting a team's defense, play by play; the second a stack of printed forms for charting its offense; and the third an ordinary tablet of yellow legal foolscap, on which to write down random observations. Tunnell then focused his attention, quietly and intentently, on the two squads warming up on the gridiron far below. Some scouts use binoculars, but Tunnell never carries them, since his eyesight is excellent and binoculars would cut down his field of vision. Just before game time, he turned to Barrick and asked him to list the defensive and offensive substitutions that the Cardinals made during the game. I inquired if there was anything I could do. "Yes," Tunnell said. "Watch that old scoreboard and let me know first thing they put up a score on that Cleveland game."

He added two fresh packs of cigarettes to the paraphernalia arrayed before him. "We might see some pretty good football right here," he said. "I'm ready for a two-pack game."

The Cardinals kicked off to the Redskins, so Tunnell started work with one of the mimeographed defense charts—a sheet of typewriter-size paper on which twenty-four horizontal lines intersected eleven vertical lines. On this chart, the vertical column at the extreme left was headed "Down." The next four columns were headed "4–3," "4–3W," "W–S," and "W–S Zone," and the rest of the vertical columns had no designation except for three at the extreme right; these were headed "Red Dog," "Short Yardage," and "Goal Line." In operation, this defense chart is far less mysterious and complicated than it appears to be at first glance. The headings "4–3," "4–3W," "W–S," and "W–S Zone" are abbreviations for fundamental defensive formations. In a 4–3, for example, which is the standard pro defense, the left end, the left tackle, the right tackle, and the right end make up the four-man line, with a left, a middle, and a right linebacker in close support. (Supporting *them* is the four-man defensive secondary.) The 4–3W, W–S, and W–S Zone formations are variations on the basic 4–3. When a team comes up with a type of defense not covered by these four formations, Tunnell inserts the necessary heading at the top of a blank column. Working with this chart, he fills in one horizontal line per play, placing a check mark in the appropriate column to describe the defensive alignment used. For example, after the notation of its being second down and six yards to go, there might be a check in the 4–3W column and a second check in the column at the right headed "Red Dog." (A linebacker "red-dogs" when he leaves his customary position and bursts across the scrimmage line as the ball is centered, in the hope of breaking up the play before it can get started.) The next line on the chart might simply show that on third down and five a straight 4–3 defense was used. Since there is an interval of twenty-five seconds between plays, Tunnell, I noticed, had ample time to make supplementary annotations on his yellow pad—say, a rough diagram of the placement of the four men in the Cardinals' excellent defensive secondary (Jimmy Hill, Pat Fischer, Larry Wilson, and Jerry Stovall) whenever the Redskins' most dangerous receiver, halfback Bobby Mitchell, was set out wide as a flanker.

When the Cardinals gained possession of the ball, Tunnell pushed his defense chart to one side and started filling in an offense chart in much the same fashion, one horizontal line per play. This chart is a somewhat more baroque form, with some twenty different vertical columns, the most important being "Down and Distance," "Yard Line," "Offensive Formation," "Play," "Offensive Blockers," "Ball-carrier," "Pass Pattern," "Pass Receiver," "Defense Formation," "Downed By," and "Gain or Loss." During the huddle that preceded each play, Tunnell penciled in the preparatory data—the down, the yards needed for first down, the yard line the ball was on, and its lateral position on the field. After each play was over, he filled in the rest of the line, using a personal shorthand. For example, to describe an offensive formation, he would write down a swift hieroglyphic on the order of "RLSL," "BRSL," or "BLRSR." In translation, the first "R" stands for "Red," the pros' conventional formation, in which one halfback is set far out to one side as a flanker, with the other halfback and the fullback aligned behind and on either side of the quarterback. "B" stands for "Brown," another standard halfback-flanker formation, "BL" for "Blue," still another—and so on. There is no need to go further into the code; once you have the proper Rosetta stone, unscrambling the meanings comes easily enough. However, it is quite a different matter to identify and record, as Tunnell did in a twinkling on down after down, the offensive formation and all the other details of a running or a pass play. As I watched him that afternoon, he not only managed to do this with dispatch but periodically found time to scribble a few remarks on his yellow pad. For example, as the Cardinals moved down the field on a passing attack directed by Charlie Johnson, their fine young quarterback, he jotted down a quick comment about Jackie Smith, a first-year man whom the Cardinals were using as a tight end: "Speed. Very big. Very good hands. Keeps his feet." When the Cardinals went on the defense again, he entered this notation on Pat Fischer, the defensive left halfback: "Good pass defender but takes his chances. Easier to beat on outside patterns." Despite his absorption in his paperwork, Tunnell was the one who first noticed, early in the second quarter, that a score had been posted on the Giants-Browns game: in the first period the Giants had already amassed a 17–0 lead. "I told you we could take them!" Tunnell exulted. "That Jimmy Brown's a good one, all right, but he's no superman. He'll go down if you hit him hard. Boy, we must be tackling out there, and we must be blocking!"

The continuing good news on the scoreboard —the Giants eventually won the game, 33–6— had the effect of making Tunnell far more chatty during the rest of the afternoon. I found his stream of remarks extremely instructive, to say the least. In my own set, where the one-eyed are kings, a man passes for an expert if he can identify the tackler on half the plays and if he occasionally drops a few dry asides on how well, or how poorly, the offensive guards are blocking. In any event, I was deeply impressed by the staggering amount of detail that an authentic football expert observes. To cite one example, after the Redskins had scored their only touchdown on a pass by George Izo that Richter, the right end, had caught after getting into the clear behind Stovall, the Cardinals' rookie safety man, I remarked to Tunnell that it was the first faulty move I had seen Stovall make all day. "Oh, he didn't play it so badly," Tunnell replied. "On that down, the Cards red-dogged with all their linebackers. They were gambling they'd shoot in so quick that Izo couldn't get his pass off. With the red dog on, Stovall had to come in and play Richter tight, and he did. The trouble was the linebackers didn't get in on Izo fast enough, and he had time to throw a good long pass."

After the game—the Cardinals won it, 21–7, about as expected, and brought their season's record to five wins and two losses, the same as the Giants'—I drove to Philadelphia with Tunnell and Barrick. Tunnell stayed up most of the night preparing his scouting report in his home in the Rosemont section of Philadelphia. In themselves, the copious tabulations that he compiles are not so important. Their value lies in providing him with the specific facts he needs to guide him through the intensive, analytical written report that he must complete overnight and turn in to Coach Sherman at nine-thirty on Monday morning. In working up this report, Tunnell's first step was to collate the information from his forms in order to supply Sherman and the assistant coaches with a full breakdown of the Cardinals' various offensive and defensive formations—how many times each was used, and in what situations. He then diagrammed these formations, pointing out the types of plays that were run from them or against them. Bearing in mind what the game film would probably show, he selected about fifteen offensive plays and defensive maneuvers that struck him as being worth special attention, and diagrammed them carefully, using colored pencils to emphasize key points, such as the blocking assign-ments on a favorite Cardinal ground play, or the patterns of the potential receivers on the staple pass plays—the routes run by Smith, the tight end; by Sonny Randle, the split end; by Bobby Joe Conrad, the flanker back; and, occasionally, by Joe Childress, the fullback, and Bill Triplett, the running halfback. He elaborated on this art work with about a dozen pages of comment on such fine points as the skill of individual players, their possible shortcomings, and (though he is not often lucky enough to detect any) the mannerisms of certain men that tip off what they are going to do. To liven up his report, Tunnell salted it with breezy headlines. For example, "They Stopped Bobby Mitchell Cold with This One" appeared in bold lettering at the top of a page given over to a diagram of a defensive arrangement that had contained the Redskins' speedy flanker. "All the Way to California" introduced the diagram of a 55-yard scoring pass that Johnson had thrown to Randle, who had got so far behind the defensive man assigned to cover him that he might as well have been on the opposite coast. The full report on the Cardinals ran to some thirty-five pages—about Tunnell's average. It took him five and a half hours to complete it. By that time, I was in New York.

On Monday morning, Tunnell took an early train to New York and, shortly after nine, delivered his scouting report to Sherman at the Giants' offices, on Columbus Circle. The team's decisive conquest of the Browns had put it back in the race again, only one game off the pace. In effect, it was almost as if a new season lay ahead, and the atmosphere at the club's headquarters that October morning was aglow. When I arrived there at ten, Sherman and Tunnell had finished a private consultation on the scouting report and were talking informally to the press in the coaching room, a fair-sized office mostly given over to wooden racks stacked with reels of film. Sherman, a modest man, was seated in the middle of the room, thanking the reporters for their congratulations on the Cleveland victory and industriously pointing out that the coming game was not going to be a snap, either. "You fellows know this league as well as I do," he said, lighting up a long cigar. "On any given Sunday, any team in this league can beat any other team. The Cardinals are not just any other team, though. They're a well-balanced young club that's just beginning to coalesce. They have the same record we have—five and two. Yesterday we played our maximum game. Now we've got to come back off that game with another major effort." At Sherman's suggestion,

Tunnell went over some of the Cardinals' strong points: both Triplett and Childress were running well, and the sound ground game was making the passing game go; Johnson, the young quarterback, had improved tremendously, and in Conrad, who had already caught forty-four passes, and Randle, who had caught twenty-six, he had two of the most reliable receivers in the league; the offensive line was much solider than it had been at the start of the year; the men in the defensive line were frequently spelled by good substitutes and were never sluggish; the three linebackers were very active, especially Dale Meinert, the middle man; and, above all, the defensive secondary of Hill, Fischer, Wilson, and Stovall had really jelled, having allowed only three touchdown passes all year.

"Are they better than the Giants' defensive secondary?" someone asked.

"I couldn't tell you. I haven't seen our club play," Tunnell answered with a big smile, pleased at his skillful evasion of the question.

A little before eleven, Andy Robustelli, the large, slow-eyed defensive end who also serves as the team's defensive coach, came in with the movie of the game in Cleveland and began to load it into a projector. A moment later, an office boy arrived with hamburgers and coffee for Sherman, Robustelli, and Tunnell, and the rest of us filed out and left them to their work. As hardly needs to be said, tight security measures surround the inner councils of a professional football team. Tunnell had been kind enough to let me glance at a few pages of his scouting report, so that I could see what one looked like, but he had been careful to show me only the most obvious material.

That Monday, after his visitors had departed, Sherman launched his preparations for the game with the Cardinals, adhering to a schedule that has now become standard. His Monday session with Robustelli and Tunnell starts with a general discussion of the scouting report. Then, with some definite ideas forming in his mind about the kind of game that should work best against the next opponent, Sherman screens the movies of the game played by the Giants the day before. For convenience, all game films are separated into two sets of reels, one composed of the offensive plays and the other of the defensive plays. The offense reels are shown first —Sherman's specialty is the offense—and then Robustelli analyzes the defense reels. That evening, Sherman meets with his offensive staff— Ed Kolman, the line coach; Ken Kavanaugh, the end coach; and Kyle Rote, the backfield coach —in a suite at the Roosevelt Hotel, where they go over the offense reels of the Giants' last game, confer on the scouting report, and eventually (by this time it is usually past midnight) settle on the offense plan to be used the following Sunday.

By Tuesday, the film of their opponent's Sunday game has been delivered and is ready to be screened in the dressing room at Yankee Stadium, the Giants' home field. It, too, is divided into offense and defense reels. In the morning, Sherman and Robustelli look at the offense reels and arrive at a rudimentary defensive plan. In the afternoon, the team is shown the complete film of the Giants' last game and is given a preliminary briefing on its opponent's personnel. In the evening, Sherman pores over the defense reels of the opponent's last game, and Robustelli takes the offense reels home with him to Stamford and studies them with Jimmy Patton, the Giants' safety man and assistant defensive coach, who lives not far away.

Wednesday is a full day for all hands. At the stadium, Sherman talks over with Robustelli and Patton any adjustments they might propose for the Giants' defensive plan. Then comes a two-hour meeting in which the team looks at the film of the opponent's last game and the coaching staff presents the complete game plan for Sunday's battle in a series of chalk talks at the blackboard. There is a long practice on Wednesday, shorter ones on Thursday, Friday, and Saturday. At these practices, Sherman and his aides not infrequently readjust a few of their earlier adjustments, for their movie-scouting goes on all week. If a half hour is lying heavy on his hands, Sherman is likely to have the projectionist run off the films of the games that the Giants played *last* year against Sunday's opponent. Throughout this strenuous preparation, no single element plays a more influential role than the scouting report. It is referred to constantly all week, studied and restudied. Tunnell himself is on hand through Thursday, in case any of the coaches want to consult him. Friday is a day of relaxation for him at home in Philadelphia, but that night he is on the move again, heading for a college game on Saturday where there are promising players to look over, and then for the pro game he is scouting on Sunday.

Because of my involvement with Tunnell, the game between the Cardinals and the Giants, in St. Louis on November 3, was one of the most absorbing I have ever watched. I saw it at home on television. At kickoff time, I was still pondering the Giants' probable strategy, as I had been all week. Would they try to move primarily on the ground, out of respect for the Cardinals' formidable pass defense? If they took to the air, would Tittle throw only the short, quick passes that he had thrown so successfully against the Browns, when he had completely abandoned the long pass? On defense, would the Giants play their linebackers up close—the adjustment that had stopped Jimmy Brown in Cleveland—or would they concentrate on frustrating the Cardinals' passing attack?

The game was not many minutes old when I began to appreciate what a first-rate job had been done in discovering and exploiting definite weaknesses in the Cardinals' strongest suit—their pass defense. Early in the first period, the Giants took the lead on a field goal that had been set up by a 55-yard pass play from Y. A. Tittle, their remarkable quarterback, to Aaron Thomas, the tight end. On that play, with Thomas and Gifford, the flanker halfback, both aligned to the right, Gifford had gone deep, and Thomas, trailing him, had beaten Fischer, the defensive left halfback, by running a "down-and-out" pattern—cutting sharply out toward the sideline. (Tunnell, I remembered, had noted on his yellow pad that Fischer could be beaten outside.) On the Cardinals' first offensive march, Johnson completed a 25-yard pass down the middle to Randle, but on two subsequent passes —longer ones—that were meant for the same receiver, Randle was very well covered; in fact, the second pass was intercepted by Dick Lynch, the Giants' defnsive right halfback.

A couple of minutes later, the Giants were in front, 10–0.

Back came the Cardinals on a sustained march. In this series of plays, Johnson, noting that his key receivers, Randle and Conrad, were being tightly covered, adroitly changed his tactics and started throwing short passes down the middle to Childress, his fullback, whom he had used only rarely as a receiver in previous games. With the ball on the Giants' 13-yard line, Johnson again looked for Childress, and found him all by himself in the end zone: 10–7. After the kickoff, Tittle capped a Giant drive with a 28-yard touchdown pass to Thomas, who, in a burst of speed, had angled behind Stovall. (This play, as I saw it, was almost an exact duplicate of the one we had watched in

Washington, when Richter, the Redskins' end, had beaten Stovall. Very interesting.) The Cards' return drive stalled almost immediately when Allan Webb intercepted a pass meant for Conrad. The pattern that Conrad ran on this play had been so precisely anticipated that Conrad and three Giant defenders—Webb, Patton, and Erich Barnes—could have fitted easily into a clothes closet. The score at the half was Giants 24, Cardinals 7. Against a defensive secondary that had allowed a total of only three touchdown passes in its first seven games, Tittle had already passed for three.

One of the repercussions of this was that Stovall, the Cardinals' rookie safety man, was replaced in the second half by Bill Stacy, a veteran defensive back who had been nursing a muscle injury but was ready for duty. Another repercussion was that the Giants, who had been so sharp and aggressive, began to let down in the second half after Tittle threw yet another touchdown pass, this one a long lead pass to Del Shofner, his split end, who had outmaneuvered Hill and then outrun him—all the way to California. The Giants' errors of commission and omission in every department from that point on played a substantial part in a rally by the Cardinals that brought them back to within ten points of the Giants, with twelve minutes still remaining in the game. However, the Cardinals' next march was abruptly halted when Barnes intercepted another pass meant for Conrad, and this, in effect, nailed down the game. Final score: Giants 38, Cardinals 21.

I learned a great deal that afternoon, and principally this—that preparation certainly helps to win football games, but only as long as a team maintains its incentive. In the modern idiom, this quality is floridly referred to as "desire," but it is nothing more nor less, of course, than what Dana X. Bible's contemporaries called "determination" and Walter Camp's called "spirit."

Tunnell seemed fairly well pleased with the results of the game when I saw him the next week, just before he left for San Francisco to scout the 49ers. "I'm really looking forward to our last game—against the Steelers," he said as he checked over the contents of his attaché case. "I've already been to forty games this season—college and pro—and I haven't seen my own team play yet."

The argument was raised by Stanley Woodward and then Army coach Earl Blaik over a decade ago, when pro football was just beginning to catch fire. But because the piece drew such loud controversy, it deserves to be reread—and argued about.

THE PRO GAME ISN'T FOOTBALL

Stanley Woodward

It had been a game to rouse the dead. The supposedly unbeatable Cleveland Football Browns had gone into the second half trailing by 21 points, and 70,000 people had howled a savage *éloge* to a team that appeared to be at the mercy of the underrated New York Yankees.

But in the second half an exhumation began to shape up and when the iron November twilight closed in on Yankee Stadium, the New Yorkers were fighting the clock to hold a 28–all tie.

The Cleveland comeback had been cruelly systematic. Marion Motley, the big fullback, had taken a series of hand-offs from quarterback Otto Graham and riddled the core of the Yankee line. Graham, keyman of a T attack that was suddenly alive, had whipped passes to his buttonhooking halfbacks and had found Dante Lavelli and Mac Speedie, his spectacular ends, with long loopers. The Stadium was in a turmoil as the Browns started for their fifth touchdown. But time ran out on them before the tie could be broken.

Going downtown I shared a cab with Colonel Earl (Red) Blaik, the Army coach. He sat in

his corner silent and apparently unmoved by the recent heroics. Trying to start a conversation, I said, "Great game, eh?"

"Yes," said the Colonel, composedly rubbing his chin, "but it wasn't football."

Not football!

Recently, when *Collier's* asked me to report the Colonel's views on college versus professional brands of the game, I reminded him of his cryptic remark in the cab after the Cleveland-Yankee hair-raiser three years ago.

He was in his shirt sleeves behind his big desk on the top floor of the West Point gymnasium during an interlude between sessions of clinical football. Down the hall the movie projector whirred as members of the staff studied the technique of some impending opponent.

"Sure, I remember it," he said, "and that's what I think. Football is a college game. It calls for these things: youth, condition, spirit, plus continuous hard work by coaches as well as players."

What's the matter with professional football?

"Nothing. It's what it aims to be. It's a show. The pros are in the entertainment business."

Subsequent questioning revealed that Earl Henry Blaik, Colonel U. S. Calvary, Retired, developer of five undefeated Army teams in nine years, doesn't think a pro eleven would stand a chance if it undertook a schedule of eight or nine games against tough college teams.

He admires the individual skills of the professional players, likes to see the games himself. But he doesn't think the pros work at team development like the colleges. He doesn't think the players keep in good condition. He thinks they lack spiritual lift. He thinks they are turning the game into basketball by depending almost wholly on the forward pass. He misses the detailed execution of the college running attack. In pro football he discerns no "second effort," i.e., getting downfield to block the secondary or pursuing a runner who has got away.

His comments are observations rather than criticisms. He says he does not know the problems of pro football and admits the pros may be proceeding in a logical manner for the promulgation of their business—which is show business.

"However," he says, "I don't learn anything from pro football. I know that if I could not develop a team which would play harder, faster and with greater coordination than the pros, my career as a college coach would be—shall I say—limited."

That day and other days I listened while Colonel Blaik expounded the revolutionary theory that the best football is not played by the pros and cannot be. His approach was positive—an evaluation of the college game rather than a mere arraignment of the shortcomings among the pros. In an attempt to get at the reasoning behind his conviction I attended meetings of the Army football staff and practice sessions of the squad. I sat in the projection room while the coaches ran movie reels of past games with prospective opponents. I listened to detailed discussions of blocking methods and faking techniques. Ultimately I began to see what the Colonel meant when, albeit without malice, he classified the pros as mere showmen.

The work a collegiate coaching staff puts into football is staggering. Blaik himself hasn't taken a vacation in nine years. Day after day around the calendar, Sundays and holidays often included, he is at work either in the football office or out on the Plains where the cadets practice.

He is not unique among college coaches. Frank Leahy of Notre Dame, Bennie Oosterbaan of Michigan, Bob Neyland of Tennessee, Dutch Meyer of Texas Christian, Lynn Waldorf

of California, Bud Wilkinson of Oklahoma and many others apply enough fanatical devotion to their profession to make them millionaires in a more rewarding field. To beat their teams you have to match them in staff work as well as man power.

The Army football office occupies a whole floor in the east tower of the West Point gymnasium. It has cubicles for assistants and scouts, a conference room, a projection room and filing space for hundreds of movie reels and scouting reports on every team and every player Army is sceduled to, or conceivably may, play against.

Blaik's office, a square room in the front of the tower, is dominated by a huge photographic blowup of General Douglas MacArthur, the Colonel's personal hero. There is also a composite chart of the schedules of all impending Army opponents, leather chairs, a sofa and ash trays strategically aligned for visitors. The Colonel doesn't smoke.

In this room, with occasional shifts to the movie room or practice field, I made Blaik the slightly unwilling victim of an inquisition on pro football.

Do you actually believe, Colonel, that a good pro team could not beat a good college team?

"Wait a minute! I don't say that. I think a good pro team might get itself up to beat a good college team in a single game. But if the pro team were put into a league with good college teams—like Notre Dame, Michigan, Ohio State, Oklahoma, Southern California, Tennessee and Texas (we'll leave West Point out of this)—it would have to learn to play football the way the colleges do or it wouldn't stand a chance. A fiery team like Tennessee would cripple a pro club."

Don't you think the professionals have better man power?

"I do not. Football is a Spartan game in which youth, spirit and condition count heavily. The colleges have the boys in their best years. Few of them ever play as well after they become professionals.

"As they grow older they acquire responsibilities and perspective, also caution. They lose the reckless abandon that marked their play in college. They get bigger and fatter. They may look imposing to the fans, but they are not the same football players. I know, and other college coaches know, that an active, enthusiastic young fellow of 190 pounds can do everything better than an old pro who weighs two-fifty or -sixty."

When Colonel Blaik is thinking things out, he has a habit of whirling his reading glasses round and round by the bows. He whirled them fiercely, as he continued:

"What happens to the leading college players who go into pro football? They take their places in the front line immediately and without exception. They become stars at once. In fact, some who don't quite make it in college become the key men of their professional clubs. Perhaps they are the best men the pros get because they're still a little hungry.

"Look at George Ratterman (New York Yanks quarterback), for instance. He's a top professional player but he never was better than second string at Notre Dame."

But you say you like to see professional games?

"That's true, and I like to take the Army squad to see them. The players have great individual skills, and a college boy—particularly a quarterback—can learn a lot about playing his position by watching the pros. Take Frankie Albert of the San Francisco 49ers. He's adept at carrying out the fakes which help set up a pass. He holds the defense in place by simulating hands-offs to his backs. He fakes in one direction and passes in another.

"But he didn't learn that in pro football. He had it all when the played for Stanford."

Have you had any players who have benefited from watching the pros?

"Yes, several of them. For instance, Arnold Tucker, who played quarterback here with Blanchard and Davis; and Dan Foldberg, offensive end and captain of our present team. Foldberg got a lot out of watching those Cleveland ends (Speedie and Lavelli). From them he has learned new ways of getting loose to receive passes, how to change direction and pace, how to make the final fast cut which shakes off the defense."

If the pros have such able individuals, why can't they make them into superior football teams?

"There are lots of reasons. One is, they don't work at it. Their main objects are to get hold of the good players after they are graduated and to get crowds into their ball parks. Everyone connected with a pro club participates in the ballyhoo. Everyone scouts players. They only work on the development of a team for a couple of months in the fall.

"After their preseason work they don't scrimmage, and you can't have a football team unless you go through your repertory over and over again under game conditions.

"Here at West Point we have about twenty basic offensive plays, with variations. In addi-

tion we have other plays devised to capitalize special weaknesses or to run against special defenses.

"In spring practice we scrimmage the basic plays more than a hundred times apiece. When the squad turns out in the fall we have to start over, the players are rusty. So we scrimmage the plays a hundred more times or so. Throughout the season we continue to use contact work to keep the players sharp.

"You don't develop good teeth by eating mush. You don't keep a blocker sharp by giving him theory and letting him go through the motions in dummy.

"I don't know whether it would be good sense for the pros to work on plays as we do. When you scrimmage you always run the risk of getting someone hurt and the pros can't afford to have the players the public wants to see on the bench.

"In addition, it may not be feasible to train pros as we train undergraduates. It's an old story to them. They probably don't have the enthusiasm for cracking skulls that you find in young fellows who haven't been overfed on football."

The Colonel whirled his glasses intensely.

"You know, even in college, players sometimes get on the downgrade in their last year. Take Red Cagle. He played here at West Point after four years at Southwestern Louisiana Institute. He was best as a yearling (sophomore). After that his performance was definitely not so good. As a pro he never came close to his early West Point form."

Colonel Blaik came to West Point from Dartmouth where he made a phenomenal record, once going through twenty-two consecutive games without a defeat. Looking for a better comparison between the potentialities of fiery youth and sated experience, he went back to that era.

"You remember the game between Dartmouth and Cornell in 1940. That was the time the referee made a mistake and gave Cornell five downs at the very end. On the last play of the game Cornell scored on a pass. This made it 7–3, but later, after conclusive evidence that the referee had made an error had been produced, Cornell ceded the game to Dartmouth; the score in the record book is Dartmouth 3, Cornell 0. Bob Krieger had kicked a field goal for Dartmouth early in the fourth period.

"What I'm trying to illustrate is that Dartmouth, a young team, beat Cornell, a veteran team, which hadn't lost in two years, strictly on youthful fire and emotional uplift. Our team hadn't any business finishing within 40 points of Cornell."

The accent on youth, the emphasis on strategy, the constant effort to build from the ground are themes from the Colonel's own career. After four years of football at Miami University, Oxford, Ohio, he played his fifth and last year at West Point. He served three years in the cavalry after graduating from the Military Academy with the two-year class of 1920, then resigned and, with his father, went into the house-building business in Dayton, Ohio, his home town.

Blaik didn't decide to become a full-time professional coach until 1934, after years of seasonal assistant coaching at West Point. Ernest Martin Hopkins, president of Dartmouth, persuaded him to come to the Indian campus that year and redeem a hopeless situation. He did that, then moved back to Army as head coach in 1941 to undertake the same kind of job.

Having built up two football teams to formidable status through extraordinary resource and application, he's a little impatient with those who think—as the pros seem to—that football coaching is not a full-time job. As a fifty-two-year-old 190-pounder who can still get into the uniform he wore as a second lieutenant, he's a little intolerant of players who handicap themselves by lugging around excess avoirdupois.

"All the pro teams are full of big fat men, some of them 40 pounds over their most efficient playing weight. I know for certain that a man who wears a rubber tire can't play football with one who is down to hard condition, no matter what the big man's weight advantage may be. The fat man is useless in the attack and he can't move laterally on the defense. He's useful only if the ball carrier runs straight into him.

"What do you find in professional football?" The Colonel pointed an accusing finger at me and went on to answer his own question.

"You find that the average defensive lineman covers the spot he's assigned to and doesn't do one thing more. He thinks he's done his job if he stops all the plays directed at him. He doesn't chase a runner who goes in the opposite direction. Here, let me show you something."

He led us into the movie room and put on a reel of the 1950 practice game between Army and Boston University. He fiddled with the projector, then found what he wanted.

"Watch this," the Colonel said. "This will show you what I think defensive men should do.

"See, Boston has the ball. There's the runner, going around our left end. See, our end is knocked down. The runner is around him. But watch now."

For a second the B.U. halfback seemed to have a clear path, then from every angle Army players started arriving. The runner was deluged by tacklers just as he turned the corner to go downfield. Even the end who had been knocked down scrambled up and got a hand on him. When the whistle blew, only two Army players were on their feet. The rest, nine of them, were in on the tackle.

"That's pursuit," said Colonel Blaik, shutting off the machine. "The pros don't have it. Sometimes they make a good first effort but they don't go through with the job. That's why Steve Van Buren of the Philadelphia Eagles and Charley Trippi of the Chicago Cardinals make so many long runs without any discernible downfield blocking. Nobody chases them. They get by the defenders in a certain sector and they're gone.

"Downfield blocking? The pros don't have that either. The pro lineman may carry out his primary block but he isn't going to chase 30 yards down the field all afternoon to hit the safety man. His nature rebels against it. It takes a young man with untarnished spirit to do that."

You'll admit, Colonel, the pros are wonderful with the forward pass.

"I'll agree with you that they have great passers and great receivers, but I do not concede that an uninterrupted succession of passes is football.

"Recently I saw a pro game in which one team threw 47 passes. Think of it! Forty-seven!

"What did the defensive linemen do when the opposition was throwing 47 passes? They stood there and looked at the ball. Rushing the passer is grueling work. It requires a great outlay of speed, strength, energy and determination. A man must drive himself if he is going to try to break through on every pass play. So the pros stand on the line of scrimmage and hope some secondary-defense man will knock the pass down.

"Now, if you don't rush the passer he will complete a large percentage of his throws. That's why you have such big scores in professional football. By using the pass as the principal weapon and by failing to put pressure on the passer, the pros have cheapened the touchdown and damaged their game, at least for some of us."

Couldn't it be said that Notre Dame, Army, Oklahoma and some of the other powerful college teams have cheapened the game by scoring so frequently?

"Perhaps that's right. But at any rate we don't trade touchdowns every few minutes. And we play balanced football by coordinating passing and running.

"The pros have practically given up the running attack. Clark Shaughnessy, who used to coach the Los Angeles Rams, had his team at Bear Mountain (nine miles from West Point) for a week last fall and he and I had several talks. He told me it's useless to run against a pro team because the defensive line is so strong. 'The men are too big,' he said.

"I couldn't let that pass. 'Now wait a minute, Clark. If the pros are so good on the defense they must have something on the offense. Do you mean to tell me your 230-pound guard can't move the other fellow's 230-pound guard at least part of the time?'

"The truth is, the pros won't pay the price to develop a running attack. After their preseason training they don't scrimmage, and I've already told you what my experience has been in the development of running plays. You soften the rugged daily schedule and the plays don't work. The blocking goes off; the timing goes off.

"Some people may argue that certain pro clubs do have a running attack—that the Philadelphia Eagles have one. I say that Steve Van Buren is a great runner and that he is helped enormously by the fact that the defensive men he plays against don't pursue."

Did the Colonel ever see a professional team with a real running attack?

"Yes, one. That was Pittsburgh when it was coached by the late Jock Sutherland. He had a bunch of castoffs from the other National League clubs and he turned them into a football team with a balanced attack in which the forward pass held its proper place.

"How did he do it? The way we do it in college football. He scrimmaged his team throughout the season. He kept the blocking and timing sharp. He was teaching college football, the same kind he taught during his years at the University of Pittsburgh. The old pros on his team may have hated him, but he kept them at it by the force of his personality, and he darned near won the championship even though he had inferior man power."

The Colonel was drawing diagrams on his desk pad, describing with X's and O's the single-wing formation which the late Sutherland made famous and which he himself used to teach.

"It's silly for Clark Shaughnessy to tell me it's impossible to run against a pro defense," he

continued. "I've seen it done. A year ago Herman Hickman put together a little All-Star team recruited entirely from graduates of Eastern colleges. It practiced less than three weeks, then played the professional New York Giants and ran all over them.

"Herman did a fine coaching job, but he didn't have much in the way of man power and I'm certain his outfit wouldn't have stayed close to any first-class college team. Yet he humiliated the Giants, who had practiced two months in preparation. How do you account for it?

"My answer is that Herman's team was full of spirit and determination—the things which make the college game what it is. Wanting to win, the boys worked intensely hard in practice. When they went on the field they were in condition and they were emotionally ready. The Giants were not."

The Colonel's contention was given additional support last August when the College All-Star football team, coached by Dr. Eddie Anderson, of Iowa and Holy Cross, gave the champion Philadelphia Eagles a severe drubbing at Soldier Field in Chicago.

The score, 17 to 7, does not fully indicate the superiority of the college team. Two or three more All-Star touchdowns barely missed fire. Once Charlie Justice of North Carolina, the running star of the game, was barely nipped by the heels en route to an apparent touchdown. Again, a sure-fire pass was dropped.

The college team was trained at Delafield, Wisconsin, far from the bright lights. It attained good physical condition and high morale. Once it directed its two-platoon power at the Eagles, it was all over. The pros were badly licked, and apparently exhausted when they went off the field at the half.

The two men who carried the burden of offense for the collegians were little fellows. Justice weighs a bare 170 pounds, and Eddie LeBaron, the offensive quarterback who ran the team and did the passing, is 10 pounds lighter. The All-Stars' savage 5–4–2 defense smothered Steve Van Buren, widely considered the greatest runner in professional football.

In summing up his ideas, the Colonel said, "I suppose I sound pretty critical. However, I go to the pro games and I take my squad whenever I can. It's good entertainment, and isn't that what it's supposed to be?"

I thought back to that roaring tie between the Cleveland Browns and the New York Yankees. Yes, I had been entertained.

But was it football?

That this is the last piece in the book is purely coincidental; one may take comfort in knowing that Mr. Yellen's prophesied Doomsday for the game was the 1960 season. However, what with the latest accent on platoons and specialists, the author may be only a few years off the mark.

HOW FOOTBALL DIED

Samuel Yellen

Given the hindsight we have now in 1960, there was a moment thirteen years ago when one might have foretold the recent debacle at Ann Arbor and the nationwide collapse of intercollegiate football. That moment occurred very early in the opening game of Michigan's 1947 season. Oddly enough, the scene then was also the stadium at Ann Arbor. I cannot recall who the opposing team was. However, having elected to receive, it had just failed to gain on three attempts and, in the orthodox manner, had punted on fourth down. The complete Michigan team then retired from the field, a full fresh team trotted out, and football fans saw a school use *two* entirely different teams—one for the defensive, the other for the offensive.

As the "Michigan System" spread, the resulting demand for football material became a serious drain on the country. Each year a number of the smaller colleges, like Wabash, Hiram, and Amherst, had to give up football. There simply were not enough players to go around.

The next fateful step leading to the ultimate catastrophe was taken by Notre Dame. It was in 1952 that the Irish came up with the specialized unit trained to execute one, and only one, particular play. So well was the secret kept that the opposing teams did not catch on until the season was well along. Of course, even during the 1940's one could have foreseen the specialized unit in the development of the specialist who came out on the field to kick the point after touchdown and then returned to the bench until his educated toe was again needed. The new unit was made up of four, five, or six key men, and was plugged into the offensive team whenever its specialty was required—that is, for an end run, a dive through center, a short screen pass, and so on. Similarly, units perfected in breaking up particular plays could be plugged into the defensive team.

Offhand one might have thought that the specialized unit would be at a disadvantage, since its very appearance on the field practically called the play coming up. Nevertheless, so thoroughly expert did each unit become in its speciality, such machine precision was drilled into it, that rarely could it be stopped, except by a defensive unit which had specialized in the same play. Nor was there any lack of deception and surprise, as can be seen by considering the variations possible in a standard play like the end run. While the "Notre Dame System" had limitations, it had the basic strength and subtlety of draw poker; whereas the older system was more like playing poker

337

wild. In 1953, all of the Big Ten and at least twenty other schools introduced the specialized unit.

The spread of the Notre Dame System meant a further drain on the already depleted football resources of the nation. In the years before 1947, a top-ranking school could get along with a squad of 60 or 70. After the Michigan System came into use, squads jumped to 100 or 120. Now, however, the development of specialized units made it necessary to have a squad of at least 150 and often 200. The coaching staff, too, had to be increased. Furthermore, it was not enough to collect simply 150 or 200 players. For no longer were men interchangeable parts on a team. Scouts had to locate not merely a good lineman or back, nor even a good tackle or fullback, but rather a good defensive screen-pass tackle or offensive end-run fullback.

It remained for the original offender, Michigan, to take the final step. Equipment, additional coaches and trainers, travel, and a network of scouts had made of football a major financial operation. Meanwhile, the revenue from football remained approximately stationary.

The trouble lay, everyone readily agreed, in the limited capacity of a stadium seating only 100,000. Yet it was extremely doubtful that the game could be made visible to 200,000 spectators. Already, half the spectators found it impossible to see clearly what was happening out on the field. Most of them had to rely on the loudspeaker to learn what the microscopic organisms off on the distant field were up to.

An impasse had been reached, but deliverance came suddenly, and from a most unexpected quarter, in the fall of 1957. The *deus ex machina* was an assistant professor in the Department of English Literature by the name of J. T. Worthington. The saving idea flashed upon him one evening as he was frowning over the cryptic reference in Milton's *Lycidas* to "that two-handed engine" and dreaming of renown won by unraveling a riddle which had puzzled scholars for so long. He little realized how soon he was to shine in a blaze of fame. The idea itself had all the simplicity of genius. What Professor Worthington proposed was that Michigan build a second stadium holding another 100,000, and then play two games simultaneously. At any one time, while the offensive team was playing in one stadium, the defensive team would be playing in the other. An underground tunnel was to connect the stadiums. The team was the two-handed engine.

The new stadium was completed for the opening of the 1959 season. On the first Saturday in October, Michigan was to play both Stanford and Wisconsin. As one might have predicted, these schools, like others, had been reluctant to sign up under the Worthington plan, since it gave them the appearance of second-rate teams which Michigan could take on two at a time. However, such was Michigan's prestige and, perhaps more significant, so alluring the share of the gate offered them that they were prevailed upon. The eyes of the college world were on Ann Arbor for this initial test of the plan. Of course, bungling was unavoidable on that Saturday; and although Michigan beat Stanford, the Wisconsin game was lost through faults in planning and timing. But toward the close of the season, things were running like clockwork.

Nevertheless, complaints were heard, both from the other schools and from the fans. The visiting teams felt that they were somehow being used. Notwithstanding the larger share they were given, they could not forget that it came from a single gate; whereas Michigan's came from a double gate. Moreover, chagrin set in as they began to comprehend what an unsurpassable lead they had allowed Michigan to attain. For, obviously, not every school could undertake to build a second stadium and schedule double games. Simple arithmetic was against it. There were not enough teams.

The fans, too, caused difficulty. They displayed a reluctance to come to Ann Arbor for the less important game. A kind of Gresham's Law in reverse came into operation. Thus on the Saturday when Michigan played Illinois and Syracuse, the first stadium was packed, the other only half-filled. And when Michigan played Notre Dame, the other stadium, where the opponent was Princeton, had a handful of spectators. Worthington, appealed to for help, came up with the daring suggestion that Michigan schedule a double game with Notre Dame in 1960. The idea was that both schools would shuttle back and forth, taking the offensive in one stadium while on the defensive in the other.

To relate the melancholy events of the fatal Saturday just a month ago seems hardly necessary. They are only too well known. The day began fine, the crowds were colorful. The 200,000 rabid fans who had descended on Ann Arbor were getting their money's worth. For the first three quarters the games went off with exceptional smoothness. The score was tied at 14–all in the old stadium, and Michigan led 21–20 in the new. Then, during the fourth quarter, through some caprice of fortune or some momentary tangle in the weary brain of one of the coaches, the irrevocable mistake was made. The Michigan offensive team shuttled from the new stadium to the old at the same time that the Notre Dame offensive shuttled from the old to the new. This brought Michigan's offensive against its own defensive, and put Notre Dame in a like predicament.

A number of factors prevented the teams from noticing the blunder until it was too late. A drizzle had started to come down in the second half, the fields had been churned to mud, and the uniforms had become unrecognizable. Furthermore, dusk having fallen, the light was poor. And, perhaps most important, the teams had grown so big, with 200 men on each squad, that a player did not know half of his teammates even by sight unless they happened to be associated with him in particular operations. Whatever the reasons, thanks to a special trick play, really a brilliant and thrilling maneuver, held in reserve for this very moment, Michigan scored against itself. Only then, after the extra point had been kicked, was the mistake discovered.

Chaos settled over the old stadium. The gridiron was a darkling plain swept with confused alarms of struggle and flight. The players wrangled. The referees could make no decision.

The snarl never was untangled. Both schools claimed the victory, and some of the Michigan alumni raised a fund to carry the case to court.

But cooler heads quickly understood that something far more serious than the score— namely, the future of football itself—was at stake. What would be the reaction of the fans? Michigan waited anxiously. On the following Saturday the worst fears were realized. Across the entire country the stadiums were deserted, and have remained so ever since. Most of the schools have not even bothered to play the scheduled games. A stupor of bewilderment overwhelmed the fans. Apparently their firm faith in football had toppled and they would have no more of it. Although a few schools have gone ahead halfheartedly to draw up a schedule for 1961, it is certain now that intercollegiate football is as dead as falconry or dueling. Most of the big schools have announced that they are quitting the game. With its usual hardheadedness and resourcefulness, Michigan has already put its best minds to work devising uses for the two stadiums at Ann Arbor, so that it need not default on the bonds. Plans are afoot to hold a festival of Greek drama in the new stadium next spring, opening with Euripides' *Hercules Distracted*.

CARTOON BY GALLAGHER

Reproduced by permission of the artist

"Okay—<u>now</u> can we use your ball?"

Index

About the Editor

JACK NEWCOMBE *was born in Burlington, Vermont, and was graduated from Brown University in 1948. He was a football enthusiast even before he made the "traveling squad" on his high school team, has written about the sport and has devoted his Saturdays and Sundays to watching it ever since. "I find that of all the spectator sports, football improves the most with age," he says. "As one passes from the joys of youth to the follies of adulthood, football becomes a better, more exciting game to watch." Mr. Newcombe, who was managing editor of* Sport *from 1950 to 1954, has contributed a number of free-lance articles on football to magazines. Since 1955 he has been a writer and text editor at* Life. *He lives with his wife and four children in Rye, N.Y.*